Undergraduate Texts in Mathematics

Editors

S. Axler
F.W. Gehring
K.A.Ribet

Undergraduate Texts in Mathematics

(continued after index)

Judith N. Cederberg

A Course in Modern Geometries

Second Edition

With 151 Illustrations

 Springer

Judith N. Cederberg
Department of Mathematics
St. Olaf College
Northfield, MN 55057
USA
cederj@stolaf.edu

Mathematics Subject Classification (2000): 51-01

Library of Congress Cataloging-in-Publication Data
Cederberg, Judith N.
    A course in modern geometries / Judith N. Cederberg—2nd ed.
        p.   cm. — (Undergraduate texts in mathematics)
    Includes bibliographical references and index.
    ISBN 0-387-98972-2 (alk. paper)
    1. Geometry.   I. Title.   II. Series.
QA445.C36 2000
516—dc21   99-057465

ISBN 0-387-98972-2   Printed on acid-free paper.

Printed in the United States of America.   (SBA)

9 8 7 6 5 4 3 2 (Corrected second printing, 2005)   SPIN 10994641

Springer-Verlag is a part of *Springer Science+Business Media*

springeronline.com

Preface to the
Second Edition

In the decade following the publication of the first edition of this text, numerous "reform" documents recommended major changes in the way mathematics should be taught. These included publications from the National Research Council (NRC), the Mathematical Association of America (MAA), the American Mathematical Association of Two-Year Colleges (AMATYC), and the National Council of Teachers of Mathematics (NCTM). In response, the National Science Foundation (NSF) funded several calculus reform and school curriculum projects.

Some of the reform documents contain specific recommendations for changes in geometry education. For example, Standards 7 and 8 in the 9–12 section of the NCTM *Curriculum and Evaluation Standards for School Mathematics* (1989) and the comparable focus areas for grades 9–12 in the updated 1998 version recommend both synthetic and analytic treatments of geometry with emphasis on the representation and use of geometric transformations and symmetry. As a result, the geometric content of several NSF school curriculum projects includes coverage of transformations and symmetry (for example, *Contemporary Mathematics in Context*, *Interactive Mathematics Program* and *Mathematics: Modeling Our World*). These curricula are producing students with new skills and ways of understanding that university-level faculty must be equipped to teach. Furthermore, they require that university-level mathematics curricula include appropriate geometric education for future teachers of secondary mathematics.

At the college/university level, the Consortium for Mathematics and its Applications (COMAP) sponsored a 1990 study conference aimed at revitalizing geometry with special attention to the survey geometry course. Their recommendations and samples of teaching materials are contained in the publication *Geometry's Future*. Among the wealth of suggestions and recommendations contained in this volume (pp. vi–vii) are the following:

- Geometric objects and concepts should be studied more from an experimental and inductive point of view rather than from an axiomatic point of view. (Results suggested by inductive approaches should be proved.)
- Recent developments in geometry should be included.
- A wide variety of computer environments should be explored . . . both as exploratory tools and for concept development.
- More use of diagrams and physical models as aids to conceptual development in geometry should be explored.
- Group learning methods, writing assignments, and projects should become an integral part of the format in which geometry is taught.

Another major factor affecting geometry has been the new widespread availability of high-speed computers. These computers enabled the development of dynamic geometry[1] software ($\mathcal{DGS}$) now used to enhance the teaching of geometry. In addition, computer-produced high-speed computations and high-resolution graphics played a major role in the development of chaos theory and fractal geometry, disciplines brought to popular attention by James Gleick's 1987 book, *Chaos: Making a New Science*.

---

[1] Here and throughout this volume, the term "dynamic geometry" is used in its broadest sense. Although Key Curriculum Press has trademarked the phrase, the author's use of the phrase does not refer to any particular computer software or published software support materials.

Renewed interest in geometry by mathematicians and scientists led NSF to fund several other geometry-related projects. These included the Geometry Center (a science and technology research center for the computation and visualization of geometric structures at the University of Minnesota), the Visual Geometry Project at Swarthmore College, and the Park City Regional Geometry Institute (now known as the IAS/Park City Math Institute) in Utah. Each of these placed major emphasis on school geometry. In addition, NSF-funded conferences at St. Olaf College in 1992 (Computers in Geometry Classrooms) and 1997 (Inquiry-Based Geometry Throughout the Secondary Curriculum), where participants investigated the reform suggestions and the use of dynamic geometry software to enhance the teaching of geometry and to increase geometric visualization throughout mathematics. Several ideas explored at these conferences are elaborated in the 1997 MAA publication, *Geometry Turned On! Dynamic Software in Learning, Teaching, and Research.*

Changes in the Second Edition

In light of these developments and recommendations, this edition extends the first edition's emphasis on transformations. New sections guide hands-on experimentation with transformations and point to web-located suggestions for similar experimentation using dynamic geometry software. The transformation emphasis is further enhanced in a new chapter-length treatment of fractal geometry. These additions and changes are detailed below.

1. New geometric explorations

The explorations offer opportunities for collaborative construction of knowledge through activities that emphasize visualization. They are designed to lead to student discovery before formal presentation of concepts, or they can be used to enhance understanding following concept introduction. The Chapter 3 explorations emphasize symmetry, a topic that has assumed major importance as mathematicians rethink the nature of mathematics. These and the other explorations can be supplemented via the use of dynamic geometry software with parallel activities written specifically for *The Geometer's Sketchpad*[2] and *Cabri Geometry II*.[3] These software-dependent activities are located on the web (with text pointers to their location) so that they can be updated as the software evolves. A list of the explorations is given in the table below.

Geometric Explorations	
Title	**Location**
Exploring Dynamic Geometry Software ($\mathcal{DGS}$)	Web
Exploring the Hyperbolic Plane with $\mathcal{DGS}$	Web
Exploring the Double Elliptic Plane	2.9
Exploring Line and Point Reflections	3.2*
Exploring Rotations and Finite Symmetry Groups	3.3*
Exploring Translations and Frieze Pattern Symmetries	3.4*
Exploring Plane Tilings	3.11*
Exploring 3-D Isometries	3.14
*Indicates web supplements using dynamic geometry software.	

2. New fractal geometry chapter

Chaos theory and fractal geometry are significant areas of mathematical and scientific interest with many results recently discovered by living mathematicians and scientists. Also, since fractal geometry is now used in many video and movie scenes, its study has contemporary appeal, and can enhance understanding of the visual images bombarding us daily. Thus, unlike the other geometries covered in this text, fractal geometry is actually "modern." In fact, it is so new that the term *fractal* is often not rigorously defined, and commonly accepted formal axiomatic treatments of this geometry do not yet exist.

The text conveys the excitement and importance of this "evolving geometry" by incorporating descriptions from the wealth of expository fractal literature and by involving readers in activities that have recently led to major discoveries. The presentation stresses the property of self-similarity (i.e., scale-invariant symmetry) and

---

[2] A trademark of Key Curriculum Press.
[3] A trademark of Université Joseph Fourier.

emphasizes the central role of transformations. Viewed from this perspective, fractal geometry is an extension of the geometry covered in Chapter 3. And its study provides an exciting *current event* setting in which to apply major concepts from that chapter.

Fractal geometry also exhibits close connections to analysis and topology. However, since the presentation of fractal geometry is intended to be introductory and descriptive with the goals of building intuition and applying geometric transformations, the chapter alludes to, but does not require substantial background in, these topics. Thus, fractal terms arising from analysis and topology (e.g., *boundary*, *connected*, etc.), are given descriptive explanations that should be adequate at this level.

3. Other changes

- *Chapter 1*: Parallel web-based explorations of *Cabri Geometry II* and *Geometer's Sketchpad* review basic concepts of Euclidean geometry. Students with access to one or both of these programs are encouraged to become familiar with this dynamic geometry software in preparation for suggested explorations in Chapters 2–5 which contain specific directions for using either of these programs.
- *Chapter 2*: (1) Parallel web-based explorations of the Poincaré model using *Cabri Geometry II* and *Geometer's Sketchpad* enable students to discover concepts of hyperbolic geometry before their formal presentation. (2) At the suggestion of several instructors, a new statement clarifies the "left versus right" distinction for sensed parallels. (3) The section on elliptic geometry now contains more guided directions for exploring double elliptic geometry via a spherical model.
- *Chapter 3*: (1) An initial discussion introduces the concept of symmetry and new explorations emphasize constructive understanding of the Euclidean transformations. In particular, reflections, rotations, translations and glide reflections are explored before the analytic model is set up and used to confirm properties of these transformations. (2) The early introduction of these transformations necessitates revisions of several theorems and their proofs. And the theorem showing that all isometries are

products of reflections has been restated to spell out the exact products involved. (3) Vectors are now used in the definition of translations, glide reflections, and dilations. (4) The particular linear transformations used are now correctly referred to as "affine."

- *Chapter 4*: Several exercise sets now include pointers to web-based instructions for carrying out specific exercises using dynamic geometry software.

Appreciation

For the additions to this second edition, I owe much to the people in our St. Olaf "geometry group," Martha Wallace and Richard Allen, faculty members of the St. Olaf mathematics department, and Dale Pearson, a secondary mathematics teacher in St. Paul, Minnesota. Their hard work and professional expertise were vital to the success of the St. Olaf geometry projects[4] for which early versions of some of these materials were prepared. Their inspiration and suggestions have supported my continued development of these materials.

In addition to the encouragement offered by these people, I am indebted to my students and to the participants in our geometry workshops for their willingness to use early versions and their thoughtful suggestions for improvements. Also, I must once again acknowledge the wonderfully encouraging environment provided by my colleagues in the St. Olaf mathematics department and, most importantly, by my husband Jim.

I am also very grateful for the support given me during two terms as a visitor in other departments: (1) the University of Washington mathematics department, during the 1991–92 academic year where James King encouraged my initial efforts at writing geometry lab

---

[4] These projects and their culminating national conferences were supported by the National Science Foundation through Teacher Enhancement Projects TPE8955118 and ESI9355671.

materials;[5] and (2) the mathematics and statistics department at the University of Canterbury in Christchurch New Zealand during the 1998–99 academic year where kind hospitality and wonderful facilities enabled me to accomplish most of the final work on this project.

Several of the changes and corrections included in this edition have been made as a result of suggestions of others. In addition to those already thanked in the third printing (David Flesner, Ockle Johnson, and Myrtle Lewin), I must add my thanks to Steven Hetzler, Janelle Sharoni, and John Wolfskill.

Note to Instructors

I have found that incorporating geometric explorations and fractal geometry in the courses I teach makes them more rewarding for both my students and myself. I sincerely hope that materials in this text will be rewarding for you and your students as well. Toward this end, I offer these suggestions.

- *Use of Explorations*: The explorations are intended to supplement and enhance student understanding (but a course based on the text can be taught without these sections). They can be used either in scheduled classes/labs or as assignments to be completed outside of formal class meetings. The explorations are designed to be done by students without instructor guidance and are most effective when used by groups of two or three with group members alternating roles as instruction reader, implementer, etc. To allow scheduling flexibility in Chapter 3, definitions first introduced in an exploration are restated later as needed.
- *Chapter Sequencing*: The new fractal geometry chapter (Chapter 5) is designed as a sequel to Chapter 3. So a course can be based on Chapters 1–3 plus either Chapter 4 or 5. If only Chapter 4 is used, Chapter 5 can be assigned to interested students as an

---

[5] The development of the original geometry labs was partially supported by the FIPSE funded project, Materials Development for Advanced Computing in the Undergraduate Mathematics Curriculum, P116B10330.

independent study project. If both Chapters 4 and 5 are used, the order of coverage of the chapters can be interchanged.

- *Supplementary References*: To find more information about the recommendations and references noted previously, check the following sources.

  - COMAP (1990). *Geometry's Future*, Arlington MA: COMAP.
  - King, James and Schattschneider, Doris (1997). *Geometry Turned On! Dynamic Software in Learning, Teaching, and Research*, MAA Notes 41.
  - NRC. (1989). *Everybody Counts*, National Research Council.
  - Lehrer, Richard, and Chazan, Daniel (1998). *Designing Learning Environments for Developing Understanding of Geometry and Space*, Mahwah NJ: Lawrence Erlbaum Associates, Inc.
  - NCTM (1989). *Curriculum and Evaluation Standards for School Mathematics*, Reston VA: National Council of Teachers of Mathematics.
  - NCTM (1998). *Principles and Standards for School Mathematics: Discussion Draft*, Reston VA: National Council of Teachers of Mathematics.

- *New Secondary Mathematics Curricula*:

  - COMAP (1998). *Mathematics: Modeling Our World*, Cincinnati OH: South-Western Educational Publishing.
  - Core-Plus Mathematics Project (1998). *Contemporary Mathematics in Context*, Chicago: Everyday Learning Corporation.
  - Fendel, D., Resek, D., Alper L., and Fraser S. (1998). *Interactive Mathematics Program*, Berkeley: Key Curriculum Press.

- *Text Website*: This site contains the dynamic software explorations and a list of other suggested resources:
  http://www.stolaf.edu/people/cederj/geotext/info.htm.

Judith N. Cederberg
cederj@stolaf.edu
http://www.stolaf.edu/people/cederj/

Preface to the First Edition

The origins of geometry are lost in the mists of ancient history, but geometry was already the preeminent area of Greek mathematics over 20 centuries ago. As such, it became the primary subject of Euclid's *Elements*. The *Elements* was the first major example of a formal axiomatic system and became a model for mathematical reasoning. However, the eventual discoveries of non-Euclidean geometries profoundly affected both mathematical and philosophical understanding of the nature of mathematics. The relation between Euclidean and non-Euclidean geometries became apparent with the development of projective geometry—a geometry with origins in artists' questions about perspective.

This interesting historical background and the major philosophical questions raised by developments in geometry are virtually unknown to current students, who often view geometry as a dead subject full of two-column proofs of patently clear results. It is no surprise that Mary Kantowski, in an article entitled "Impact of Computing on Geometry," has called geometry "the most troubled and controversial topic in school mathematics today" (Fey, 1984, p. 31). However, this and many other recent articles provide evidence for an increasing realization that the concepts and methods of geometry are becoming more important than ever in this age of computer graphics. The geometry of the artists, projective geometry, has become the tool of computer scientists and engineers as they work on the frontiers of CAD/CAM (computer-aided design/computer-aided manufacturing) technology.

The major emphasis of this text is on the geometries developed after Euclid's *Elements* (circa 300 B.C.). In addition to the primary goal of studying these "newer" geometries, this study provides an excellent opportunity to explore aspects of the history of mathematics. Also, since algebraic techniques are frequently used, this study demonstrates the interaction of several areas of mathematics and serves to develop geometrical insights into mathematical results that previously appeared to be completely abstract in nature.

Since Euclid's geometry is historically the first major example of an axiomatic system and since one of the major goals of teaching geometry in high school is to expose students to deductive reasoning, Chapter 1 begins with a general description of axiomatic (or deductive) systems. Following this general introduction, several finite geometries are presented as examples of specific systems. These finite geometries not only demonstrate some of the concepts that occur in the geometries of Chapters 2 through 4, but also indicate the breadth of geometrical study.

In Chapter 2, Euclid's geometry is first covered in order to provide historical and mathematical preparation for the major topic of non-Euclidean geometries. This brief exposure to Euclid's system serves both to recall familiar results of Euclidean geometry and to show how few substantial changes have occurred in Euclidean geometry since Euclid formulated it. The non-Euclidean geometries are then introduced to demonstrate that these geometries, which appear similar to Euclidean geometry, have properties that are radically different from comparable Euclidean properties.

The beginning of Chapter 3 serves as a transition from the synthetic approach of the previous chapters to the analytic treatment contained in the remainder of this chapter and the next. There follows a presentation of Klein's definition of geometry, which emphasizes geometrical transformations. The subsequent study of the transformations of the Euclidean plane begins with isometries and similarities, and then progresses to the more general transformations called affinities.

By using an axiomatic approach and generalizing the transformations of the Euclidean plane, Chapter 4 offers an introduction to projective geometry and demonstrates that this geometry provides a general framework within which the geometries of Chapters 2 and 3 can be placed. Mathematically, the next logical step in this process is the study of topology, which is usually covered in a separate course.

This text is designed for college-level survey courses in geometry. Many of the students in these courses are planning to pursue secondary-school teaching. However, with the renewed interest in geometry, other students interested in further work in mathematics or computer science will find the background provided by these courses increasingly valuable. These survey courses can also serve as an excellent vehicle for demonstrating the relationships between mathematics and other liberal arts disciplines. In an attempt to encourage student reading that further explores these relationships, each chapter ends with a section that lists suggested bibliographic sources for relevant topics in art, history, applications, and so on. I have found that having groups of students research and report on these topics not only introduces them to the wealth of expository writing in mathematics, but also provides a way for them to share their acquired insights into the liberal arts nature of mathematics.

The material contained in this text is most appropriate for junior or senior mathematics majors. The only geometric prerequisite is some familiarity with elementary secondary-school geometry. Since the text makes frequent use of matrix algebra and occasional references to more general concepts of linear algebra, a background in elementary linear algebra is helpful. Because the text introduces the concept of a group and explores properties of geometric transformations, a course based on this text provides excellent preparation for the standard undergraduate course in abstract algebra.

I am especially grateful for the patient support of my husband and the general encouragement of my colleagues in the St. Olaf Mathematics Department. In particular, I wish to thank our department chair, Theodore Vessey, for his support and our secretary, Donna Brakke, for her assistance. I am indebted to the many St. Olaf alumni who studied from early drafts of the text and to Charles M. Lindsay for his encouragement after using preliminary versions of the text in his courses at Coe College in Cedar Rapids, Iowa. Others who used a preliminary version of the text and made helpful suggestions are Thomas Q. Sibley of St. John's University in Collegeville, Minnesota, and Martha L. Wallace of St. Olaf College. I am also indebted to Joseph Malkevitch of York College of the City University of New York for serving as mathematical reader for the text, and to Christina Mikulak for her careful editorial work.

Judith N. Cederberg

Contents

---

* Supplementary dynamic geometry software activities using *Cabri Geometry II* and *Geometer's Sketchpad* are available at the website: http://www.stolaf.edu/ people/cederj/geotext/info.htm.

1 CHAPTER

Axiomatic Systems and Finite Geometries

1.1 Gaining Perspective*

Finite geometries were developed in the late nineteenth century, in part to demonstrate and test the axiomatic properties of *completeness, consistency,* and *independence*. They are introduced in this chapter to fulfill this historical role and to develop both an appreciation for and an understanding of the revolution in mathematical and philosophical thought brought about by the development of non-Euclidean geometry. In addition, finite geometries provide relatively simple axiomatic systems in which we can begin to develop the skills and techniques of geometric reasoning. The finite geometries introduced in Sections 1.3 and 1.5 also illustrate some of the fundamental properties of non-Euclidean and projective geometry.

Even though finite geometries were developed as abstract systems, mathematicians have applied these abstract ideas in designing statistical experiments using Latin squares and in developing error-correcting codes in computer science. Section 1.4 develops a simple

---

* Supplementary dynamic geometry software activities are available at the website: http://www.stolaf.edu/people/cederj/geotext/info.htm.

error-correcting code and shows its connection with finite projective geometries. The application of finite affine geometries to the building of Latin squares is equally intriguing. Since Latin squares are clearly described in several readily accessible sources, the reader is encouraged to explore this topic by consulting the resources listed at the end of this chapter.

In studying finite axiomatic systems, you are encouraged to take advantage of the visual nature of geometry by constructing illustrations. These can be drawn using paper and pencil, or built with concrete objects such as yarn and game chips. While working through this first chapter, you are also encouraged to become familiar with dynamic geometry software (DGS). This new tool enables accurate renditions of traditional compass and straightedge constructions that then can be dynamically rearranged by dragging initial objects. Introductions featuring activities that review basic ideas in Euclidean geometry are available for both *Geometer's Sketchpad* and *Cabri Geometry* at the website: http://www.stolaf.edu/people/cederj/geotext/info.htm. You are encouraged to become familiar with one or both of these programs so that you can carry out explorations suggested in Chapters 2 through 5.

1.2   Axiomatic Systems

The study of any mathematics requires an understanding of the nature of deductive reasoning; frequently, geometry has been singled out for introducing this methodology to secondary school students. There are important historical reasons for choosing geometry to fulfill this role, but these reasons are seldom revealed to secondary school initiates. This section introduces the terminology essential for a discussion of deductive reasoning so that the extraordinary influence of the history of geometry on the modern understanding of deductive systems will become evident.

Deductive reasoning takes place in the context of an organized logical structure called an *axiomatic* (or *deductive*) system. Such a system consists of the components listed below:

Components of an Axiomatic System

1. Undefined terms.
2. Defined terms.
3. Axioms.
4. A system of logic.
5. Theorems.

Undefined terms are included since it is not possible to define all terms without resorting to circular definitions. In geometrical systems these undefined terms frequently, but not necessarily, include *point, line, plane* and *on*. *Defined terms* are not actually necessary, but in nearly every axiomatic system certain phrases involving undefined terms are used repeatedly. Thus, it is more efficient to substitute a new term, that is, a defined term, for each of these phrases whenever they occur. For example, in Euclidean geometry we substitute the term "parallel lines" for the phrase "lines that do not intersect." Furthermore, it is impossible to prove all statements constructed from the defined and undefined terms of the system without circular reasoning, just as it is impossible to define all terms. So an initial set of statements is accepted without proof. The statements that are accepted without proof are known as *axioms*. From the axioms, other statements can be deduced or proved using the rules of inference of a *system of logic* (usually Aristotelian). These latter statements are called *theorems*.

As noted earlier, the axioms of a system must be statements constructed using the terms of the system. But they cannot be arbitrarily constructed since an axiom system must be consistent.

Definition 1.1
An axiomatic system is said to be *consistent* if there do not exist in the system any two axioms, any axiom and theorem, or any two theorems that contradict each other.

It should be clear that it is essential that an axiomatic system be consistent, since a system in which both a statement and its negation can be proved is worthless. However, it soon becomes evident that it would be difficult to verify consistency directly from this definition, since all possible theorems would have to be considered.

Instead, models are used for establishing consistency. A *model* of an axiomatic system is obtained by assigning interpretations to the undefined terms so as to convert the axioms into true statements in the interpretations. If the model is obtained by using interpretations that are objects and relations adapted from the real world, we say we have established *absolute consistency*. In this case, statements corresponding to any contradictory theorems would lead to contradictory statements in the model, but contradictions in the real world are supposedly impossible. On the other hand, if the interpretations assigned are taken from another axiomatic system, we have only tested consistency relative to the consistency of the second axiomatic system; that is, the system we are testing is consistent only if the system within which the interpretations are assigned is consistent. In this second case, we say we have demonstrated *relative consistency* of the first axiomatic system. Because of the number of elements in many axiomatic systems, relative consistency is the best we are able to obtain. We illustrate the use of models to determine consistency of the axiomatic system for four-point geometry.

Axioms for Four-Point Geometry

Undefined Terms. Point, line, on.
Axiom 4P.1. There exist exactly four points.
Axiom 4P.2. Two distinct points are on exactly one line.
Axiom 4P.3. Each line is on exactly two points.

Before demonstrating the consistency of this system, it may be helpful to make some observations about these three statements which will also apply to other axioms in this text. Axiom 4P.1 explicitly guarantees the existence of exactly four points. However, even though lines are mentioned in Axioms 4P.2 and 4P.3, we cannot ascertain whether or not lines exist until theorems verifying this are proved, since there is no axiom that explicitly insures their existence. This is true even though in this system the proof of the existence of lines is almost immediate. Axioms 4P.2 and 4P.3, like many mathematical statements, are disguised "if ... then" statements. Axiom 4P.2 should be interpreted as follows: If two distinct points exist,

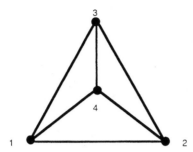

FIGURE 1.1 A four-point geometry model.

then these two points are on exactly one line. Similarly, Axiom 4P.3 should be interpreted: If there is a line, then it is on exactly two points. In other axiomatic systems, we will discover that the axioms actually lead to theorems telling us that there are many more points and/or lines than those guaranteed to exist by the axioms.

These observations suggest that the construction of any model for four-point geometry must begin with the objects known to exist, that is, four points. In model 4P.1 these points are interpreted as the letters A, B, C, D whereas in model 4P.2 (see Fig. 1.1) these points are interpreted as dots. In continuing to build either model, we must interpret the remaining undefined terms so as to create a system in which Axioms 4P.2 and 4P.3 become true statements.

Model 4P.1

Undefined Term	Interpretation
Points	Letters A, B, C, D
Lines	Columns of letters given below
On	Contains, or is contained in

Lines					
A	A	A	B	B	C
B	C	D	C	D	D

Model 4P.2

Undefined Term	Interpretation
Points	Dots denoted 1, 2, 3, 4
Lines	Segments illustrated in Fig. 1.1
On	A dot is an endpoint of a segment or vice versa

There are several other important properties that an axiomatic system *may* possess.

Definition 1.2
An axiom in an axiomatic system is *independent* if it cannot be proved from the other axioms. If each axiom of a system is independent, the system is said to be independent.

Clearly an independent system is more elegant since no unnecessary assumptions are made. However, the increased difficulty of working in an independent system becomes obvious when we merely note that accepting fewer statements without proof leaves more statements to be proved. For this reason the axiomatic systems used in secondary-school geometry are seldom independent.

The verification that an axiomatic system is independent is also done via models. The independence of Axiom A in an axiomatic system S is established by finding a model of the system S' where S' is the system obtained from S by replacing Axiom A with a negation of A. Thus, to demonstrate that a system consisting of n axioms is independent, n models must be exhibited—one for each axiom. The independence of the axiomatic system for four-point geometry is demonstrated by the following three models, all of which interpret points as letters of the alphabet and lines as the columns of letters indicated.

Models Demonstrating Independence of Axioms for Four-Point Geometry

Model 4P I.1
A model in which a negation of Axiom 4P.1 is true (i.e., there do not exist four points):

Points	Lines
A, B	A
	B

Since this model contains only two points, the negation of Axiom 4P.1 is clearly true and it is easy to show that Axioms 4P.2 and 4P.3 are true statements in this interpretation.

Model 4P I.2
A model in which a negation of Axiom 4P.2 is true (i.e., there are two distinct points not on one line):

Points	Lines	
A, B, C, D	A	C
	B	D

Note that in this model there is no line on points A and C. What other pairs of points fail to be on a line?

Model 4P I.3
A model in which a negation of Axiom 4P.3 is true (i.e., there are lines not on exactly two points):

Points	Lines			
A, B, C, D	A	A	B	C
	B	D	D	D
	C			

In this model one line is on three points, whereas the remaining lines are each on two points, so the negation of Axiom 4P.3 is true in this interpretation.

Since we have demonstrated the independence of each of the axioms of four-point geometry, we have shown that this axiomatic system is independent.

Another property that an axiomatic system may possess is *completeness*.

Definition 1.3
An axiomatic system is *complete* if every statement containing undefined and defined terms of the system can be proved valid or invalid, or in other words, if it is not possible to add a new independent axiom to the system.

In general, it is impossible to demonstrate directly that a system is complete. However, if a system is complete, there cannot exist two essentially different models. This means all models of the system must be pairwise *isomorphic*.

Definition 1.4

Two models α and β of an axiomatic system are said to be *isomorphic* if there exists a one-to-one correspondence ϕ from the set of points and lines of α onto the set of points and lines of β that preserves all relations. In particular if the undefined terms of the system consist of the terms "point," "line," and "on," then ϕ must satisfy the following conditions:

1. For each point P and line l in α, $\phi(P)$ and $\phi(l)$ are a point and line in β.
2. If P is on l, then $\phi(P)$ is on $\phi(l)$.

If all models of a system are pairwise isomorphic, it is clear that each model has the same number of points and lines. Furthermore, if a new independent axiom could be added to the system, there would be two distinct models of the system: a model α in which the new axiom would be valid and a model β in which the new axiom would *not* be valid. The models α and β could not then be isomorphic. Hence, if all models of the system are necessarily isomorphic, it follows that the system is complete.

In the example of the four-point geometry, it is clear that models 4P.1 and 4P.2 are isomorphic. The verification that all models of this system are isomorphic follows readily once the following theorem is verified (see Exercises 5 and 6).

Theorem 4P.1

There are exactly six lines in the four-point geometry.

Finally, any discussion of the properties of axiomatic systems must include mention of the important result contained in Gödel's theorem. Greatly simplified, this result says that any consistent axiomatic system comprehensive enough to contain the results of elementary number theory is not complete.

Exercises

For Exercises 1–4, consider the following axiomatic system:

Axioms for Three-Point Geometry

Undefined Terms. Point, line, on.
Axiom 3P.1. There exist exactly three points.
Axiom 3P.2. Two distinct points are on exactly one line.
Axiom 3P.3. Not all points are on the same line.
Axiom 3P.4. Two distinct lines are on at least one common point.

1. (a) Prove that this system is consistent. (b) Did the proof in part (a) demonstrate absolute consistency or relative consistency? Explain.

2. Prove that this system is independent.

3. Prove the following theorems in this system: (a) Two distinct lines are on exactly one point. (b) Every line is on exactly two points. (c) There are exactly three lines.

4. Is this system complete? Why?

5. Prove Theorem 4P.1.

6. Prove that any two models of four-point geometry are isomorphic.

Use the following definition in Exercises 7 and 8.

Definition
The *dual* of a statement p in four-point geometry is obtained by replacing each occurrence of the term "point" in p by the term "line" and each occurrence of the term "line" in p by the term "point."

7. Obtain an axiomatic system for *four-line geometry* by dualizing the axioms for four-point geometry.

8. Verify that the dual of Theorem 4P.1 will be a theorem of four-line geometry. How would its proof differ from the proof of Theorem 4P.1 in Exercise 5?

1.3   Finite Projective Planes

As indicated by the examples in the previous section, there are geometries consisting of only a finite number of points and lines. In this section we will consider an axiomatic system for an important collection of finite geometries known as *finite projective planes*. These geometries may, at first glance, look much like finite versions of plane Euclidean geometry. However, there is a very important difference. In a finite projective plane, each pair of lines intersects; that is, there are no parallel lines. This pairwise intersection of lines leads to several other differences between projective planes and Euclidean planes. A few of these differences will become apparent in this section; others will not become evident until we study general plane projective geometry in Chapter 4.

Some of the first results in the study of finite projective geometries were obtained by von Staudt in 1856, but it wasn't until early in this century that finite geometries assumed a prominent role in mathematics. Since then, the study of these geometries has grown considerably and there are still a number of unsolved problems currently engaging researchers in this area.

Axioms for Finite Projective Planes

Undefined Terms. Point, line, incident.

Defined Terms. Points incident with the same line are said to be *collinear*. Lines incident with the same point are said to be *concurrent*.

Axiom P.1. There exist at least four distinct points, no three of which are collinear.

Axiom P.2. There exists at least one line with exactly $n + 1$ ($n > 1$) distinct points incident with it.

Axiom P.3. Given two distinct points, there is exactly one line incident with both of them.

Axiom P.4. Given two distinct lines, there is at least one point incident with both of them.

Any set of points and lines satisfying these axioms is called a *projective plane of order n*. Note that the word "incident" has been used in place of the undefined term "on" in this axiom system, since "incident" is commonly used in the study of general projective planes.

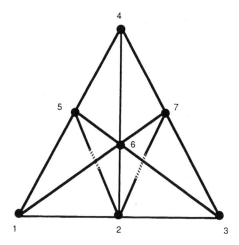

FIGURE 1.2 A finite projective plane model.

The consistency of this axiomatic system is demonstrated by either of the following models which use the same interpretations as models 4P.1 and 4P.2 in Section 1.2.

Model P.1

Points	Lines						
A, B, C, D, E, F, G	A	A	B	A	B	C	C
	B	D	D	F	E	D	E
	C	E	F	G	G	G	F

Model P.2

Points	Lines
Dots denoted 1, 2, 3, 4, 5, 6, 7	Segments illustrated in Fig. 1.2

Note that Models P.1 and P.2 depict a projective plane of order 2 and both have exactly three points on each line, but there are projective planes with more than three points on a line as shown by the next model.

Model P.3

Points	Lines												
$A, B, C, D, E,$	A	A	A	A	B	B	B	C	C	C	D	D	D
$F, G, H, I, J,$	B	E	H	K	E	F	G	E	F	G	E	F	G
K, L, M	C	F	I	L	H	I	J	I	J	H	J	H	I
	D	G	J	M	K	L	M	M	K	L	L	M	K

Whereas models P.1 and P.2 have three points on each line, three lines on each point, and a total of seven points and seven lines, model P.3 has four points on each line, four lines on each point, and a total of thirteen points and thirteen lines. To determine if finite projective planes exist with more points and lines, it is clearly impractical to employ trial-and-error procedures. Instead we develop a series of theorems that lead to a general result regarding the number of points and lines in a finite projective plane of order n.

The proofs of these theorems are simplified by noting that this axiom system satisfies the *principle of duality*, which Coxeter has described as "one of the most elegant properties of projective geometry" (Coxeter, 1969, p. 231). As noted in the exercises in Section 1.2, the *dual* of a statement is obtained by replacing each occurrence of the word "point" by the word "line" and vice versa (consequently, the words "concurrent" and "collinear" must also be interchanged).

Definition 1.5
An axiomatic system in which the dual of any theorem is also a theorem is said to satisfy the *principle of duality*.

Thus, in an axiomatic system that satisfies the principle of duality, the proof of any theorem can be "turned into" a proof of a dual theorem merely by dualizing the original proof. To show that an axiom system has the property of duality it is necessary to prove that the duals of each axiom are theorems of the system. The theorems that are the dual statements of the four axioms of this system are listed here. The proofs of the duals of Axioms P.1, P.3, and P.4 are left to you.

Theorem P.1 (Dual of Axiom P.1)
There exist at least four distinct lines, no three of which are concurrent.

Theorem P.2 (Dual of Axiom P.3)
Given two distinct lines, there is exactly one point incident with both of them.

Theorem P.3 (Dual of Axiom P.4)
Given two distinct points, there is at least one line incident with both of them.

Theorem P.4 (Dual of Axiom P.2)
There exists at least one point with exactly $n + 1$ ($n > 1$) distinct lines incident with it.

Proof

By Axiom P.2 there is a line l with $n + 1$ points $P_1, P_2, \ldots, P_{n+1}$ and by Axiom P.1 there is a point P not incident with l. Then by Axiom P.3 there exist lines $l_1, l_2, \ldots, l_{n+1}$ joining the point P to points $P_1, P_2, \ldots, P_{n+1}$, respectively (see Fig. 1.3). It is sufficient to show that these lines are all distinct and that there are no other lines through P. If $l_i = l_j$ for $i \neq j$ then the two points P_i and P_j would be incident with both l and $l_i = l_j$, and it would follow by Axiom P.3 that $l = l_i = l_j$. But P is on l_i and *not* on l so we have a contradiction. Thus, $l_i \neq l_j$ for $i \neq j$. Now assume there is an additional line, l_{n+2} through P. This line must also intersect l at a point Q (Axiom P.4). Since l has exactly $n + 1$ points, Q must be one of the points $P_1, \ldots, P_{n+1}$. Assume $Q = P_1$, then, since $Q = P_1$ and P are two distinct points on both l_1 and l_{n+2}, it follows that $l_{n+2} = l_1$. Therefore, the point P is incident with exactly $n + 1$ lines. ∎

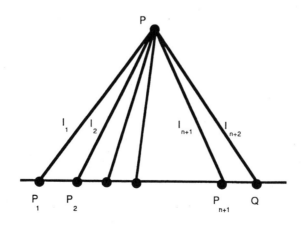

FIGURE 1.3 Proof P.4.

The previous proof demonstrates several geometric conventions. First, to make the proof less awkward, the phrase "is incident with" is frequently replaced by a variety of other familiar terms such as "is on," "contains," and "through." The meanings of these substitute terms should be obvious by their context. Second, uppercase letters are used to designate points while lowercase letters are used for lines. Finally, since diagrams are extremely helpful both in constructing and following a proof, figures are included as part of the proofs whenever appropriate; but the narrative portions of the proofs are constructed so as to be completely independent of the figures.

In models P.1, P.2, and P.3, the number of points on each line and the number of lines on each point is the same for all lines and points in each model. That this must be true in general is verified by the following theorems.

Theorem P.5

In a projective plane of order n, each point is incident with exactly $n + 1$ lines.

Proof

Let P be a point of the plane. Axiom P.2 guarantees the existence of a line l containing $n + 1$ points, $P_1, P_2, \ldots, P_{n+1}$. Then there are

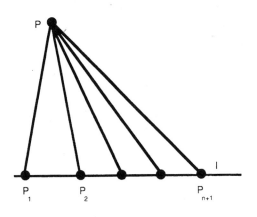

FIGURE 1.4 Proof P.5, P not on l.

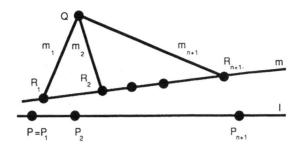

FIGURE 1.5 Proof P.5, P on l.

two cases to consider, depending on whether P is on l or not (see Figs. 1.4 and 1.5).

Case 1 (P is not on l): If P is not on l there are at least $n + 1$ lines through P, namely, the lines joining P to each of the points $P_1, P_2, \ldots, P_{n+1}$. Just as in the proof of the previous theorem, it can be shown that these lines are distinct and there are no other lines through P. So in this case there are exactly $n + 1$ lines through P.

Case 2 (P is on l): Assume $P = P_1$. Axiom P.1 guarantees the existence of a point Q not on l. It is also possible to verify the existence of a line m that contains neither P nor Q (see Exercise 7). By case 1, Q is on exactly $n + 1$ lines $m_1, m_2, \ldots, m_{n+1}$. But each of these lines intersects m in a point R_i for $i = 1, \ldots, n + 1$. It can easily be shown that these points are distinct and that these are the only points on line m. Thus, P is not on the line m, which contains exactly $n + 1$ points, so as in case 1, P is incident with exactly $n + 1$ lines. ∎

With this theorem in hand, the following theorem follows immediately by duality.

Theorem P.6

In a projective plane of order n, each line is incident with exactly $n + 1$ points.

Using these results, we can now determine the total number of points and lines in a projective plane of order n.

Theorem P.7

A projective plane of order n contains exactly $n^2 + n + 1$ points and $n^2 + n + 1$ lines.

Proof

Let P be a point in a projective plane of order n. Then every other point is on exactly one line joining it with the point P. By Theorem P.5 there are exactly $n + 1$ lines through P and by Theorem P.6 each of these lines contains exactly $n+1$ points, that is, n points in addition to P. Thus, the total number of points is $(n+1)n+1 = n^2+n+1$. A dual argument verifies that the total number of lines is also n^2+n+1. ∎

Thus, a finite projective plane of order two must have seven points and seven lines and a projective plane of order three must have thirteen points and thirteen lines. But one of the unresolved questions in the study of finite geometries is the determination of the orders for which finite projective planes exist. A partial answer to this question was given in 1906 when Veblen and Bussey proved that there exist finite projective planes of order n whenever n is a power of a prime. It has long been conjectured that these are the only orders for which finite projective planes exist. In 1949 Bruck and Ryser proved that if n is congruent to 1 or 2 (modulo 4), and if n cannot be written as the sum of two squares, then there are no projective planes of order n. This proved the conjecture for an infinite number of cases including $n = 6, 14, 21$, and 22. However, it also left open an infinite number of cases including $n = 10, 12, 15, 18$, and 20. In late 1988, a group of researchers in the computer science department at Concordia University in Montreal completed a case-by-case computer analysis requiring several thousand hours of computer time. By investigating the implications of the existence of an order 10 projective plane, they concluded that the conjecture is also correct for $n = 10$; that is, finite projective planes of order 10 do not exist. This leaves $n = 12$ as the smallest number for which the conjecture is unproved (Cipra, 1988).

The study of the infinite projective plane from both synthetic and analytic viewpoints yields a wealth of interesting geometric properties which are generalizations of both Euclidean and non-Euclidean properties. We pursue this study in Chapter 4, following an introduction of non-Euclidean geometry (Chapter 2) and the development of an analytic model for Euclidean geometry (Chapter 3). However, as we shall see in the following section, even one of the simplest projective geometries, namely the finite projective plane of order 2, has an application that demonstrates the relevance of geometry to exciting new areas of mathematics.

Exercises

1. Which axioms for a finite projective plane are also valid in Euclidean geometry? Which are not?

2. Prove that the axiomatic system for finite projective planes is incomplete.

3. Verify that models P.1 and P.2 are isomorphic.

4. Prove Theorem P.1.

5. Prove Theorem P.2.

6. Prove Theorem P.3.

7. Verify the existence of the line m used in case 2 of the proof of Theorem P.5.

8. How many points and lines does a finite projective plane of order 7 have?

The axioms for a *finite affine plane of order n* are given below. The undefined terms and definitions are identical to those for a finite projective plane.

Axioms for Finite Affine Planes

Axiom A.1. There exist at least four distinct points, no three of which are collinear.

Axiom A.2. There exists at least one line with exactly n ($n > 1$) points on it.

Axiom A.3. Given two distinct points, there is exactly one line incident with both of them.

Axiom A.4. Given a line l and a point P not on l, there is exactly one line through P that does not intersect l.

9. How do the axioms for a finite affine plane differ from those for a finite projective plane?

10. Show that a finite affine plane does not satisfy the principle of duality.

11. Find models of affine planes of orders 2 and 3.

The following exercises ask you to prove a series of theorems about finite affine planes. You should prove these in the order indicated since some will require that you use a previous result.

12. Prove: In an affine plane of order n, each point lies on exactly $n + 1$ lines. [*Hint*: Consider two cases as in the proof of Theorem P.5.]

13. Prove: In an affine plane of order n, each line contains exactly n points.

14. Prove: In an affine plane of order n, each line l has exactly $n - 1$ lines that do not intersect l.

15. Prove: In an affine plane of order n, there are exactly n^2 points and $n^2 + n$ lines.

16. Verify that if one line and its points are deleted from the finite projective plane of order 2 given in model P.1 or P.2, the remaining points and lines form a model of an affine plane. What is its order?

1.4 An Application to Error-Correcting Codes

The finite projective plane of order 2 illustrated in models P.1 and P.2 of the previous section is known as a *Fano plane*. A concise way of representing this and other finite planes is a configuration known as an *incidence table*. The lines of the plane are represented by columns in Table 1.1, while the points of the plane are represented by rows. Entries of 0 and 1 represent nonincidence and incidence, respectively.

This table demonstrates that we can represent each point in a Fano plane uniquely by a vector consisting of the entries in the corresponding row of the incidence table. Thus, point A can be represented by the vector $(1, 0, 0, 0, 0, 1, 1)$. Similarly, every point in a

TABLE 1.1 Incidence Table for a Fano Plane.

	l_1	l_2	l_3	l_4	l_5	l_6	l_7
A	1	0	0	0	0	1	1
B	0	1	0	0	1	0	1
C	0	0	1	0	1	1	0
D	1	0	0	1	1	0	0
E	0	1	0	1	0	1	0
F	0	0	1	1	0	0	1
G	1	1	1	0	0	0	0

Fano plane can be represented by a binary 7-tuple; that is, a vector with seven components, each of which is a 0 or 1. Note that the vector for any given point contains exactly three 1's, so in the language of coding theory, we say that each vector has *weight* 3. Following a brief introduction to the area of coding theory, we shall see that these seven vectors play an important role in an elementary error-correcting code.

Coding theory is devoted to the detection and correction of errors that are introduced when messages are transmitted. Such codes have found application in transmission of pictures from space and in the development of the compact disk. The impetus for developing these codes arose from the frustrations that Richard W. Hamming encountered in 1947 when working with a mechanical relay computer, which dumped his program whenever it detected an error. Having a computer that could detect but not find and correct an error led to the development of error-correcting codes.

Since then, coding theory has become an important research area, using results from projective geometry, group theory, the theory of finite fields, and linear programming. Error-correcting coding has been described as "the art of adding redundancy efficiently so that most messages, if distorted, can be correctly decoded" (Pless, 1982, p. 2).

One of the simplest error-correcting codes is a projective geometry code known as the *Hamming (7,4) code*. This code can be generated by the four rows of the matrix G below, known as the *generator matrix* for the code. In this matrix, the first row vector is the code word for 1000, the binary representation of the decimal number 8; the second row is the code word for 0100, the binary representation of the decimal number 4; and so on. The first four digits of these code words occupy the so-called *information positions*, since they represent the actual number or message to be transmitted. The remaining three positions are called the *redundancy positions*.

$$G = \begin{bmatrix} 1 & 0 & 0 & 0 & 0 & 1 & 1 \\ 0 & 1 & 0 & 0 & 1 & 0 & 1 \\ 0 & 0 & 1 & 0 & 1 & 1 & 0 \\ 0 & 0 & 0 & 1 & 1 & 1 & 1 \end{bmatrix}$$

Other code words are obtained by adding these rows where the addition is the usual componentwise vector addition modulo 2. Note that when we find all possible sums of these rows (see Table 1.2), we obtain in the first four positions all 16 possible strings of 0's and 1's; that is, all binary representations of the decimal numbers 0 through 15.

The redundancy digits in the last three positions allow single error corrections; that is, if a transmitted message contains a single digit error these extra digits allow us to find and correct the error.

TABLE 1.2 Possible Code Words.

0	0	0	0	0	0	0	Adding no words
1	0	0	0	0	1	1	Adding one word
0	1	0	0	1	0	1	
0	0	1	0	1	1	0	
0	0	0	1	1	1	1	
1	1	0	0	1	1	0	Adding two words
1	0	1	0	1	0	1	
1	0	0	1	1	0	0	
0	1	1	0	0	1	1	
0	1	0	1	0	1	0	
0	0	1	1	0	0	1	
1	1	1	0	0	0	0	Adding three words
1	1	0	1	0	0	1	
1	0	1	1	0	1	0	
0	1	1	1	1	0	0	
1	1	1	1	1	1	1	Adding four words

For example, the message $x = 1010010$ does not appear in Table 1.2 as a possible code word. Assuming that a single error has occurred in the transmission of a code word we can locate the error and correct it using the parity check matrix H. This parity check matrix consists of seven column vectors, which give the binary representations of the decimal numbers 1 through 7.

$$Hx = \begin{bmatrix} 0 & 0 & 0 & 1 & 1 & 1 & 1 \\ 0 & 1 & 1 & 0 & 0 & 1 & 1 \\ 1 & 0 & 1 & 0 & 1 & 0 & 1 \end{bmatrix} \begin{bmatrix} 1 \\ 0 \\ 1 \\ 0 \\ 0 \\ 1 \\ 0 \end{bmatrix} = \begin{bmatrix} 1 \\ 0 \\ 0 \end{bmatrix}$$

Since the result is $(1, 0, 0)$, namely, the binary representation of the decimal number 4, the error occurs in the fourth position; hence the original code word was 1011010. Similarly, we can show that each of the 2^7 possible binary 7-tuples differs from a possible code word in at most one digit; and if there is a difference, the digit in which the "error" occurs can be located with the parity check matrix. However, when an actual code word is multiplied by this parity check matrix, the result is $(0, 0, 0)$ (see Exercises 6 and 7).

The parity check matrix H can be thought of as the defining matrix for this code. Note that the matrix H clearly has rank 3, and since H is a 3×7 matrix it represents a linear transformation from a vector space of dimension 7 to one of dimension 3. As we recall from linear algebra the kernel of this linear transformation is the set of solutions of $Hx = 0$ and the dimension of this kernel is $7 - 3 = 4$. By demonstrating that $Hx = 0$ whenever x is a code word, we can show that the row vectors of the generator matrix G are basis vectors for this kernel. Thus, the code words of the Hamming $(7, 4)$ code from a subspace of a vector space. Any code for which the code words form a subspace is said to be *linear*.

The code words of the Hamming $(7, 4)$ code can be considered to be coordinates of points in a seven-dimensional space where the entire space consists of points corresponding to the 2^7 possible messages, that is, the possible binary 7-tuples. Distance in this space is defined in terms of a function known as the *Hamming distance*.

Definition

The *Hamming distance* $d(x, y)$ between two binary n-tuples x and y is the number of components by which the n-tuples differ.

Thus, if $x = 1001110$ and $y = 1011101$, $d(x, y) = 3$. Clearly, the maximum distance between binary 7-tuples is 7, and, as you can easily verify, the minimum distance between any pair of nonzero code words in the Hamming $(7, 4)$ code is 3. Since the minimum distance is 3 this is also known as the Hamming $(7, 4, 3)$ code. Also note that the distance between 0000000 and any other binary 7-tuple x is just the number of ones in x, that is, the weight of x. Thus the *minimum weight* of this code is said to be 3.

To further illustrate the role of the Hamming distance in the Hamming $(7, 4, 3)$ code, we first consider a more elementary code consisting of just the two code words 000 and 111. These two code words can be identified as opposite vertices in a three-dimensional cube with vertices consisting of all ordered triples of 0 and 1 where edges join pairs of vertices whose Hamming distance is 1, as shown in Fig. 1.6. Notice that the Hamming distance between two vertices in this cube counts the number of edges of the cube that must be traversed to go from one vertex to the other.

Whereas the Hamming distance between the two code words 000 and 111 is 3, the binary 3-tuples that could occur if exactly one error is made in transmitting the code word 000 would be those at distance

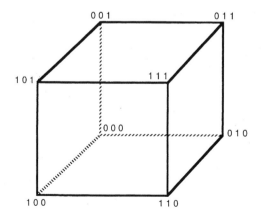

FIGURE 1.6 Cube determined by binary triples.

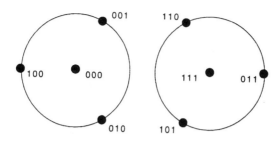

FIGURE 1.7   Spheres of binary 3-tuples.

1 from 000, namely, 001, 010, and 100. The set {001, 010, 100} is said to form a 1-*sphere*, centered at the code word 000. These same binary 3-tuples are located at a distance 2 from the other code word, 111. The vertex 111 is the center of a second 1-sphere consisting of all binary 3-tuples that could occur if exactly one error is made in transmitting 111 (Fig. 1.7). These two spheres partition the set of binary 3-tuples, so that every binary 3-tuple appears in one of these two spheres. Thus, if we assume that a given message contains one or fewer errors, we can decode it by locating the unique nearest code word.

Similarly, we can view the code words in the Hamming $(7, 4, 3)$ code as select vertices in a seven-dimensional cube where edges again join pairs of vertices located a Hamming distance of 1 unit apart. Here the minimum distance between code words is also 3 and all binary 7-tuples lie in a set of nonoverlapping 1-spheres that exhaust the seven-dimensional cube (see Exercise 6). The decoding process we are using is that of locating the nearest code word. Codes with the property that all possible messages lie within or on nonoverlapping spheres of radius t, are called *perfect t-error correcting codes*. Thus, the Hamming $(7, 4, 3)$ code, in addition to being linear, is a perfect 1-error-correcting code.

A result from coding theory (Blake, 1975, p. 185) shows that a perfect linear code is spanned by its minimum weight vectors. This means that the vectors of weight 3 span the Hamming $(7, 4, 3)$ code. As we can easily verify, these are the vectors in the rows of the incidence table for the Fano plane. Furthermore, the rows of the generator matrix G form a basis for this set.

Exercises

1. Show that the points and lines of the incidence table (Table 1.1) satisfy the axioms for a projective plane.

2. Demonstrate that the Fano plane given by the incidence table (Table 1.1) is isomorphic to that given in model P.1 of Section 1.3.

3. Verify that any pair of coordinate vectors in the incidence table (Table 1.1) differ in exactly four components, that is, their Hamming distance is 4.

4. Write out the binary representations of the decimal numbers 1 through 15.

5. Verify that there are exactly $2^7 - 16$ binary 7-tuples that are not code words in the Hamming $(7, 4, 3)$ code.

6. (a) Show that there are exactly seven binary 7-tuples that differ from the code word 1000011 in exactly one digit. (b) Apply the parity check matrix H to one of these seven and verify that it does locate the position in which the digit differs.

7. Show that $Hx = 0$ for each row vector in the generator matrix G.

8. Obtain all possible code words in the linear $(5, 3)$ binary code with generator matrix G'.

$$G' = \begin{bmatrix} 1 & 0 & 0 & 1 & 1 \\ 0 & 1 & 0 & 0 & 1 \\ 0 & 0 & 1 & 1 & 1 \end{bmatrix}$$

9. Show that the Hamming distance is a metric, that is, that it satisfies each of the following conditions:

   (i) $d(x, y) = 0$ iff $x = y$.

   (ii) $d(x, y) = d(y, x)$.

   (iii) $d(x, z) \leq d(x, y) + d(y, z)$.

10. Verify that the minimum distance between any pair of code words in the Hamming $(7, 4, 3)$ code is 3.

11. Show that the set of code words in the Hamming $(7, 4, 3)$ code can be obtained by adding the two 7-tuples 0000000 and 1111111 to the fourteen 7-tuples that occur either as rows of Table 1.1 or as rows of the incidence table obtained from Table 1.1 by interchanging 0's and 1's.

1.5 Desargues' Configurations

In this section we consider an axiomatic system for one more finite structure. We shall see that this structure not only satisfies the principle of duality but also exhibits an interesting relation between points and lines similar to the *polarity* relation of projective geometry. This relation involves points that do not lie on a line. Since the term "geometry" is usually reserved for structures in which each pair of points determines a unique line, we refer to the structures that satisfy our axioms as Desargues' configurations. Desargues' configurations are so named because they illustrate a theorem in real projective geometry known as *Desargues' theorem*. This theorem is stated in terms of two particular properties of triangles, that is, sets of three noncollinear points. If two triangles ABC and DEF have the

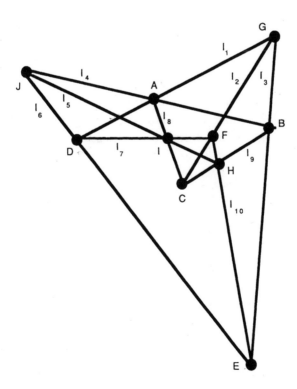

FIGURE 1.8 A Desargues' configuration.

property that lines joining corresponding vertices (i.e., *AD, BE, CF*) are concurrent, the triangles are said to be *perspective from a point*. Similarly, if the triangles possess the dual property that the intersections of corresponding sides are collinear, they are said to be *perspective from a line*. With these definitions, Desargues' theorem can be stated succinctly.

Desargues' Theorem
If two triangles are perspective from a point, then they are perspective from a line.

An example of a Desargues' configuration and its corresponding incidence table is shown in Fig. 1.8 and Table 1.3 (as in Section 1.4 entries of 0 and 1 represent nonincidence and incidence, respectively). As you can see, either from the configuration or the incidence table, *ABC* and *DEF* are triangles that are perspective from point *G* and line l_5.

Careful scrutiny of either the structure shown in Fig. 1.8 or the corresponding incidence table (Table 1.3) will lead to the observation that for each point *M* in the structure there is a line *m* such that no lines join *M* with points on *m*. The point *M* and line *m* are referred to as *pole* and *polar*, respectively. This *pole–polar* relation is described in detail by the following definitions and axioms.

TABLE 1.3 Incidence Table for a Desargues' Configuration.

	l_1	l_2	l_3	l_4	l_5	l_6	l_7	l_8	l_9	l_{10}
A	1	0	0	1	0	0	0	1	0	0
B	0	0	1	1	0	0	0	0	1	0
C	0	1	0	0	0	0	0	1	1	0
D	1	0	0	0	0	1	1	0	0	0
E	0	0	1	0	0	1	0	0	0	1
F	0	1	0	0	0	0	1	0	0	1
G	1	1	1	0	0	0	0	0	0	0
H	0	0	0	0	1	0	0	0	1	1
I	0	0	0	0	1	0	1	1	0	0
J	0	0	0	1	1	1	0	0	0	0

Axioms for Desargues' Configurations

Undefined Terms. Point, line, on.

Defined Terms. If there are no lines joining a point M with points on line m (M not on m), m is called a *polar* of M and M is called a *pole* of m.

Axiom DC.1. There exists at least one point.

Axiom DC.2. Each point has at least one polar.

Axiom DC.3. Each line has at most one pole.

Axiom DC.4. Two distinct points are on at most one line.

Axiom DC.5. There are exactly three distinct points on each line.

Axiom DC.6. If line m does not contain point P, then there is a point on both m and any polar of P.

It should be no surprise that the Desargues' configuration shown in Fig. 1.8 provides a model for this axiomatic system. Furthermore, as you can easily verify, this axiomatic system satisfies the principle of duality (see Exercise 3).

Other properties of Desargues' configurations are given by the following theorems. The first of these theorems describes an important property of poles and polars. We encounter this property again when we study the polarity relation in projective geometry in Chapter 4.

Theorem DC.1

If P is on a polar of point Q, then Q is on each polar of P.

Proof

Let P be on q where q is a polar of Q (Fig. 1.9). Thus, since Q is not on q (why?), q must contain two more points, R and S, which are distinct from P and Q (Axiom DC-5). Let p be a polar of P and assume Q is not on p. Then by Axiom DC-6, p and q must intersect at a point, namely, P, R, or S. But P is not on p by definition. And if R or S are on p, then q is a line joining P with a point on its polar, contradicting the definition. Thus, Q is on p. ∎

The usefulness of the property described in Theorem DC.1 is illustrated in the proofs of the following two theorems, which verify that the correspondence between poles and polars is one-to-one.

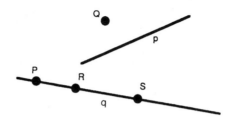

FIGURE 1.9   Proof DC.1.

Theorem DC.2
Each point has exactly one polar.

Proof
Let P be an arbitrary point. By Axiom DC.2, P has at least one polar p. Assume P has a second polar p'. By Axioms DC.4 and DC.5 there is a point T on p' but not on p. Let t be a polar of T. Then by Axiom DC.6, p and t intersect. But since T is on p', P is on t by the previous theorem, and so line t joins P to a point on p, contradicting the definition of polar. Thus P has exactly one polar.   ∎

Theorem DC.3
Each line has exactly one pole.

Proof
By Axiom DC.3 each line has at most one pole. Hence, it suffices to show that an arbitrary line p has at least one pole. Let R, S and T be the three points on p, and let r and s be the unique polars of R and S (Theorem DC.2). Clearly, S is not on r (why?). Therefore, by Axiom DC.6, there is a point P on r and s. But P is on the polars of R and S; hence, by Theorem DC.1, R and S are on the unique polar of P. So p is the polar of P or P is the pole of p.   ∎

These theorems and the following exercises illustrate that even though a finite structure may involve a limited number of points and lines, the structure may possess "strange' properties such as duality and polarity, which are not valid in Euclidean geometry. Another unexpected property illustrated by the exercises is that in Desargues' configurations, a line has exactly three lines parallel to it through its pole; that is, there are points through which there are three lines parallel to a given line (see Exercise 6). Because of this latter property, Desargues' configurations can be classified as non-Euclidean.

Exercises

1. In the Desargues' configuration shown in Fig. 1.8 find the pole of line AB and the polar of C.

2. (a) Find two triangles in the Desargues' configuration in Fig.1.8 that are perspective from point C. From which line are these two triangles perspective? (b) Find two triangles in the Desargues' configuration in Fig. 1.8 that are perspective from line AB. From which point are these two triangles perspective?

The following exercises ask you to verify theorems in the axiom system for Desargues' configurations. This means you must justify your proofs on the basis of the axioms— you cannot verify your reasoning on the basis of the model or incidence table given in this section.

3. Verify the duals of Axioms DC.1 through DC.6.

4. Prove: There is a line through two distinct points iff their polars intersect.

5. Prove: If p and q are two lines both parallel to m (i.e., p and m have no common points, nor do q and m), then p and q intersect at the pole of m.

6. Prove: Through a point P there are exactly three lines parallel to p, the polar of P (i.e., the three lines have no points in common with line p).

7. Prove: There are exactly 10 points and 10 lines in a Desargues' configuration.

8. Prove Desargues' theorem. That is, show that if ABC and $A'B'C'$ are two triangles perspective from a point P, then they are perspective from a line. (Assume that the points A, B, C, A', B', C', and P are all distinct and that no three of the points A, B, C, A', B', C' are collinear.)

The following exercises ask you to work in an axiomatic system for finite structures known as *Pappus' configurations*. These axioms are as follows:

Axioms for Pappus' Configurations

Undefined Terms. Point, line, on.
Defined Terms. Two lines without a common point on them are *parallel*.
Two points without a common line on them are *parallel*.
Axiom PC.1. There exists at least one line.
Axiom PC.2. There are exactly three distinct points on every line.
Axiom PC.3. Not all points are on the same line.
Axiom PC.4. There is at most one line on any two distinct points.
Axiom PC.5. If P is a point not on a line m, there is exactly one line on P parallel to m.
Axiom PC.6. If m is a line not on a point P, there is exactly one point on m parallel to P.

9. (a) Construct a model of a Pappus' configuration. (b) Construct an incidence table for this model.

10. Verify that this axiomatic system satisfies the principle of duality.

11. Prove: If m is a line, there are exactly two lines parallel to m.

12. Prove: There are exactly nine points and nine lines in a Pappus' configuration.

13. Prove: If m and n are parallel lines with distinct points A, B, C on m and A', B', C' on n, then the three intersection points of AC' with CA', AB' with BA', and BC' with CB' are collinear. (This result, which is valid in some projective planes, is known as the Theorem of Pappus.)

1.6 Suggestions for Further Reading

Albert, A. A., and Sandler, R. (1968). *An Introduction to Finite Projective Planes*. New York: Holt, Rinehart and Winston. (Contains a thorough group theoretic treatment of finite projective planes.)

Anderson, I. (1974). *A First Course in Combinatorial Mathematics*. Oxford, England: Clarendon Press. (Chapter 6 discusses block designs and error-correcting codes.)

Beck, A., Bleicher, M. N., and Crowe, D. W. (1972). *Excursions into Mathematics*. New York: Worth. (Sections 4.9–4.15 give a very readable discussion of finite planes, including the development of analytic models.)

Benedicty, M., and Sledge, F. R. (1987). *Discrete Mathematical Structures*. Orlando, FL: Harcourt Brace Jovanovich. (Chapter 13 gives an elementary presentation of coding theory.)

Cipra, B. A. (1988). Computer search solves old math problem. *Science* 242:1507–1508. (Reports on verification that there is no projective plane of order 10.)

Gallian, J. (1996). Error detection methods. *ACM Computing Surveys*. Vol. 28, No. 3, pp. 504–517.

Gensler, H. J. (1984). *Gödel's Theorem Simplified*. Lanham, MD: University Press of America.

Hofstadter, D. R. (1984). Analogies and metaphors to explain Gödel's theorem. In *Mathematics: People, Problems, Results*. D. M. Campbell and J. C. Higgins (Eds.), Vol. 2, pp. 262–275. Belmont, CA: Wadsworth.

Kolata, G. (1982). Does Gödel's theorem matter to mathematics? *Science* 218: 779–780.

Lam, C. W. H. (1991). The Search for a Projective Plane of Order 10. *The American Mathematical Monthly*. Vol. 98, No. 4, pp. 305–318.

Lockwood, J. R., and Runion, G. E. (1978). *Deductive Systems: Finite and Non-Euclidean Geometries*. Reston, VA: NCTM (Chapter 1 contains an elementary discussion of axiomatic systems.)

Nagel, E. and Newman, J. R. (1956). Gödel's proof. In *The World of Mathematics*. J. R. Newman (Ed.), Vol. 3, pp. 1668–1695. New York: Simon and Schuster.

Pless, V. (1982). *Introduction to the Theory of Error-Correcting Codes*. New York: Wiley. (A well-written explanation of this new discipline and the mathematics involved.)

Smart, J. R. (1998). *Modern Geometries*, 5th ed. Pacific Grove, CA: Brooks/Cole. (Chapter 1 contains an easily readable discussion of axiomatic systems and several finite geometries.)

Thompson, T. M. (1983). *From Error-Correcting Codes Through Sphere Packings to Simple Groups*. The Carus Mathematical Monographs, No. 21. Ithaca, NY: MAA (Incorporates numerous historical anecdotes while tracing 20th century mathematical developments involved in these topics.)

Readings on Latin Squares

Beck, A., Bleicher, M. N. and Crowe, D. W. (1972). *Excursions into Mathematics*, pp. 262–279. New York: Worth.

Crowe, D. W., and Thompson, T. M. (1987). Some modern uses of geometry. In *Learning and Teaching Geometry, K-12, 1987 Yearbook*, M. M. Lindquist and A. P. Schulte (Eds.), pp. 101–112. Reston, VA: NCTM.

Gardner, M. (1959). Euler's spoilers: The discovery of an order-10 Graeco-Latin square. *Scientific American* 201: 181–188.

Sawyer, W. W. (1971). Finite arithmetics and geometries. In *Prelude to Mathematics*, Chap. 13. New York: Penguin Books.

2

CHAPTER

Non-Euclidean Geometry

2.1 Gaining Perspective

Mathematics is not usually considered a source of surprises, but non-Euclidean geometry contains a number of easily obtainable theorems that seem almost "heretical" to anyone grounded in Euclidean geometry. A brief encounter with these "strange" geometries frequently results in initial confusion. Eventually, however, this encounter should not only produce a deeper understanding of Euclidean geometry, but it should also offer convincing support for the necessity of carefully reasoned proofs for results that may have once seemed obvious. These individual experiences mirror the difficulties mathematicians encountered historically in the development of non-Euclidean geometry. An acquaintance with this history and an appreciation for the mathematical and intellectual importance of Euclidean geometry is essential for an understanding of the profound impact of this development on mathematical and philosophical thought. Thus, the study of Euclidean and non-Euclidean geometry as mathematical systems can be greatly enhanced by parallel readings in the history of geometry. Since the mathematics of the ancient Greeks was primarily geometry, such readings provide an introduction to the history of mathematics in general.

The sources recommended at the end of this chapter are intended to provide insight into the following:

1. The nature and uses of geometry in ancient civilizations like those of Babylon, China, and Egypt.
2. The mystical qualities that were associated with mathematical and geometric relations by groups like the Pythagoreans.
3. The importance of compass and straight edge constructions and the dilemma posed by three particular construction problems.
4. The emergence of deductive reasoning and the understanding of the nature of axioms in ancient Greece.
5. The importance of Euclidean geometry in the philosophies of Plato and Kant.
6. The reasons for the repeated attempts to prove Euclid's fifth postulate.
7. The numerous "false starts" and the reasons for the delay in the development of non-Euclidean geometry.
8. The influence of the development of non-Euclidean geometry on mathematical and philosophical thought.

2.2 Euclid's Geometry

To understand the significance of non-Euclidean geometry it is essential to become familiar with the geometry developed by the ancient Greeks. This geometry reached its apogee in approximately 300 B.C. with the appearance of the *Elements* of Euclid. In the 13 books comprising this treatise, Euclid organized 465 propositions summarizing the currently known results not only in geometry but also in number theory and elementary (geometric) algebra.

The *Elements* of Euclid is important for its significant mathematical content, but it also has become a landmark in the history of mathematics because it is the earliest extensive example of the use of the axiomatic method. Euclid realized that not every mathematical statement can be proved, that certain statements must be accepted as basic assumptions. Euclid referred to these assumptions as *postulates* and *common notions*, but they are now known as *axioms*.

Euclid's work was immediately accorded the highest respect and recognized as a work of genius. As a result all previous work in geometry was quickly overshadowed so that now there exists little information about earlier efforts. It is a further mark of the monumental importance of this work, that the *Elements* was used essentially unmodified as a standard geometry text for centuries. (The geometry contained in the *Elements* became known as Euclidean geometry.)

Euclid's definitions, postulates, common notions, and first 30 propositions (theorems) as translated by Sir Thomas Heath are given in Appendix A. A careful consideration of these should make the following observations apparent:

1. Even though Euclid realized the necessity of axioms, he apparently did not realize the need for undefined terms. However, a consideration of the first seven definitions suggests that these seven terms are essentially undefined.
2. In the listing of his axioms, Euclid makes a distinction between those he called postulates and those he called common notions. The former were supposedly geometric in nature, whereas the latter were supposedly common to all mathematics.
3. The statement of the fifth postulate is much more involved than the other four.

The third observation led geometers to suspect that the fifth postulate was not independent of the first four postulates, but that it could be proved on the basis of the common notions and the first four postulates. The fact that Euclid had proved his first 28 propositions without resorting to the use of this postulate added fuel to this speculation. The attempts to prove the fifth postulate began soon after the appearance of the *Elements*. In these attempts, geometers frequently made an assumption and used this assumption to prove the fifth postulate. However, each of these assumptions was eventually proved equivalent to the fifth postulate. A list of some of these equivalent formulations is both interesting and instructive. One of these statements involves the notion of equidistant lines. Recall that the *distance from a point P to a line m* is the length of the perpendicular segment from P to m. If the distance from each point on a line l to line m is the same, then l is said to be *equidistant* from m.

Statements Equivalent to Euclid's Fifth Postulate

1. *Playfair's Axiom*: Through a given point not on a given line, exactly one parallel can be drawn to a given line.
2. The sum of the angles of any triangle is equal to two right angles.
3. There exists a pair of similar triangles.
4. There exists a pair of straight lines everywhere equidistant from one another.
5. Given any three noncollinear points, there exists a unique circle passing through them.
6. If three angles of a quadrilateral are right angles, then the fourth angle is also a right angle.

The proof of the equivalence of the fifth postulate and Playfair's axiom is presented later. This proof demonstrates the two steps required to prove that a statement is equivalent to Euclid's fifth postulate: (1) We must construct a proof of Playfair's axiom using Euclid's five postulates; and (2) we must construct a proof of Euclid's fifth postulate using Euclid's first four postulates together with Playfair's axiom. Note that in both (1) and (2), Euclid's Propositions 1 through 28 can be used. Proofs of the equivalence of the fifth postulate and statements 2 through 6 are contained in *Introduction to Non-Euclidean Geometry* by Harold E. Wolfe (1945).

Proof of the Equivalence of Playfair's Axiom and Euclid's Fifth Postulate

Proof of Playfair's axiom based on Euclid's postulates

Let the given point be P and the line be l (Fig. 2.1). Through P construct a line perpendicular to l at Q (Proposition 12). Then through P construct a second line PR perpendicular to PQ (11). The lines PR and l are parallel (27). Now assume PS is a second line through P as shown. Then by common notion (C.N.) 5, $\angle QPS$ is less than $\angle QPR$. Hence, $\angle BQP$ and $\angle QPS$ (where B is a point on l as shown) are together less than $\angle BQP$ and $\angle QPR$ (C.N. 1). But $\angle BQP$ and $\angle QPR$ are right angles; therefore, PS and l are not parallel by Postulate 5. ∎

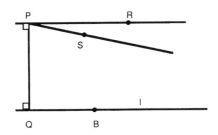

FIGURE 2.1 Fifth postulate ⇒ Playfair's axiom.

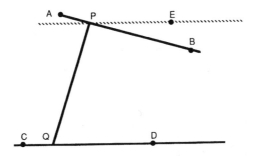

FIGURE 2.2 Playfair's axiom ⇒ fifth postulate (1).

Proof of the fifth postulate based on postulates 1 through 4 and Playfair's axiom

Let AB and CD be lines cut by a transversal PQ so that $\angle DQP$ and $\angle QPB$ are together less than two right angles. At P, construct line PE so that $\angle DQP$ and $\angle QPE$ are together equal to two right angles (Proposition 23). Then PE is parallel to QD (28). So by Playfair's axiom, AB is not parallel to CD, and thus AB and CD intersect (Fig. 2.2). Now assume AB and CD intersect in a point S on the other side of PQ (Fig. 2.3). Then $\angle SPQ$ and $\angle SQP$ are together greater than two right angles. But this contradicts Proposition 17. So AB and CD intersect on the appropriate side. ∎

Returning to a consideration of Euclid's work, it is useful to investigate some of the proofs presented in the *The Thirteen Books of Euclid's Elements* as translated by Heath. In particular, we consider the proofs of Propositions 1, 16, 21, and 27, reprinted with the permission of Cambridge University Press. These proofs demonstrate

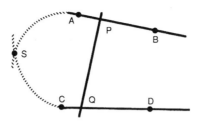

FIGURE 2.3   Playfair's axiom $\Rightarrow$ fifth postulate (2).

some of the geometric properties that Euclid took for granted, that is, properties he assumed without stating them explicitly as postulates or common notions. The essential role of these properties in Euclid's geometry became evident with the development of non-Euclidean geometries.

Euclid's Proposition 1

On a given finite straight line to construct an equilateral triangle.

Let *AB* be the given finite straight line.

Thus it is required to construct an equilateral triangle on the straight line *AB*.

With centre *A* and distance *AB* let the circle *BCD* be described;

[Post. 3]

again, with centre *B* and distance *BA* let the circle *ACE* be described;

[Post. 3]

and from the point *C*, in which the circles cut one another, to the points *A, B* let the straight lines *CA, CB* be joined.   [Post. 1]

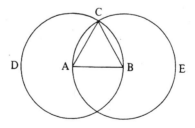

Now, since the point *A* is the centre of the circle *CDB*,

AC is equal to *AB*.   [Def. 15]

Again, since the point *B* is the centre of the circle *CAE*,

BC is equal to *BA*.   [Def. 15]

But *CA* was also proved equal to *AB*; therefore each of the straight lines *CA*, *CB* is equal to *AB*.

And things which are equal to the same thing are also equal to one another; [C.N. 1]

therefore *CA* is also equal to *CB*.

Therefore the three straight lines *CA*, *AB*, *BC* are equal to one another.

Therefore the triangle *ABC* is equilateral; and it has been constructed on the given finite straight line *AB*.

(Being) what it was required to do.

In the proof of Proposition 1 Euclid assumed that the circles in his construction intersect at a point *C*; that is, he assumed the *continuity* of circles without previously proving this as a proposition or stating it as a postulate. Later axiom systems for Euclidean geometry included explicit axioms of continuity, for example, Dedekind's axiom of continuity (see Appendix B). Note that Dedekind's axiom requires the concept of *betweenness*, which was also assumed by Euclid.

Euclid's Proposition 16

In any triangle, if one of the sides be produced, the exterior angle is greater than either of the interior and opposite angles.

Let *ABC* be a triangle, and let one side of it *BC* be produced to *D*;

I say that the exterior angle *ACD* is greater than either of the interior and opposite angles *CBA*, *BAC*.

Let *AC* be bisected at *E* [1.10],
and let *BE* be joined and produced in a straight line to *F*;

let *EF* be made equal to BE [1.3],
let *FC* be joined [Post. 1],
and let *AC* be drawn through to *G* [Post. 2].

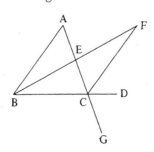

Then, since AE is equal to EC, and BE to EF,

the two sides AE, EB are equal to the two sides CE, EF respectively;

and the angle AEB is equal to the angle FEC, for they are vertical angles.   [1.15]

Therefore the base AB is equal to the base FC, and the triangle ABE is equal to the triangle CFE, and the remaining angles are equal to the remaining angles respectively, namely those which the equal sides subtend;   [1.4]

therefore the angle BAE is equal to the angle ECF.

But the angle ECD is greater than the angle ECF;   [C.N. 5]

therefore the angle ACD is greater than the angle BAE.

Similarly, also, if BC be bisected, the angle BCG, that is, the angle ACD [1.15], can be proved greater than the angle ABC as well.

Therefore etc.   Q.E.D.

In the proof of Proposition 16 Euclid extended segment BE to a segment twice as long (BF). In doing so he implicitly assumed that a segment can be extended without coming back on itself so that F does not lie on segment BE. In more formal language, Euclid assumed that a line is *infinite in extent*, not merely *boundless*. As an example of a line that is boundless, but not of infinite extent, interpret the undefined term "line" as a great circle on a sphere.

Euclid's Proposition 21

If on one of the sides of a triangle, from its extremities, there be constructed two straight lines meeting within the triangle, the straight lines so constructed will be less than the remaining two sides of the triangle, but will contain a greater angle.

On BC, one of the sides of the triangle ABC, from its extremities B, C, let the two straight lines BD, DC be constructed meeting within the triangle;

I say that BD, DC are less than the remaining two sides of the triangle BA, AC, but contain an angle BDC greater than the angle BAC.

For let BD be drawn through to E.

Then, since in any triangle two sides are greater than the remaining one,   [1.20]

therefore, in the triangle ABE, the two sides AB, AE are greater than BE.

Let *EC* be added to each;
therefore *BA, AC* are greater than *BE, EC*.

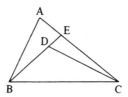

Again, since, in the triangle *CED*,
the two sides *CE, ED* are greater than *CD*,
let *DB* be added to each;
therefore *CE, EB* are greater than *CD, DB*.
But *BA, AC* were proved greater than *BE, EC*;
therefore *BA, AC* are much greater than *BD, DC*.
Again, since in any triangle the exterior angle is greater than the interior and opposite angle,   [1.16]
therefore, in the triangle *CDE*,
the exterior angle *BDC* is greater than the angle *CED*.
For the same reason, moreover, in the triangle *ABE* also,
the exterior angle *CEB* is greater than the angle *BAC*. But the angle *BDC* was proved greater than the angle *CEB*;
therefore the angle *BDC* is much greater than the angle *BAC*.
Therefore etc.   Q.E.D.

In the proof of Proposition 21, Euclid assumed that a line that contains the vertex (*B*) of a triangle (△*ABC*) and an interior point (*D*) must intersect the opposite side (*AC*) at a point (*E*). Either this assumption or its equivalent, which was formulated by Pasch in the 19th century, is known as *Pasch's axiom*. The equivalent forms are as follows.

Pasch's Axiom 1. A line containing a vertex of a triangle and a point interior to the triangle will intersect the opposite side of the triangle.
Pasch's Axiom 2. Let *A, B, C* be three points not on the same line and let *l* be a line in the plane containing *A, B, C* that does not pass through *A, B,* or *C*. Then if *l* passes through a point of the segment *AB* and contains a point interior to △*ABC*, it will also pass through a point of segment *AC* or a point of segment *BC*.

Pasch's axiom can be shown to be equivalent to the separation properties of points and lines that Euclid also assumed; that is, he assumed that *a point separates a segment* into two distinct sets and that *a line separates the plane* into two distinct sets.

Euclid's Proposition 27

If a straight line falling on two straight lines makes the alternate angles equal to one another, the straight lines will be parallel to one another.

For let the straight line *EF* falling on two straight lines *AB, CD* make the alternate angles, *AEF, EFD* equal to one another;

I say that *AB* is parallel to *CD*.

For, if not, *AB, CD* when produced will meet either in the direction of *B, D* or towards *A, C*.

Let them be produced and meet, in the direction of *B, D*, at *G*.

Then, in the triangle *GEF*, the exterior angle *AEF* is equal to the interior and opposite angle *EFG*:

which is impossible. [1.16]

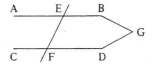

Therefore *AB, CD* when produced will not meet in the direction of *B, D*.

Similarly it can be proved that neither will they meet towards *A, C*.

But straight lines which do not meet in either direction are parallel; [Def. 23]

therefore *AB* is parallel to *CD*.

Therefore etc. Q.E.D.

The major point to be made in considering Proposition 27 is that the proof of this proposition, which guarantees the existence of parallel lines, depends on the validity of Proposition 16, whose proof in turn requires that lines be of infinite extent.

These "shortcomings" in Euclid's work did not become significant until the development of non-Euclidean geometry. But then they presented a very real dilemma and had to be resolved. As a result, a number of new axiom systems for Euclidean geometry were developed. Obviously these systems were necessarily much longer and more involved than Euclid's. Appendices B, C and D contain systems developed by Hilbert, Birkhoff, and the School Mathematics Study Group (SMSG), respectively. Examine these to determine how each system eliminates the shortcomings encountered in Euclid. Note that Appendix F contains proofs of one theorem (the angle-side-angle theorem) in all three systems.

Exercises

1. Prove the following statements equivalent to Euclid's fifth postulate: (a) If a line intersects one of two parallel lines, it also intersects the other. (b) Straight lines that are parallel to the same straight line are parallel to one another. (This is Proposition 30.)

2. Prove that the two versions of Pasch's axiom are equivalent.

3. Work through each of the following examples using Euclid's postulates and propositions (see Appendix A) to determine which steps are valid. As you do so, you may want to use dynamic geometry software to recreate the constructions. Then find the "flaw" in each. [Examples a through c are reprinted from Dubnov (1963) with the permission of D. C. Heath and Company. Example d is reprinted from Maxwell (1961) with the permission of Cambridge University Press.]

Example a. A right angle is congruent to an obtuse angle.

Proof
From the endpoints of segment AB construct two congruent line segments AC and BD lying on the same side of AB so that $\angle DBA$ is a right angle and $\angle CAB$ is an obtuse angle. We shall prove that $\angle DBA \simeq \angle CAB$. Construct CD. Clearly, AB and CD are not parallel. Construct the perpendicular bisectors of segments AB and CD and let their point of intersection be N. Construct NA, NB, NC, and ND.

 Case 1: The point N lies on the same side of AB as do C and D (Fig. 2.4). Clearly,

$$\triangle NAC \simeq \triangle NBD \quad \text{so} \quad \angle NAC \simeq \angle NBD \tag{1}$$

Furthermore,

$$\angle NAB \simeq \angle NBA \tag{2}$$

Thus, by adding (1) and (2), $\angle CAB \simeq \angle DBA$.

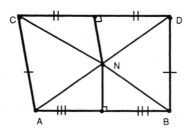

FIGURE 2.4 Example a, case 1.

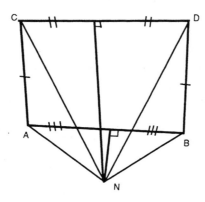

FIGURE 2.5 Example a, case 3.

Case 2: The point N lies on AB; that is, N is the midpoint of segment AB. Then, as in case 1, $\triangle NAC \simeq \triangle NBD$, and again $\angle NAC \simeq \angle NBD$. Thus, by substitution, $\angle BAC \simeq \angle ABD$.

Case 3: The point N lies on the opposite side of AB from C and D (Fig. 2.5). Then as in case 1, $\triangle NAC \simeq \triangle NBD$ and again

$$\angle NAC \simeq \angle NBD \tag{1}$$

Furthermore,

$$\angle NAB \simeq \angle NBA \tag{2}$$

Thus, by subtracting (2) from (1), $\angle CAB \simeq \angle DBA$. ∎

Example b. A rectangle inscribed in a square is also a square.

Proof

Let rectangle $MNPQ$ be inscribed in square $ABCD$ as shown in Fig 2.6. Drop perpendiculars from P to AB and from Q to BC at R and S, respec-

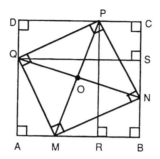

FIGURE 2.6   Example b.

tively. Clearly $PR \simeq QS$. Furthermore, $PM \simeq QN$. So $\triangle PMR \simeq \triangle QNS$, and hence $\angle PMR \simeq \angle QNS$. Consider quadrilateral $MBNO$ where O is the point of intersection of QN and PM. Its exterior angle at the vertex N is congruent to the interior angle at the vertex M, so that the two interior angles at the vertices N and M are supplementary. Thus, the interior angles at the vertices B and O must also be supplementary. But $\angle ABC$ is a right angle, and hence, $\angle NOM$ must also be a right angle. Therefore the diagonals of rectangle $MNPQ$ are perpendicular. Hence, $MNPQ$ is a square.   ■

Example c. Two lines, exactly one of which is perpendicular to a third line, do not intersect.

Proof
At points A_0 and B_0 of the line l, draw A_0Q and B_0P so that Q and P are on the same side of A_0B_0 and so that $\angle QA_0B_0$ is acute and $\angle PB_0A_0$ is a right angle (Fig. 2.7). We shall prove that the rays A_0Q and B_0P do not intersect. Locate A_1 on A_0Q and B_1 on B_0P such that $d(A_1, A_0) = d(B_1, B_0) =$

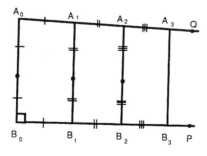

FIGURE 2.7   Example c.

$\frac{1}{2}(d(A_0, B_0))$. Then for $i \geq 1$ locate points A_i on A_0Q such that A_i is between A_{i-1} and A_{i+1} and $d(A_{i+1}, A_i) = \frac{1}{2}(d(A_i, B_i))$. Also locate points B_i on B_0P such that B_i is between B_{i-1} and B_{i+1} and $d(B_{i+1}, B_i) = \frac{1}{2}(d(A_i, B_i))$. Clearly, for any i, segments $A_{i+1}A_i$ and $B_{i+1}B_i$ cannot have any points in common since if K were a common point, there would exist a triangle, $\triangle A_iKB_i$ in which the sum of two sides, A_iK and B_iK, is less than or equal to the length of the third side, A_iB_i. ■

Example d. Every point inside a circle, other than the center, lies on its circumference.

Proof
Consider an arbitrary circle with center O and radius r and an arbitrary point $P \neq O$ inside it. Let Q be the point on OP such that P is between O and Q and such that $d(O, P) \cdot d(O, Q) = r^2$ (Fig. 2.8). Let the perpendicular bisector of segment PQ at R intersect the circle at points U and V. Then

$$d(O, P) = d(O, R) - d(R, P)$$

and

$$d(O, Q) = d(O, R) + d(R, Q)$$
$$= d(O, R) + d(R, P).$$

So

$$
\begin{aligned}
d(O, P) \cdot d(O, Q) &= [d(O, R) - d(R, P)] \cdot [d(O, R) + d(R, P)] \\
&= d^2(O, R) - d^2(R, P) \\
&= [d^2(O, U) - d^2(R, U)] - [d^2(P, U) - d^2(R, U)] \\
&= d^2(O, U) - d^2(P, U)
\end{aligned}
$$

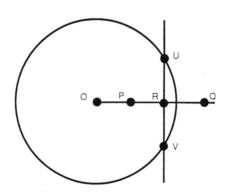

FIGURE 2.8   Example d.

$$= d(O, P) \cdot d(O, Q) - d^2(P, U).$$

Therefore, $d(P, U) = 0$, so $P = U$. ∎

2.3 Non-Euclidean Geometry*

The struggle to prove Euclid's fifth postulate, which began shortly after the appearance of the *Elements* (ca. 300 B.C.) continued well into the 18th century, but eventually mathematicians realized that the fifth postulate is independent of the first four. In other words, there can exist geometries in which the negation of the fifth postulate is an axiom. These geometries came to be known as *non-Euclidean*. To initiate our study of these non-Euclidean geometries, we will consider the equivalent version of Euclid's fifth postulate, known as *Playfair's axiom*.

Postulate 5′ (Playfair's Axiom)
Through a given point not on a given line can be drawn exactly one line not intersecting the given line.

Thus, Euclid's geometry can be said to be based on Postulates 1 through 4 and Playfair's axiom. Non-Euclidean geometry, on the other hand, is based on Euclid's Postulates 1 through 4 and a negation of Playfair's axiom. The two possible negations of Playfair's axiom given here lead to two vastly different non-Euclidean geometries—*hyperbolic* and *elliptic* (for elliptic geometry, a modification of Postulate 2 must also be made).

Hyperbolic Axiom
Through a given point, not on a given line, at least two lines can be drawn that do not intersect the given line.

Elliptic Axiom
Two lines always intersect.

The presentation of hyperbolic geometry that begins in the next section reflects the manner in which the subject developed historically. The proofs are based on Euclid's Postulates 1 through 4 and the hyperbolic axiom, with additional justification offered for the previously cited unstated assumptions of Euclid. This approach has the disadvantage that it lacks the rigorous nature of modern mathematics; but it does expedite exploration of many of the unexpected results of this fascinating subject. Since the proofs of Euclid's Propositions 1 through 28 are based only on Postulates 1 through 4, we already have 28 theorems of hyperbolic geometry. With these theorems in hand, we are able to jump into the heart of plane hyperbolic geometry and develop almost immediately several interesting and strange results in this subject. The development of these results is, for the most part, surprisingly easy; although a few of the theorems necessary in the development are more difficult to prove than comparable theorems in Euclidean geometry. (More rigorous proofs for each of our results can be developed using Hilbert's axiom system with the hyperbolic axiom in place of Playfair's axiom.)

Many of the theorems we will encounter were developed by the Italian mathematician Gerolamo Saccheri (1667–1733) in his attempt to find a reductio ad absurdum proof of the fifth postulate. Influenced by the contemporary view that Euclidean geometry was the only possible geometry and faced with results radically different from those in Euclidean geometry, Saccheri allowed himself to think he had obtained a contradiction to the hyperbolic hypothesis after producing a long list of hyperbolic theorems. (He also rejected a second alternative hypothesis after much briefer consideration.) He recorded his work in a book with the intriguing title *Euclides ab Omni Naevo Vindicatus* (Euclid Freed of Every Flaw).

Credit for the discovery of hyperbolic geometry is generally given instead to the Russian mathematician Nicolai Ivanovich Lobachevsky (1793–1856) and the Hungarian mathematician János Bolyai (1802–1860), who published their independent work in 1829 and 1832, respectively. The eminent mathematician Karl Friedrich Gauss (1777–1855) also worked extensively in hyperbolic geometry but left his results unpublished. The details of the discoveries of these three men and the resistance they encountered provide one of the most fascinating episodes in the history of mathematics.

As the results of hyperbolic geometry unfold, the difficulty of visualizing these results within a world that most of us view as

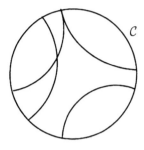

FIGURE 2.9 Poincaré model.

Euclidean becomes increasingly difficult. There are two frequently used geometric models that can aid our visualization of hyperbolic plane geometry. These are known as the *Poincaré model* and the *Klein model* (Figs. 2.9 and 2.10). Both of these models assign interpretations to hyperbolic terms within the context of Euclidean geometry.

Poincaré Model

Hyperbolic Term	Interpretation
Point	Point interior to a given Euclidean circle C
Line	Portion interior to C of a circle orthogonal to C or a diameter of C
Plane	Interior of C

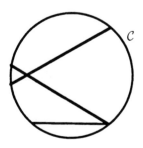

FIGURE 2.10 Klein model.

Under these interpretations the axioms and theorems of hyperbolic geometry become statements in Euclidean geometry. The Poincaré model is important historically since it was used to demonstrate the consistency of hyperbolic geometry relative to Euclidean geometry.

Within this model, the measure of an angle determined as in Euclidean geometry is the measure of the hyperbolic angle. However, the correspondence between the hyperbolic and Euclidean distances is not nearly so straightforward. Essentially, Euclidean meter sticks must be viewed as getting longer as they are placed closer to the circumference of C. A description of the life of people inhabiting the Poincaré model is given in Trudeau (1987, pp. 235–244). To explore the world of these inhabitants, that is, the hyperbolic geometry depicted in the Poincaré model, you can use dynamic geometry software. Information on obtaining the needed menus/scripts and specific directions for guided hyperbolic explorations are available at the website: http://www.stolaf.edu/people/cederj/geotext/info.htm.

The Klein model uses a similar interpretation of the term "point" but uses a more easily visualized interpretation of the term "line." However, in this model neither the distance nor the angle measures for hyperbolic geometry agree with their Euclidean counterparts.

Klein Model

Hyperbolic Term	Interpretation
Point	Point interior to a given Euclidean circle C
Line	Open chord of C
Plane	Interior of C

This model will play an important role in Chapter 4, when we use Klein's definition of geometry to develop hyperbolic geometry as a subgeometry of the more general projective geometry.

The presentation of elliptic geometry, which ends this chapter uses an intuitive approach via spherical models rather than resorting to a drawn out axiomatic development. The aim of both presentations is to merely familiarize the reader with properties of non-Euclidean geometry.

2.4 Hyperbolic Geometry—Sensed Parallels

Since hyperbolic geometry results from the replacement of the fifth postulate by the hyperbolic axiom, we will begin our study of this geometry by determining the consequences of this new axiom. In doing so, we will immediately need to make use of one of the properties Euclid assumed without stating it, namely, the continuity of lines. In the development that follows, we will accept Dedekind's axiom as an explicit statement of this property.

Dedekind's Axiom of Continuity
For every partition of the points on a line into two nonempty sets such that no point of either lies between two points of the other, there is a point of one set that lies between every other point of that set and every point of the other set.

Let P be a point and l a line not containing P as described in the hypothesis of the hyperbolic axiom. From P, construct a perpendicular to l at Q (Proposition 12). Also construct a line m through P perpendicular to PQ at $P(11)$. Let S be a second point on line m and construct QS (Fig. 2.11). Then the points of QS can be partitioned into sets A and B as described below:

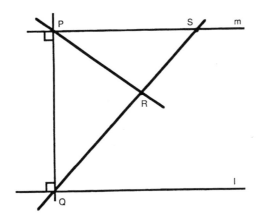

FIGURE 2.11   Existence of sensed parallel.

    i. Let $A = \{X : X$ is on QS and PX intersects $l\}$.

   ii. Let $B = \{Y : Y$ is on QS and PY does not intersect $l\}$.

Clearly, Q is in set A and S is in set B (why?), so the sets are nonempty. And if X, X' are elements of A, and Y, Y' are elements of B, Y cannot be between X and X' and X cannot be between Y and Y' (see Exercise 1). Thus, by Dedekind's axiom there is some point T in either set A or set B such that T is between X and Y for all X in A and Y in B. It soon becomes apparent that T is in B (see Exercise 2). If a point R on QS moves along QS from Q to S then the line PR will rotate about the point P and $m\angle QPR$ will take on values from 0 to 90°. (In Fig. 2.11 this rotation would be counterclockwise.) Clearly, when R coincides with the point T given by Dedekind's axiom, $m\angle QPR = m\angle QTP < 90°$ and the line PT can be described as the first line in the rotation process that does not intersect l. Note that a similar situation arises on the other side of PQ; that is, there is another first line that does not intersect l, say PT'. For convenience we refer to these as the first lines on the *right* and *left* of PQ that do not intersect l. Furthermore, $\angle QPT \simeq \angle QPT'$. For if not, assume that $m\angle QPT$ is greater than $m\angle QPT'$ (Fig. 2.12). Then construct PU so that $\angle QPU \simeq \angle QPT'$ where U is on the right side of PQ. Then, since PT is the first line on the right of PQ that does not intersect l, PU must intersect l at some point V. Let V' be a point on l to the left of PQ such that segment $V'Q$ is congruent to segment VQ. Construct PV'. Since PQ is perpendicular to l, $\angle PQV' \simeq \angle PQV$. Thus, $\angle QPV' \simeq \angle QPV$ (4), and therefore $\angle QPV' \simeq \angle QPT'$. So V'

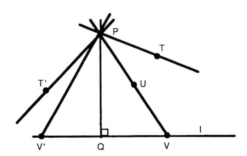

FIGURE 2.12 Symmetry of sensed parallels.

is on PT' and PT' intersects l. But this is a contradiction; therefore $\angle QPT \simeq \angle QPT'$.

Note that any of the lines lying within the angle $\angle(PT, PT')$, that is, the angle formed by lines PT and PT' that does not contain PQ, will not intersect l either.

The previous discussion is summarized in the following definition and theorem.

Definition 2.1
The first line through P relative to the counterclockwise (clockwise) rotation from PQ that does not intersect l (Fig. 2.12) is said to be *right-(left-)sensed parallel* to l through P. Any other line through P that does not intersect l is said to be *ultraparallel* to l through P or *nonintersecting* with l.

Theorem 29h
If l is any line and P is any point not on l, then there are exactly two lines through P that do not intersect l and that make equal acute angles with the perpendicular from P to l and that are such that every line through P lying within the angle containing that perpendicular intersects l, while every other line through P does not.

Corollary
Two lines with a common perpendicular are ultraparallel.

Before using this relation of sensed parallelism, some important properties of this relation must be established. Recall that in Euclidean geometry the parallelism relation satisfies the following properties:

1. If line l is the parallel to line m through P, then l is also the parallel to m through any other point R on l.
2. If line l is parallel to line m, then m is parallel to l (symmetry).
3. If line l is parallel to line m and m is parallel to line n, then l is parallel to n (transitivity).

The first of these merely states that the property of parallelism is independent of the point P. The second and third properties are the well-known properties of symmetry and transitivity, as labeled.

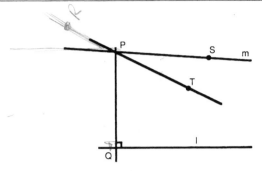

FIGURE 2.13 Sensed parallel demonstration.

Before verifying that the relation of sensed parallelism in hyperbolic geometry satisfies these same properties, we shall first outline the procedure involved in proving that line *l* is sensed parallel to line *m*. From Definition 2.1 it should be apparent that in addition to verifying that *l* and *m* do not intersect, we must also show that at any point *P* on *m*, *m* is the first line in the rotation from the perpendicular to *l* that does not intersect *l*. In practice this second property is demonstrated by verifying in Figure 2.13 that any line *PT* that intersects line *m* at *P* and enters ∠*QPS* must intersect *l*. (Here, *PQ* is perpendicular to *l* at *Q*, and *S* is a point on *m* in the direction of parallelism from *P*.) This procedure is used in the proofs of the next three theorems. Each of these proofs is written for right-sensed parallels. The proofs for left-sensed parallels can be obtained by substituting the term "left" for "right" throughout.

Theorem 30h
If a line l is the right-(left-)sensed parallel through a point P to a line m, it is at each of its points the right-(left-)sensed parallel to the line m.

Proof
Assume *l* is right-sensed parallel to *m* through *P*. Let *R* be any other point on *l*.

Case 1: *R* is on the right side of *P*. Let *PQ* and *RS* be the perpendiculars to *m* at *Q* and *S* (12). Let *B* be any point on *l* to the right of *R*. It is sufficient to show that every line *RU* lying within ∠*BRS* must intersect *m* (Fig. 2.14). Construct *PU*. Clearly, *PU* lies within ∠*QPR*, and hence must intersect *m* at a point *M* (definition of sensed parallels). Construct *QR*. By Pasch's axiom for △*PQR*, *PU* must intersect

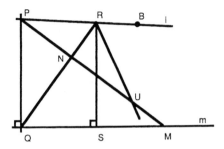

FIGURE 2.14   Proof 30h.

segment QR in a point N. In $\triangle QNM$, RU intersects segment NM. But it does not intersect segment QN. Therefore, by Pasch's axiom, it must intersect segment QM and hence m.

Case 2: R is on the left side of P. (See Exercise 5).   ■

It can now be said that l is sensed parallel to m without specifying through which point, just as the relation of parallelism in Euclidean geometry does not depend on particular points on the lines. The term *parallel* may also suggest that sensed parallel lines have other properties analogous to those of parallel lines in Euclidean geometry. And Theorems 31h and 32h below demonstrate that the relation of *right-(left-)sensed parallelism* is both symmetric and transitive, making the relation an equivalence relation (assuming that a line is sensed parallel to itself). However, the designation of *right* versus *left* used above and in the statements of Theorems 31h and 32h indicates that in hyperbolic geometry each line belongs to two equivalence classes of "first-parallel" lines, not just one, as in Euclidean geometry. The *right* versus *left* designation is a classic way of identifying these two classes without resorting to the terminology of equivalence classes.[1] But this *right* versus *left* designation can easily be confusing, since, for example, if the entire configuration shown

---

[1] For example, in Wolfe's *Introduction to Non-Euclidean Geometry*, the following appears (p. 68): "On occasion it will be found possible and convenient to distinguish between the two parallels by describing one as the 'right-hand,' the other as the 'left-hand' parallel."

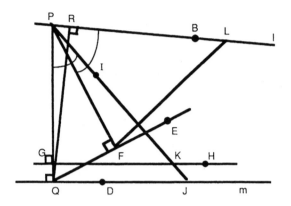

FIGURE 2.15   Proof 31h.

in Figure 2.15 is rotated 180° about *P*, it then appears to show *left-sensed* parallels.

One possible way to clarify the situation is to use the terminology of *ideal points*. If *l* and *m* are sensed parallel lines, they are said to intersect in an *ideal point*. Ideal points will be represented by Greek letters, for example, Ω. Since there are right- and left-sensed parallels to every line, any line *l* will have exactly two ideal points and these two ideals points can be used to identify the two equivalence classes of lines sensed parallel to *l*. In the Poincaré and Klein models, the ideal points are represented by the points lying on the circumference of *C*. For convenience we will say that two sensed parallel lines *l* and *m* "intersect" at a point Ω, but we must be careful not to let this familiar terminology suggest that ideal points possess the same properties as ordinary hyperbolic points.

Theorem 31h
If line l is right-(left-)sensed parallel to line m, then m is right-(left-)sensed parallel to l.

Proof
Assume that *l* is right-sensed parallel to *m*. Let *P* be a point on *l*, *PQ* the perpendicular to *m* at *Q*, and *QR* the perpendicular to *l* at *R*. We can show that *R* will be on the right side of *PQ*. (See Exercise 6.) Also, let *D* be a point on *m* to the right of *PQ*. It is sufficient to show

that every line QE lying within ∠RQD must intersect l (Fig. 2.15). Let PF be the perpendicular to QE at F. As before, the exterior angle theorem guarantees that F will lie to the right of PQ. Furthermore, segment PF is shorter than segment PQ (19). Thus, on segment PQ there is a point G such that segment PG is congruent to segment PF (3). Draw GH perpendicular to PQ. Let B be a point on l such that B is to the right of R and construct ∠GPI ≃ ∠FPB. Then PI will intersect m at J (definition of sensed parallel). Since GH intersects segment PQ in ∆PQJ and cannot intersect QJ, it must intersect segment PJ at some point K. On line PB find a point L to the right of PQ such that segment PL is congruent to segment PK and construct FL. Now ∆PGK ≃ ∆PFL(4). So ∠PFL is a right angle. But ∠PFE is also a right angle. Hence, FE = FL. Therefore, QE intersects l at L. ∎

Thus, the relation of sensed parallelism is symmetric. The verification that this relation is also transitive is simplified by using the following lemma.

Lemma
If m is right-sensed parallel to n, P and S are points on m (S to the right of P), and R is a point on n, then any line l entering ∠RPS will intersect n at a point T on the right side of R.

Proof
Let U be a point on line l below line m and let PQ be the perpendicular to n at Q.

Case 1: Q coincides with or lies to the left of R (Fig. 2.16). Then clearly m∠QPU is less than m∠QPS so PU intersects line n to the right

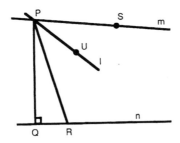

FIGURE 2.16 Lemma proof, case 1.

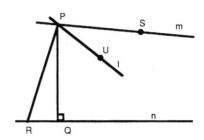

FIGURE 2.17 Lemma proof, case 2.

of Q (definition of right-sensed parallel). Since PU cannot intersect segment QR (see Exercise 7), it must intersect n to the right of R.

Case 2: Q lies to the right of R (Fig. 2.17). Then line l will either enter $\triangle PQR$ and intersect side RQ (Pasch's axiom), and therefore line n as desired, or $m\angle UPQ$ will be less than $m\angle SPQ$, and thus l will intersect n to the right of R by the definition of right-sensed parallels. ∎

Theorem 32h

If two lines are both right-(left-)sensed parallel to a third line, then they are right-(left-)sensed parallel to one another.

Proof

Assume that l is right-sensed parallel to n, and m is right-sensed parallel to n. We shall show that l is right-sensed parallel to m.

Case 1: l and m lie on opposite sides of n. Clearly, l and m do not intersect since they lie on opposite sides of n. Let P and S be points on l, S to the right of P. Construct PQ, the perpendicular to m at Q. Then, since l and m lie on opposite sides of n, PQ will intersect n at a point R. Let PU be a line entering $\angle QPS$. It is sufficient to show that PU intersects m to the right of Q (Fig. 2.18). Since l is right-sensed parallel to n, PU will intersect n at a point T by the preceding lemma. Construct line TQ and let W be a point on n to the right of T. Then line PU enters $\angle QTW$ at T. Since m is right-sensed parallel to n, n is right-sensed parallel to m by Theorem 31h, and the lemma can be used again to show that PT intersects m as desired.

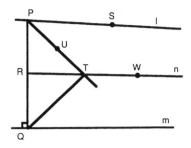

FIGURE 2.18   Proof 32h, case 1.

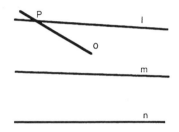

FIGURE 2.19   Proof 32h, case 2.

Case 2: m is between l and n. Assume that l is not right-sensed parallel to m and let P be a point on l (Fig. 2.19). By Theorem 29h there is a line o through P that is the right-sensed parallel to m. Since m is right-sensed parallel to n, n is right-sensed parallel to m (Theorem 31h). Furthermore, o is right-sensed parallel to m, and o and n lie on opposite sides of m. Therefore, by case 1, o is right-sensed parallel to n. This gives us two lines through P, both right-sensed parallel to n, contradicting the uniqueness guaranteed by Theorem 29h. Thus, it follows that l is right-sensed parallel to n.   ∎

Hence, the relation of sensed parallelism is transitive. Note, however, that the hypothesis of this theorem requires that the direction of parallelism be the same in both cases. But if, for example, l is right-sensed parallel to n, and m is left-sensed parallel to n, l and m may *not* be sensed parallel. This is demonstrated using Klein models (Fig. 2.20).

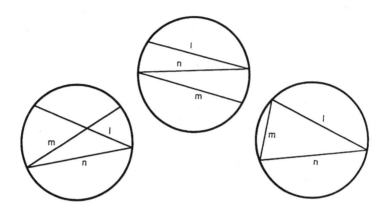

FIGURE 2.20   Sensed parallels in Klein models.

Exercises

1. Show that sets A and B described at the beginning of this section have the property that no point of either lies between two points of the other.

2. Verify that the point T guaranteed by Dedekind's axiom cannot be in set A and therefore must be in set B (where sets A and B are the sets described at the beginning of this section).

3. (a) Use a Klein model to show the right- and left-sensed parallels to a line l through a point P not on l. (b) In the same model, show two lines through P that are ultraparallel to l.

4. (a) Use a Poincaré model to show the right- and left-sensed parallels to a line l through a point P not on l. (b) In the same model, show two lines through P that are ultraparallel to l.

5. Prove case 2 of Theorem 30h. [*Hint*: Choose U above l.]

6. Prove the claim in the proof of Theorem 31h, that R will be on the right side of PQ.

7. In case 1 of the proof of the lemma used to prove Theorem 32h, prove that line PU cannot intersect segment Q. [*Hint*: You may need to refer to the separation of the plane by a line.]

8. Explain why there are no more than two ideal points on a hyperbolic line.

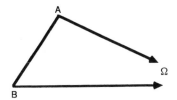

FIGURE 2.21 Asymptotic triangle, $\triangle AB\Omega$.

2.5 Hyperbolic Geometry — Asymptotic Triangles

We will continue the study of sensed parallels by examining the figures formed by two sensed parallel lines and a transversal. Because these figures resemble triangles, they have come to be known as *asymptotic triangles* (Fig. 2.21). In order to make use of the usual convention of naming a triangle by its three vertices, we will use the ideal point determined by the two sensed parallel lines as the third point in the notation. Thus we will speak of asymptotic triangle $\triangle AB\Omega$, where the two lines are represented by $A\Omega$ and $B\Omega$ and the transversal is the segment AB. Once again, it is important to note that although convenient notationally, Ω does not represent an actual point in hyperbolic geometry.

Definition 2.2
The figure consisting of two sensed parallel lines and a transversal intersecting the lines at A and B is referred to as an *asymptotic triangle*. If Ω is the ideal point determined by the sensed parallels, we refer to this asymptotic triangle as $\triangle AB\Omega$.

It is important to note that asymptotic triangles, despite the name, are *not* triangles so we cannot apply previous theorems about triangles to asymptotic triangles. However, asymptotic triangles do have some properties in common with triangles. In particular, Theorems 33h and 34h show that a modified Pasch's axiom holds for asymptotic triangles. Note that Theorem 33h is an extension of the lemma used in the proof of Theorem 32h, but here it is proved using the notation of asymptotic triangles.

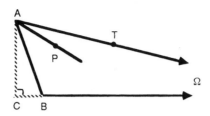

FIGURE 2.22   Proof 33h, Case 1.

Theorem 33h

If a line passes within asymptotic triangle △ABΩ *through one of its vertices (including* Ω*), it will intersect the opposite side.*

Proof

Let *AP* be a line passing through *A*, and *P* a point interior to △ABΩ. Let *AC* be the perpendicular to *B*Ω through *A*.

Case 1: AC coincides with *AB* or falls outside △ABΩ (Fig. 2.22). Then clearly ∠*PAC* is smaller than ∠*TAC* where *T* lies on side *A*Ω. Hence, *AP* intersects side *C*Ω (definition of sensed parallels). Since *AP* cannot intersect segment *CB*, it must intersect side *B*Ω.

Case 2: AC lies within △ABΩ (Fig. 2.23). Then *P* may fall inside △*ABC* and hence *AP* intersects side *BC* (Pasch's axiom) and therefore side *B*Ω; or *P* may fall inside △*AC*Ω or on side *AC*. In this latter instance, as in case 1, *AP* must intersect side *C*Ω and hence side *B*Ω.

The proof for a line through *B* is the same; so assume the line passes through Ω, that is, *P*Ω is sensed parallel to *A*Ω and *B*Ω (Fig. 2.24). Construct *AP*. Then by the previous part of the proof, *AP* intersects side *B*Ω at some point *Q*. But *P*Ω intersects side *AQ* in △*ABQ* and therefore intersects side *AB* (Pasch's axiom).   ∎

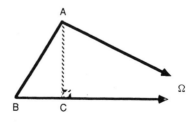

FIGURE 2.23   Proof 33h, case 2.

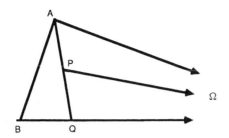

FIGURE 2.24 Proof 33h, line through Ω.

Theorem 34h

If a straight line intersects one of the sides of asymptotic triangle $\triangle AB\Omega$ but does not pass through a vertex (including Ω), it will intersect exactly one of the other two sides.

Proof

See Exercise 1. ∎

The analog of the exterior angle theorem for ordinary triangles (Proposition 16) can also be verified for asymptotic triangles. Note, however, that in an ordinary triangle each exterior angle has two opposite interior angles; whereas each exterior angle of an asymptotic triangle has only one.

Theorem 35h

The exterior angles of asymptotic triangles $\triangle AB\Omega$ at A and B made by extending AB are greater than their respective opposite interior angles.

Proof

Let AB be extended through B to C. It is sufficient to show that $\angle CB\Omega$ is greater than $\angle BA\Omega$. To do this, assume that the opposite is true, that is, $\angle CB\Omega$ is less than or equal to $\angle BA\Omega$. Through B construct BD such that D lies in the direction of parallelism from AB, and $\angle CBD \simeq \angle BA\Omega$.

Case 1: D lies inside $\triangle AB\Omega$ (Fig. 2.25). Then by Theorem 33h, BD intersects $A\Omega$ at some point E. But then in $\triangle ABE$, the exterior angle at B is congruent to the interior angle at A, which contradicts Proposition 16.

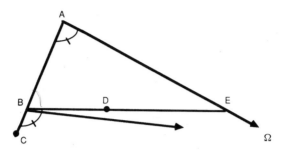

FIGURE 2.25   Proof 35h, case 1.

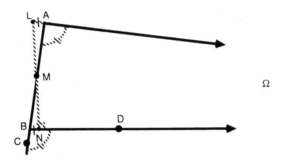

FIGURE 2.26   Proof 35h, case 2.

Case 2: D lies on $B\Omega$ (Fig. 2.26). Let M be the midpoint of segment AB (Proposition 10). Construct MN perpendicular to $B\Omega$ at N. Clearly, N cannot coincide with B (why?). We shall assume that N falls to the right of B (if $A\Omega$ and $B\Omega$ are right-sensed parallel as shown in Fig. 2.26). The proof for the case when N falls to the left of B is similar (see Exercise 2). Extend $A\Omega$ to L so the segment LA is congruent to segment BN. Construct ML. Then $\angle LAM \simeq \angle NBM$, since they are supplements of congruent angles. Hence, $\triangle LAM \simeq \triangle NBM$, and $\angle BMN \simeq \angle AML$. Therefore, $LM = MN$. Furthermore, $\angle ALM \simeq \angle BNM$. So $\angle ALM$ is a right angle. Thus, $A\Omega$ is ultraparallel to $B\Omega$. But this contradicts the hypothesis. Thus, both cases lead to a contradiction, and hence it follows that $m\angle CB\Omega$ is greater than $m\angle BA\Omega$.   ■

Note that case 2 of this proof demonstrates the following theorem.

Theorem 36h

Two lines cut by a transversal so as to make alternate angles congruent are ultraparallel.

As a result of this theorem, Euclid's Propositions 27 and 28 refer to ultraparallel lines.

The familiar triangle congruence theorems of Euclidean geometry also have analogs in hyperbolic geometry. Here, since two of the three sides of an asymptotic triangle are infinite, there are only two angles and one side to consider. In other words, two asymptotic triangles are said to be congruent whenever their finite sides and the two pairs of corresponding angles are congruent.

Theorem 37h

If segment AB is congruent to segment $A'B'$ and $\angle BA\Omega$ is congruent to $\angle B'A'\Omega'$ in asymptotic triangles $\triangle AB\Omega$ and $\triangle A'B'\Omega'$, then $\angle AB\Omega$ is congruent to $\angle A'B'\Omega'$.

Proof

Assume $\angle AB\Omega \not\cong \angle A'B'\Omega'$; in particular assume that $m\angle AB\Omega$ is greater than $m\angle A'B'\Omega'$. Let C be a point in the direction of parallelism from AB such that $\angle ABC \simeq \angle A'B'\Omega'$ (Fig. 2.27). By Theorem 33h, BC intersects side $A\Omega$ at some point D. On $A'\Omega'$ find D' such that segment AD is congruent to segment $A'D'$. Construct $B'D'$. Then $\triangle ABD \simeq \triangle A'B'D'$, so $\angle A'B'D' \simeq \angle ABD$. But $\angle ABD \simeq \angle A'B'\Omega'$, and thus $\angle A'B'D' \simeq \angle A'B'\Omega'$. And $B'D' = B'\Omega'$. But this is a contradiction so $\angle AB\Omega \simeq \angle A'B'\Omega'$. ∎

Two other congruence theorems for asymptotic triangles are stated below (see Exercises 3 and 4).

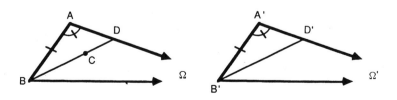

FIGURE 2.27 Proof 37h.

Theorem 38h

In asymptotic triangles $\triangle AB\Omega$ and $\triangle A'B'\Omega'$, if $\angle BA\Omega \simeq \angle B'A'\Omega'$ and $\angle AB\Omega \simeq \angle A'B'\Omega'$, then segment AB is congruent to segment $A'B'$.

Theorem 39h

In asymptotic triangles $\triangle AB\Omega$ and $\triangle A'B'\Omega'$, if segment AB is congruent to segment $A'B'$, $\angle AB\Omega \simeq \angle BA\Omega$, and $\angle A'B'\Omega' \simeq \angle B'A'\Omega'$, then $\angle AB\Omega \simeq \angle A'B'\Omega' \simeq \angle BA\Omega \simeq \angle B'A'\Omega'$.

These asymptotic triangle theorems lead to a unique concept in hyperbolic geometry, namely, the *angle of parallelism*. The definition of this concept uses a mapping on the set of positive real numbers.

Let PQ be a segment of length h, that is, $m(PQ) = h$. Let QS be the line perpendicular to PQ at Q and PR the line sensed parallel to QS through P (Fig. 2.28). Then there is a mapping a such that $a(h) = m\angle QPR$ where $m\angle QPR$ denotes the measure of $\angle QPR$.

Theorems 37h and 29h can be used to show that the mapping $a(h)$ is well defined. As shown in Exercise 5, this mapping is also one-to-one and order reversing [i.e., if $h < h'$, then $a(h) > a(h')$]. Furthermore, it can be shown that $a(h)$ is a continuous mapping. These results are summarized in the following theorem.

Theorem 40h

The mapping $a(h)$ just described is continuous, one-to-one, and order reversing.

Definition 2.3

An angle with measure $a(h)$ is called an *angle of parallelism of h*.

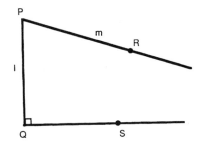

FIGURE 2.28 Angle of parallelism.

In *A Survey of Geometry* (pp. 414–416), Howard Eves (1972) demonstrates that

$$a(h) = 2\arctan(e^{-h})$$

if the unit of length is chosen as the distance corresponding to the angle of parallelism $a = 2\arctan(e^{-1})$.

This leads to another interesting property of hyperbolic geometry not possessed by Euclidean geometry. Note that in both Euclidean and hyperbolic geometry, angles possess a natural unit of measure that can be geometrically constructed since right angles can be constructed. Because of this, angles are said to be *absolute* in both geometries. In Euclidean geometry, lengths are not absolute; since there is no natural unit of length structurally connected with the geometry. However, in hyperbolic geometry lengths are absolute because the mapping $a(h)$ associates to any angle (e.g., 45°) a definite distance h; and once an angle of measure 45° is constructed, the corresponding angle of parallelism can be constructed. [Note that this statement assumes that it is possible to *construct* a line perpendicular to one of two intersecting lines and sensed parallel to the other; that is, if lines l and m intersect at point P as shown in Figure 2.28, it is possible to construct the line QS perpendicular to l at Q and sensed parallel to m. This construction is demonstrated in Wolfe (1945, pp. 97–99).]

Exercises

1. Prove Theorem 34h.

2. Complete the verification of case 2 in the proof of Theorem 35h by considering the case where N falls to left of B.

3. Prove Theorem 38h.

4. Prove Theorem 39h.

5. Prove using a synthetic proof: If $h < h'$, then $a(h) > a(h')$.

6. Prove that the sum of the measures of the two angles at the ordinary vertices of an asymptotic triangle is less than 180°. [*Hint*: Use Theorem 35h.]

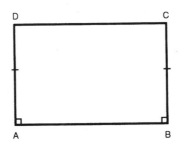

FIGURE 2.29 Saccheri quadrilateral.

2.6 Hyperbolic Geometry—Saccheri Quadrilaterals

A second figure of importance in hyperbolic geometry is the *Saccheri quadrilateral* (Fig. 2.29) in honor of the efforts of Gerolamo Saccheri, who, as noted previously, almost discovered non-Euclidean geometry.

Definition 2.4
A *Saccheri quadrilateral* is a quadrilateral *ABCD* with two adjacent right angles at *A* and *B* and with sides $AD \simeq BC$. Side *AB* is called the *base* and side *DC* is called the *summit*.

We shall soon see that one of the implications of the hyperbolic axiom is that the angles at *C* and *D* in this figure are not right angles as they are in Euclidean geometry. There are, however, properties of Saccheri quadrilaterals common to both Euclidean and hyperbolic geometry since their proofs require results based only on Euclid's first four postulates. Two of these common properties are stated in Theorem 41h and conclusion (1) of Theorem 42h.

Theorem 41h
The line joining the midpoints of the base and summit of a Saccheri quadrilateral is perpendicular to both of them.

Proof
See Exercise 1. ■

Corollary

The base and summit of a Saccheri quadrilateral are ultraparallel.

Theorem 42h

The summit angles of a Saccheri quadrilateral are (1) *congruent and* (2) *acute.*

Proof

See Exercise 3. ∎

As indicated earlier, the proof of part (2) depends on the hyperbolic axiom. In Euclidean geometry this conclusion must be changed to "right," whereas in elliptic geometry this conclusion must be changed to "obtuse." In fact, Theorem 42h is equivalent to the hyperbolic axiom whereas the Euclidean version is equivalent to Euclid's parallel postulate. This theorem also leads to one of the dramatic results in hyperbolic geometry, namely, that the angle sum of every triangle is less than 180°. As we shall see in the next section, the angle sum is *not even constant* for all triangles, in hyperbolic geometry.

Theorem 43h

The sum of the angles of every triangle is less than two right angles.

Proof

Assume $\triangle ABC$ is an arbitrary triangle with base BC. Let D and E be the midpoints of sides AB and AC, respectively. And let BF, AG, and CH be the perpendiculars to DE from B, A, and C. Then, as shown in Exercise 5, there are three possible cases (Fig. 2.30).

Case 1: Since $\angle BDF \simeq \angle ADG$ (15), it follows that $\triangle BDF \simeq \triangle ADG$, and thus $\angle FBD \simeq \angle GAD$, and segment BF is congruent to segment AG(26). Likewise, $\angle HCE \simeq \angle GAE$ and segment AG is congruent to segment CH. Hence, segment BF is congruent to segment CH, and quadrilateral $BFHC$ is a Saccheri quadrilateral. Thus, by Theorem 42h, $\angle FBC \simeq \angle HCB$ and both are acute, so their sum is

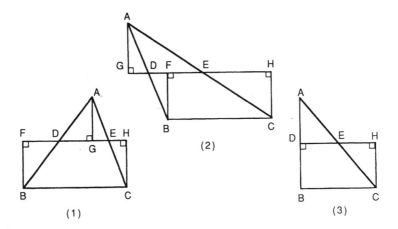

FIGURE 2.30 Proof 43h.

less than two right angles. But

$$m\angle FBC + m\angle HCB = m\angle FBD + m\angle DBC + m\angle HCE + m\angle ECB$$
$$= m\angle GAB + m\angle ABC + m\angle GAE + m\angle ACB$$
$$= m\angle ABC + m\angle BAC + m\angle ACB.$$

It follows that the angle sum of $\triangle ABC$ is less than two right angles.
Cases 2 and 3: See Exercise 6. ∎

In the preceding proof, $\triangle ABC$ is said to be *equivalent* to Saccheri quadrilateral *BFHC*.

Several important results are immediate corollaries of this theorem.

Corollary 1
The sum of the angles of a quadrilateral is less than four right angles.

Corollary 2
Two lines cannot have more than one common perpendicular.

Corollary 3
There do not exist lines that are everywhere equidistant.

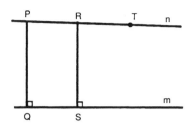

FIGURE 2.31 Proof 44h.

As Corollary 3 states, lines are never equidistant. Instead the distance between sensed parallels varies from point to point as shown in the following theorem.

Theorem 44h

The perpendicular distance from a point on one of two sensed parallels to the other line decreases as the point moves in the direction of parallelism.

Proof

Let lines n and m be right-sensed parallel. Choose points P and R on n (Fig. 2.31). Construct PQ and RS perpendicular to m from P and R, respectively. (Assume R is to the right of PQ.) Then it suffices to show that $m(RS) < m(PQ)$. Let T be to the right of R. Now $m\angle PRS + m\angle SRT = 180°$, and $m\angle QPR + m\angle PRS < 180°$ by Corollary 1 of Theorem 43h. Thus, $m\angle QPR < m\angle SRT$, so $m(PQ) = a^{-1}m\angle QPR > a^{-1}m\angle SRT = m(RS)$. ∎

Theorem 43h yields still another result that is vastly different from what happens in Euclidean geometry.

Theorem 45h

If the three angles of one triangle are congruent respectively to the three angles of a second triangle, then the triangles are congruent.

Proof

Let $\triangle ABC$ and $\triangle A'B'C'$ be two triangles with corresponding angles congruent. Now if any pair of corresponding sides is congruent, then the triangles are congruent (Proposition 26). Hence, assume that none of the three pairs of corresponding sides is congruent.

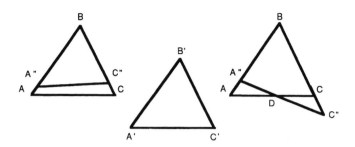

FIGURE 2.32 Proof 45h.

In particular, assume that $AB \not\simeq A'B'$; assume furthermore that $m(AB) > m(A'B')$. So find A'' on AB such that $A''B \simeq A'B'$; and on BC find C'' such that $BC'' \simeq B'C'$ (Fig. 2.32). Now $\triangle A''BC'' \simeq \triangle A'B'C'$ by Proposition 4. So $\angle BA''C'' \simeq \angle B'A'C'$ and $\angle BC''A'' \simeq \angle B'C'A'$. Thus, $\angle BA''C'' \simeq \angle BAC$ and $\angle BC''A'' \simeq \angle BCA$.

Case 1: C is between B and C''. Then by Pasch's axiom, $A''C''$ intersects AC at a point D. And in $\triangle DCC''$, $\angle CC''D \simeq \angle BCD$. But $\angle BCD$ is an exterior angle and this is a contradiction to the exterior angle theorem.

Case 2: C'' is between B and C. Then $A''ACC''$ is a quadrilateral and

$$m\angle C''A''A + m\angle A''AC + m\angle ACC'' + m\angle CC''A''$$
$$= (180 - m\angle BA''C'') + m\angle A''AC + m\angle ACC'' + (180 - m\angle BC''A'')$$
$$= 180 - m\angle A''AC + m\angle A''AC + m\angle ACC'' + 180 - m\angle C''CA$$
$$= 360.$$

But this contradicts Corollary 1 of Theorem 43h. Therefore,

$$\triangle ABC \simeq \triangle A'B'C'. \qquad \blacksquare$$

Recall that in Euclidean geometry, two triangles are said to be *similar* if there is a one-to-one correspondence between the vertices of the two triangles such that corresponding angles are congruent and the lengths of corresponding sides are proportional. However, the preceding theorem indicates that in hyperbolic geometry any two triangles satisfying these properties are automatically congruent. Thus, we do not have any similar but noncongruent triangles in hyperbolic geometry.

Exercises

1. Prove Theorem 41h.

2. Prove the corollary of Theorem 41h.

3. Prove Theorem 42h. [*Hint*: To prove (2), construct right-sensed parallels to AB at C and D and apply Theorem 35h to asymptotic triangle $\triangle CD\Omega$.]

4. Prove that Theorem 42h is equivalent to the hyperbolic axiom.

5. Show that in $\triangle ABC$, where D and E are the midpoints of AB and AC, respectively, the perpendiculars to line DE from A and B must either coincide with or lie on opposite sides of AB. (Thus, there are only the three possible cases as shown in Fig. 2.30.)

6. Prove cases 2 and 3 of Theorem 43h.

7. Why can there be no squares or rectangles in hyperbolic geometry?

8. Show that in Fig. 2.33, if $m(AD) > m(BC)$, then $m\angle BCD > m\angle ADC$.

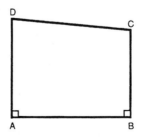

FIGURE 2.33 Exercise 8.

2.7 Hyperbolic Geometry—Area of Triangles

In the previous section we discovered that in hyperbolic geometry the angle sum of every triangle is less than 180° and that similar triangles do not exist. We now show that in this geometry the area of a triangle is determined by its angle sum. However, before proceeding with the necessary theorems it is prudent to recall the axioms that any area function must satisfy.

Area Axioms

Axiom Ar.1. The area of any set must be nonnegative.
Axiom Ar.2. The area of congruent sets must be the same.
Axiom Ar.3. The area of the union of disjoint sets must equal the sum of the areas of the sets.

To begin the sequence of theorems that will lead to the desired results, we need to return to a consideration of Saccheri quadrilaterals.

Theorem 46h

Two Saccheri quadrilaterals with congruent summits and summit angles are congruent.

Proof

Let $ABCD$ and $EFGH$ be two Saccheri quadrilaterals with $AB \simeq EF$, and $\angle DAB \simeq \angle HEF \simeq \angle EFG \simeq \angle ABC$. We must show that $AD \simeq EH$ (consequently $BC \simeq FG$), and that $DC \simeq HG$.

Part 1: $AD \simeq EH$. Assume that this is not true; in particular, assume that $m(AD) < m(EH)$. Find H' on EH and G' on FG so that $EH' \simeq AD$ and $FG' \simeq BC$. Construct $H'G'$ (Fig. 2.34). Let O and O' be the midpoints of AB and EF, respectively. Construct DO, CO, $H'O'$ and $G'O'$. Clearly, $\triangle DAO \simeq \triangle H'EO'$, and $\triangle OCB \simeq \triangle O'G'F'$. Thus, $DO \simeq H'O'$, $OC \simeq O'G'$, and $\angle DOC \simeq \angle H'O'G'$. So $\triangle DOC \simeq \triangle H'O'G'$. Then $\angle EH'G' \simeq \angle ADC$ and both are right angles. Likewise $\angle FG'H' \simeq \angle BCD$ and both are right angles. Therefore, $\angle HH'G'$ and

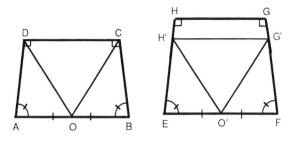

FIGURE 2.34 Proof 46h.

$\angle GG'H'$ are also right angles. Thus, quadrilateral $HH'G'G$ has four right angles, contradicting Corollary 1 of Theorem 43h. So $AD \simeq EH$.

Part 2: $DC \simeq HG$. (See Exercise 3.) ∎

With this result, we can prove a specialized version of the general area theorem for triangles.

Theorem 47h

Two triangles with the same angle sum and one pair of congruent sides have the same area.

Proof

Let $\triangle ABC$ and $\triangle DEF$ be two triangles with the same angle sum and assume $AB \simeq DE$. Let G and H be the midpoints of AC and BC. Construct GH. Let AI, CJ, BK be perpendiculars to GH from A, C, and B, respectively. As in the proof of Theorem 43h, there are three

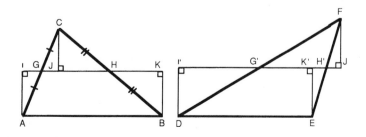

FIGURE 2.35 Proof 47h.

possible cases. In the case shown in Fig. 2.35, $\triangle AIG \simeq \triangle CJG$, and $\triangle CJH \simeq \triangle BKH$. So $IA \simeq KB$, and $AIKB$ is a Saccheri quadrilateral. Then clearly area($AIKB$) = area($\triangle ABC$) by the area axioms.

Furthermore, $m\angle IAB = m\angle CAB + m\angle GCJ$ and $m\angle KBA = m\angle CBA + m\angle HCJ$. Also, $m\angle CAB + m\angle CBA + m\angle GCJ + m\angle HCJ = m\angle CAB + m\angle CBA + m\angle ACB$. Therefore, since $AIKB$ is a Saccheri quadrilateral,

$$m\angle IAB = m\angle KBA = \frac{1}{2}[m\angle CAB + m\angle CBA + m\angle ACB].$$

As shown by Exercise 4, similar proofs for the other two cases demonstrate that a triangle and its equivalent Saccheri quadrilateral always have the same area, and furthermore the angle sum of the triangle equals the sum of the summit angles of the equivalent Saccheri quadrilateral.

Completing the same construction on DEF creates the Saccheri quadrilateral $I'DEK'$ with area($I'DEK'$) = area($\triangle DEF$) and with $m\angle I'DE = m\angle DEK' = \frac{1}{2}(m\angle FDE + m\angle FED + m\angle DFE)$. But since the summit angles of the two Saccheri quadrilaterals are congruent from the preceding and the hypothesis, and since $AB \simeq DE$, it follows by Theorem 46h that $I'DEK' \simeq IABK$. So area($I'DEK'$) = area($IABK$), and hence area($\triangle ABC$) = area($\triangle DEF$). ∎

In order to prove Theorem 48h, the generalized version of the previous theorem, we first demonstrate the following result.

Lemma
In $\triangle ABC$ if FE is perpendicular to the perpendicular bisector of BC and intersects AC at its midpoint, it will also intersect AB at its midpoint.

Proof
As in the proof of Theorem 43h there again are three cases. For the first case Figure 2.36 can be used to complete the proof and similar arguments can be used in the other two cases. ∎

Theorem 48h
Any two triangles with the same angle sum have the same area.

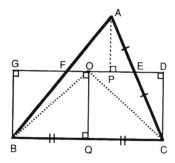

FIGURE 2.36   Lemma.

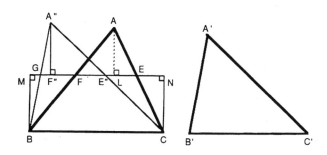

FIGURE 2.37   Proof 48h.

Proof

Let $\triangle ABC$ and $\triangle A'B'C'$ be two triangles with the same angle sum. Without loss of generality, assume that $m(A'C') > m(AC)$. (Note that if any pair of sides is congruent, the result follows immediately from Theorem 47h.) As in the proof of Theorem 47h, construct the Saccheri quadrilateral on BC (Fig. 2.37). Then let E'' be on FE so that $m(CE'') = \frac{1}{2}m(A'C')$. E'' will not coincide with E or N since $\frac{1}{2}m(A'C') > \frac{1}{2}m(AC) > m(CN)$. Construct CE'' and extend it to a point A'' so that $E''A'' \simeq CE''$. Construct $A''B$. Now let AF'' be the perpendicular to MN at F''. Since FE is perpendicular to the perpendicular bisector of BC by Theorem 41h and intersects $A''C$ at its midpoint, it will also intersect $A''B$ at its midpoint G by the previous lemma. Therefore, $\triangle BMG \simeq \triangle A''F''G$ and $\triangle A''E''F'' \simeq \triangle CE''N$. So area$(\triangle A''BC) =$ area$(MBCN)$. But as in the proof of Theorem 47h, area$(\triangle ABC) =$ area$(MBCN)$. And so area$(\triangle A''BC) =$ area$(\triangle ABC)$.

Furthermore, as in the proof of Theorem 47h, the angle sum of $\triangle A''BC = m(\angle MBC) + m(\angle BCN) =$ angle sum of $\triangle ABC$. Therefore, the angle sum of $\triangle A''BC =$ angle sum of $\triangle A'B'C'$, and $A''C \simeq A'C'$. So by Theorem 47h, $\text{area}(\triangle A''BC) = \text{area}(\triangle A'B'C')$, and thus $\text{area}(\triangle ABC) = \text{area}(\triangle A'B'C')$. ■

Thus, unlike Euclidean geometry, where the area of a triangle is determined by the lengths of its base and altitude, the preceding theorem demonstrates that the area of a triangle in hyperbolic geometry is completely determined by its angle sum. The relation between the area and the angle sum for triangles is stated in terms of the *defect* of a triangle.

Definition 2.5
The *(angular)* *defect* of a triangle is the numerical difference, $180-$ the angle sum of the triangle; that is, the angular defect of $\triangle ABC = 180 - [m\angle ABC + m\angle BCA + m\angle CAB]$.

Theorem 49h
If a triangle is divided into two triangles by a line from a vertex to a point on the opposite side, the defect of the original triangle is equal to the sum of the defects of the two smaller triangles.

Proof
See Exercise 6. ■

Theorem 48h implies that the area of a triangle can be considered either as a function of the angle sum of the triangle or as a function of the angular defect of the triangle. From Theorem 49h and the axioms of area, it follows that the area function A must preserve addition of angular defects. Since this function A must be a continuous function, then a result of elementary calculus says that there is a constant k such that

$$A(\triangle ABC) = k^2(\text{defect}(\triangle ABC)).$$

This result is summarized in the following theorem. One proof of this theorem is credited to Gauss (Coxeter, 1969, p. 296); another proof can be found in Moise (1974, p. 345).

Theorem 50h

There is a constant k such that

$$\text{area}(\triangle ABC) = k^2\{180 - [m\angle ABC + m\angle BCA + m\angle CAB]\}.$$

Exercises

1. Using only Postulates 1 through 4 (and Propositions 1 through 28) prove the following: If the sum of the angles of a triangle is the same for all triangles, then that sum is 180°. [*Hint:* Consider a triangle partitioned by a line joining a vertex with a point on the opposite side.] What does this result say about triangles in hyperbolic geometry?

2. The following "proof" of the existence of a triangle with angle sum equal to 180° is reprinted from Dubnov's *Mistakes in Geometric Proofs* (1963) with the permission of D. C. Heath and Co. (a) Does this "proof" make use of the parallel postulate? (b) What is wrong with the proof?

Claim. There exists a triangle with angle sum equal to 180°.

Proof

Since the angle sum of a triangle is less than or equal to 180°, let $\triangle ABC$ (Fig. 2.38) be a triangle with the greatest angle sum; call this sum a. We shall prove that $a = 180°$.
$m\angle 1 + m\angle 2 + m\angle 6 \le a$ and $m\angle 3 + m\angle 4 + m\angle 5 \le a$ (Why?) So $m\angle 1 + m\angle 2 + m\angle 3 + m\angle 4 + m\angle 5 + m\angle 6 \le 2a$. But $m\angle 5 + m\angle 6 = 180°$, and $m\angle 1 + m\angle 2 + m\angle 3 + m\angle 4 = a$. So $a + 180° \le 2a$ or $a \ge 180°$. Thus, $a = 180°$. ∎

3. Verify part 2 in the proof of Theorem 46h.

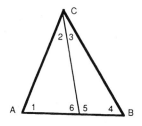

FIGURE 2.38 Exercise 2.

4. Prove that a triangle and its equivalent Saccheri quadrilateral have the same area, and that the angle sum of the triangle equals the sum of the summit angles of the equivalent Saccheri quadrilateral.

5. Prove the lemma used in the proof of Theorem 48h.

6. Prove Theorem 49h.

7. Prove that the angle sum of a convex polygon of n sides is less than $(n-2)180°$.

2.8 Hyperbolic Geometry—Ultraparallels

In this final section on hyperbolic geometry, we will briefly consider the second type of parallel lines, namely, ultraparallels. Recall that if l is a line and P a point not on l, then a line m through P is said to be ultraparallel to l if l and m do not intersect and are not sensed parallel. As in the case of sensed parallels, the definition of ultraparallelism is independent of the point P and the relation is symmetric. These properties are formalized in the following theorems, which can be verified by indirect proofs (see Exercises 2 and 3).

Theorem 51h
If a line is ultraparallel through a given point to a given line, it is at each of its points ultraparallel to the given line.

Theorem 52h
If one line is ultraparallel to a second, then the second is ultraparallel to the first.

However, unlike sensed parallelism, ultraparallelism is *not* transitive. In terms of line l and point P, any line lying within the vertical angles formed by the sensed parallels to l through P is ultraparallel to l. In particular, any two of these lines, say m and n, are both ultraparallel to l, but m and n are not ultraparallel, since they intersect at P (Fig. 2.39).

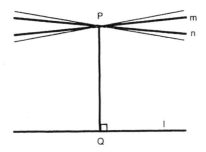

FIGURE 2.39 *m* and *n* within angles formed by sensed parallels to *l*.

Two familiar properties in Euclidean geometry are: (1) two parallel lines have an infinite number of common perpendiculars; and
(2) the (perpendicular) distance between two parallel lines is constant (i.e., parallel lines are everywhere equidistant). In hyperbolic
geometry, we have already observed that sensed parallel lines do
not have common perpendiculars and that the perpendicular distance between sensed parallel lines decreases in the direction of
parallelism (Theorem 44h). Furthermore, one of the corollaries of
Theorem 43h demonstrates that two ultraparallel lines do *not* have
more than one common perpendicular. That a common perpendicular between two ultraparallel lines does exist is verified by the
following theorem. Since the proof of this theorem is somewhat involved you may find it enlightening to sketch the specific points and
lines one by one as you encounter them in your reading.

Theorem 53h
Two ultraparallel lines have a common perpendicular.

Proof
Let *n* and *m* be ultraparallel. Let *A* and *B* be any two points on *n*
and construct *AC* and *BD* perpendicular to *m* at *C* and *D*. Now if segments *AC* and *BD* are congruent, *ABCD* is a Saccheri quadrilateral
(Fig. 2.40) and the common perpendicular is the line connecting the
midpoints of *AB* and *CD*. If *AC* and *BD* are not congruent, assume
that $m(AC) > m(BD)$. Find *E* on *AC* such that $CE \simeq BD$. At *E* draw
EF on the side of *AC* determined by *BD* such that $\angle CEF \simeq \angle BDG$
where *G* is a point on *n* such that *B* is between *A* and *G*.

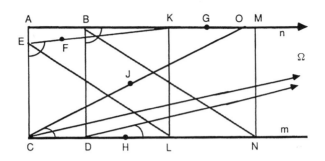

FIGURE 2.40 Proof 53h.

It will be shown that EF intersects n. Let $C\Omega$ and $D\Omega$ be sensed parallel to n in the direction from A to B. Let H be a point on m such that D is between C and H. Then $C\Omega$ contains points in the interior of $\angle ACH$, and $D\Omega$ likewise contains points in the interior of $\angle BDH$ since m is ultraparallel to n. Now $m\angle HD\Omega > m\angle HC\Omega$ by the exterior angle theorem for asymptotic triangles. Construct CJ such that $\angle JCH \simeq \angle \Omega DH$. Then CJ will intersect n at a point O. Now since $EC \simeq BD$, $\angle FEC \simeq \angle GBD$, and $\angle ECJ \simeq \angle BD\Omega$, EF is sensed parallel to CJ and hence cannot intersect segment CO. Therefore, EF must intersect segment AO in a point K. Construct KL perpendicular to m. On n and m on the side of BD opposite A, find M and N such that $BM \simeq EK$, and $DN \simeq CL$. Construct MN. Then $\triangle ECL \simeq \triangle BDN$ and consequently $\triangle EKL \simeq \triangle BMN$, and thus $KL \simeq MN$. Furthermore, $m\angle DNM = m\angle DNB + m\angle BNM = m\angle CLE + m\angle ELK = 90°$. So $KMNL$ is a Saccheri quadrilateral and the line joining the midpoints of segments KM and LN is perpendicular to both n and m. ∎

Corollary
Two ultraparallel lines have exactly one common perpendicular.

Note that the proof of the previous theorem demonstrates that the common perpendicular exists but the actual construction cannot be accomplished without the ability to construct sensed parallels. This construction can be done and is demonstrated in Wolfe (1945).

The question of the distance between ultraparallel lines can now be answered in terms of the unique common perpendicular. The proof of this theorem is left for the exercises.

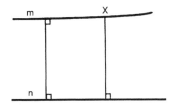

FIGURE 2.41   Theorem 54h.

Theorem 54h

If X is an arbitrary point on m, a line ultraparallel to n, then the perpendicular distance from X to n is a minimum along the common perpendicular to m and n (Fig. 2.41).

With this theorem, we conclude our introduction to hyperbolic geometry. The approach we have taken is similar to the historic development of the subject; that is, we started with Euclid's five postulates and replaced the fifth postulate (in the form of Playfair's axiom) by a negation in the form of the hyperbolic axiom. With this one change, we have obtained a new geometry with several strange properties that make it radically different from Euclidean geometry. In the next section, we will explore the geometry that results when we replace Euclid's fifth postulate by a second possible negation.

Exercises

1. Sketch each of the following in a Klein model. (Draw one model for each.) (a) Two intersecting lines that are both sensed parallel to a third line. (b) Two intersecting lines that are both ultraparallel to a third line. (c) Two sensed parallel lines that both intersect a third line. (d) Two sensed parallel lines that are both sensed parallel to a third line. (e) Two sensed parallel lines that are both ultraparallel to a third line. (f) Two ultraparallel lines that both intersect a third line. (g) Two ultraparallel lines that are both ultraparallel to a third line.

2. Prove Theorem 51h.

3. Prove Theorem 52h.

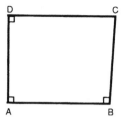

FIGURE 2.42 Lambert quadrilateral.

4. Without using Theorem 54h, prove that in Figure 2.42, $m(DC) > m(AB)$. (Any such quadrilateral with three right angles is known as a *Lambert quadrilateral*.)

5. Using the result of Exercise 4, prove that the summit of a Saccheri quadrilateral is greater than the base.

6. Using the result of Exercise 4, prove Theorem 54h.

2.9 Elliptic Geometry

The consequences of the hyperbolic axiom had been thoroughly explored before the systematic study of elliptic geometry began. The initiation of the study of this second non-Euclidean geometry can be traced to 1854 when G.B.F. Riemann gave an inaugural lecture at the University of Göttingen entitled "On the Hypotheses Which Underlie the Foundations of Geometry."

As with hyperbolic geometry, an axiomatic system for elliptic geometry is obtained from Euclid's geometry by replacing the fifth postulate (in the form of Playfair's axiom) with a negation. In this case the negation is known as the *elliptic axiom*.

Elliptic Axiom
Two lines always intersect.

Unfortunately, it soon becomes evident that the axiomatic system consisting of this axiom and Euclid's first four postulates is not consistent, since the first four postulates imply the validity of

Proposition 27, which asserts the existence of parallel (i.e., noninter-secting) lines. In order to obtain a consistent system that contains the elliptic axiom and maintains as many of the properties of Eu-clidean geometry as possible, Euclid's proof of Proposition 27 must be invalidated. An examination of this proof (see Section 2.2) shows that it makes use of Proposition 16, but in the proof of this latter proposition, Euclid inferred from Postulate 2 the infinite extent of a line. If Postulate 2 is interpreted as saying only that a line is bound-less but *not* necessarily of infinite extent, the proof of Proposition 16 and therefore the proof of Proposition 27 becomes invalid.

Thus, to obtain a consistent non-Euclidean geometry containing the elliptic axiom, Euclid's second postulate must be modified as follows:

Postulate 2′

A finite line (i.e., segment) can be produced continuously in a line. The line obtained is boundless but not necessarily of infinite extent.

Even with this modification, the axiomatic system consisting of Euclid's first four postulates and the elliptic axiom remains incon-sistent, since it still yields the following proof of the existence of parallel lines.

Another proof of the existence of parallel lines

Let A and B be two points on a line l. Let m and n be lines perpen-dicular to l at A and B, respectively (Proposition 11). Assume that m and n are not parallel. Let C be their point of intersection. Then find C' on m on the side of l opposite C such that the segments AC and AC' are congruent (3). Construct $C'B$ (Fig. 2.43). Then since $\triangle ABC \simeq \triangle ABC'$, and $\angle C'BA \simeq \angle CBA$ (4); it follows that $\angle C'BA$ is also a right angle. Thus, by Proposition 14, C', B, and C are collinear, and hence m and n intersect in two distinct points C and C', which yields a contradiction. Thus, m and n are parallel lines. ■

So to obtain a consistent axiom system, including the elliptic axiom, the preceding proof must also be invalidated. After some consideration, it should become apparent that the following unstated assumptions were used in the proof:

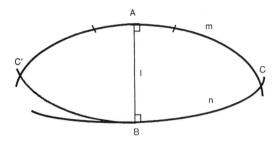

FIGURE 2.43   Existence of parallels.

1. A line separates the plane.
2. Two distinct points lie on a unique line.

Thus, this proof would be invalidated if either of these two as-sumptions were negated. It is the need to negate one of these two assumptions that leads to two types of elliptic geometry. If the first assumption is maintained and the second assumption is negated, that is, if it is assumed that two distinct points do not necessarily lie on a unique line, the geometry known as double elliptic geometry is obtained. If, on the other hand, the second assumption is main-tained and the first assumption is negated, that is, if it is assumed that a line does not separate the plane, the geometry known as sin-gle elliptic geometry is obtained. Either choice, together with the modification of Postulate 2, results in a system radically different from Euclid's. Hence, it is nearly impossible to salvage any of Eu-clid's work, and it becomes essential to develop an entirely new set of axioms for both single and double elliptic geometry. Axioms for these geometries can be found in Chapters 7 and 8 of *An Introduc-tion to Non-Euclidean Geometry* by David Gans (1973). Since models of both double and single elliptic geometry are easily accessible, we can achieve considerable familiarity with these geometries by ex-ploring properties in these models. Thus, we can sample the flavor of elliptic geometries without considering a series of detailed proofs.

Models of Double and Single Elliptic Geometry

Term	Interpretation for Double Elliptic	Interpretation for Single Elliptic
Point	Point on the surface of a Euclidean sphere	Point on the surface of a Euclidean hemisphere if the point is not on the edge; points on the edge are identified with their diametric opposite
Line	Great circle	Semigreat circle
Length	Euclidean length	Euclidean length with the modification implied by the preceding
Angle measure	Euclidean angle measure	Euclidean angle measure

Exploring Double Elliptic Geometry

Equipment Requirements

- A spherical surface[2] and water-based markers that will write on the surface of the sphere.
- Tools for measuring distances, measuring angles, and drawing circles on the sphere; these could be a length of string (long enough to reach around the sphere), rubber bands that will reach around the sphere, and a flexible protractor.

Activities

The following activities ask you to use this equipment and the model of double elliptic geometry described above to "discover" fundamental properties of double elliptic geometry. Describe your findings in paragraph summaries that include answers to the summary questions and a com-

---

[2]Use a moderate-size ball or a Lénárt Sphere (TM Key Curriculum Press).

parison of the properties observed with those in Euclidean and hyperbolic geometries.

1. Points and Lines

   a. Construct and label several pairs of points on the surface of your sphere.
   b. Find the lines determined by some of the pairs of points you located.
   c. Summary questions:

      i. Do two points always lie on a line? Is the line determined by two points unique?
      ii. Can the distance between two points be made arbitrarily large? Why or why not? (The *elliptic distance* between points is the Euclidean distance along the shortest arc of the great circle between them.)
      iii. How long is a line? Are all lines the same length?
      iv. If *l* and *m* are two lines, do *l* and *m* necessarily intersect? If so, how often?
      v. Does this geometry satisfy Playfair's axiom? If not, can Playfair's axiom be modified so that it becomes a true statement in this model? If so, how?

2. Perpendiculars

   a. Construct a line *l* and a point *P* not on *l* on your sphere. Now find a line *m* through *P* that is perpendicular to *l*. Label a point of intersection of these two lines *Q*. (Note: The *elliptic angle measure* is the Euclidean angle measure between tangents to the two great circles.)
   b. Find a line *n* perpendicular to *m* at *P*.
   c. Repeat the previous two constructions with varying distances between *P* and *l*.
   d. Summary questions:

      i. Can a perpendicular to a line *l* always be drawn through a point *P* if *P* lies off the line *l*? If so, is the perpendicular to *l* through *P* unique?

  ii. Can a perpendicular to a line l always be drawn through a point P if P is on the line l? If so, is the perpendicular to l through P unique?

  iii. Can two lines have a common perpendicular? Can two lines have more than one common perpendicular?

  iv. Can two lines be equidistant?

3. Circles

 a. Construct several circles by constructing two points, one to serve as the center and one as a point on the circle. Be sure to vary the distance d between the two points, including examples with $d < \pi r/2$, $\pi r/2 < d < \pi r$, and $d = \pi r$ (r represents the radius of the sphere).

 b. Recall that in Euclidean geometry, it is also possible to construct a unique circle through any 3 given noncollinear points. Determine how the center of such a circle is constructed in Euclidean geometry. Why does this construction always work in Euclidean geometry?

 c. Construct 3 noncollinear points on your spherical model. Try using the usual Euclidean construction for locating the center of a circle that would pass through these three points.

 d. Summary questions:

  i. What happens to the size of the circle as the radius increases? Why?

  ii. Is it possible to specify the same circle with different center and radii pairs?

  iii. Will there always be a unique circle passing through 3 noncollinear points in this geometry? Why?

4. Triangles, Saccheri Quadrilaterals, and 2-gons

 a. Construct several triangles including one with exactly one right angle and one with exactly two right angles. Measure the nonright angles and the sides of each.

 b. Construct two triangles that have two pairs of congruent angles and a pair of congruent sides opposite one of the pair of congruent angles. Try making the two triangles noncongruent.

   c. Construct a triangle with three right angles. Measure the sides and angles of this triangle. Compute the fraction of the surface area of the sphere covered by your triangle.

   d. Construct a 2-gon, i.e., a two-sided figure, with two right angles.

   e. Construct a Saccheri quadrilateral. Measure its summit angles, its base length, and its summit length.

   f. Summary questions:

      i. Do three points determine a unique triangle? Why?

     ii. In a right triangle, i.e., a triangle with exactly one right angle, what is the maximum length of a side opposite an acute angle? What is the minimum length of a side opposite an obtuse angle?

    iii. What is true about the angle sum of triangles? Is there an upper bound for such angle sums? A lower bound? Why?

    iv. What appears to be the relation between the angle sum of a triangle and its area?

     v. What appears to be true about the summit angles of a Saccheri quadrilateral in this geometry? How is this related to the angle sum of triangles in this geometry? How does the length of the summit compare to the length of the base?

The activities above should give insight into the special properties of double elliptic geometry. Lists of some of the major properties for this geometry and for single elliptic geometry follow. Hopefully, the items in the first list agree with your observations. As a real test of your visualization skills, try explaining the differences between the properties in the first list for double elliptic geometry (Fig. 2.44) and those in the second list for single elliptic geometry (Fig. 2.45).

Properties of Double Elliptic Geometry

1. A line separates the plane.
2. There is at least one line through each pair of points.
3. Each pair of lines meets in exactly two points.

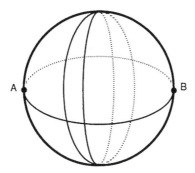

FIGURE 2.44 Model of double elliptic plane.

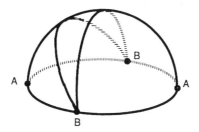

FIGURE 2.45 Model of single elliptic plane.

4. There is a positive constant k such that the distance between two points never exceeds πk. Two points at the maximum distance are called *opposite* points.
5. All lines have the same length, $2\pi k$.
6. Corresponding to each point there is a unique opposite point.
7. Two points lie on a unique line if and only if the points are not opposite.
8. All the lines through a given point also pass through the point opposite the given point.
9. All the lines perpendicular to any given line meet in the same pair of opposite points. The distance from each of these points to any point of the given line is $\pi k/2$. These two opposite points are called *poles* of the given line and the line is called the *polar* of the two points.
10. All the lines through a point are perpendicular to the polar of that point.

11. There exists a unique perpendicular to a given line through a given point if and only if the point is not the pole of the line.
12. The summit angles of a Saccheri quadrilateral are congruent and obtuse.
13. The angle sum of every triangle exceeds 180°.
14. The area of a triangle is given by

$$\text{area}(\triangle ABC) = k^2(m\angle ABC + m\angle BCA + m\angle CAB - 180°).$$

Properties of Single Elliptic Geometry

1. A line does not separate the plane.
2. There is at least one line through each pair of points.
3. Each pair of lines meets in exactly one point.
4. There is a positive constant k such that the distance between two points never exceeds $\pi k/2$. Two points that divide a line into equal segments are called *opposite* points.
5. On a given line, corresponding to each point there is an opposite point on the line.
6. All lines have the same length πk.
7. All lines perpendicular to any given line go through the same point. The distance from this point to any point of the given line is $\pi k/2$. The point is called the *pole* of the given line and the line is called the *polar* of the point.
8. All the lines through a point are perpendicular to the polar of that point.
9. There exists a unique perpendicular to a given line through a given point if and only if the point is not the pole of the given line.
10. The summit angles of a Saccheri quadrilateral are congruent and obtuse.
11. The angle sum of every triangle exceeds 180°.
12. The area of a triangle is given by

$$\text{area}(\triangle ABC) = k^2(m\angle ABC + m\angle BCA + m\angle CAB - 180°).$$

2.10 Significance of the Discovery of Non-Euclidean Geometries

The development of non-Euclidean geometry began historically with the attempt to prove Euclid's fifth postulate from his first four postulates. By the early 19th century, mathematicians began to accept the possibility that the fifth postulate might be independent. That this postulate is indeed independent was demonstrated when in 1868 the Italian mathematician Eugenio Beltrami (1835–1900) exhibited the first in a series of geometric models of hyperbolic geometry. The best known of these geometric models is the Poincaré model introduced in Section 2.3. Under the interpretations of these models, the axioms of hyperbolic geometry become theorems in Euclidean geometry. Thus hyperbolic geometry was shown to be relatively consistent, and in particular, the models demonstrated that hyperbolic geometry is consistent if Euclidean geometry is consistent. The question of the independence of the fifth postulate had finally been settled.

That the development of non-Euclidean geometry had profound mathematical and philosophical consequences has already been mentioned at the beginning of this chapter. The abstract considerations of these geometries also had important implications in other areas. Riemann's lecture of 1854 used a method that created an infinite number of geometries, and Einstein adopted one of these Riemannian geometries in his study of relativity. A description of this geometry and Einstein's use of it is contained in an essay by Penrose (1978). Furthermore, research since World War II indicates that binocular visual space is hyperbolic. Descriptions of this research are recorded in Trudeau (1987) and in articles by Ogle (1962) and Zage (1980).

2.11 Suggestions for Further Reading

Aleksandrov, A. D. (1969). Non-Euclidean Geometry. In *Mathematics: Its Content, Methods and Meaning*, A. D. Aleksandrov, A. N. Kolmogorov,

TABLE 2.1   A Comparison of Euclidean and Non-Euclidean Geometries.[a]

	Euclidean	Hyperbolic	Elliptic	
Two distinct lines intersect in	at most one	at most one	one (single) two (double)	point(s).
Given a line m and point P not on m, there exist	exactly one	at least two	no lines	through P not intersecting m.
A line	does not	does not	does	have finite length.
A line	is	is	is not	separated by a point.
A line	does	does	does not (single) does (double)	separate the plane.
Nonintersecting lines	are equidistant.	are never equidistant.	do not exist.	
If a line intersects one of two nonintersecting lines, it	must	may or may not		intersect the other.
The summit angles in a Saccheri quadrilateral are	right	acute	obtuse	angles.
Two distinct lines perpendicular to the same line are	parallel.	ultraparallel.	intersecting.	
The angle sum of a triangle is	equal to	less than	greater than	180°.
The area of a triangle is	independent	proportional to the defect	proportional to the excess	of its angle sum.
Two triangles with congruent corresponding angles are	similar.	congruent.	congruent.	

[a] Reprinted with permission from Meserve (1983), *Fundamental Concepts of Geometry*.

and M. A. Lavrent'ev (Eds.), Vol. 3, pp. 97–189. Cambridge, MA: M.I.T. Press. (This is an expository presentation of non-Euclidean geometry.)

Davis, D. M. (1993). *The Nature and Power of Mathematics.* Princeton: Princeton University Press. (Written for the liberal arts students, Chapters 1 and 2 provide a substantial introduction to early Greek mathematics and non-Euclidean geometry.)

Gans, D. (1973). *An Introduction to Non-Euclidean Geometry.* New York: Academic Press. (This is an easy-to-read and detailed presentation.)

Gray, J. (1979). *Ideas of Space: Euclidean, Non-Euclidean and Relativistic.* Oxford: Clarendon Press.

Heath, T. L. (1956). *The Thirteen Books of Euclid's Elements,* 2d ed. New York: Dover.

Henderson, L. D. (1983). *The Fourth Dimension and Non-Euclidean Geometry in Modern Art.* Princeton, NJ: Princeton University Press.

Lieber, L. R. (1940). *Non-Euclidean Geometry: or, Three Moons in Mathesis,* 2d ed. New York: Galois Institute of Mathematics and Art. (This is an entertaining poetic presentation.)

Lockwood, J. R. and Runion, G. E. (1978). *Deductive Systems: Finite and Non-Euclidean Geometries.* Reston, VA: N.C.T.M. (This is a brief elementary introduction that can be used as supplementary material at the secondary-school level.)

Ogle, K. N. (1962). The visual space sense. *Science* 135: 763–771.

Penrose, R. (1978). The geometry of the universe. In *Mathematics Today: Twelve Informal Essays.* Edited by L. A. Steen, pp. 83–125. New York: Springer-Verlag.

Ryan, P. J. (1986). *Euclidean and Non-Euclidean Geometry: An Analytic Approach.* Cambridge: Cambridge University Press. (Uses groups and analytic techniques of linear algebra to construct and study models of these geometries.)

Sommerville, D. (1970). *Bibliography of Non-Euclidean Geometry,* 2d ed. New York: Chelsea.

Trudeau, R. J. (1987). *The Non-Euclidean Revolution.* Boston: Birkhauser. (This presentation of both Euclid's original work and non-Euclidean geometry is interwoven with a nontechnical description of the revolution in mathematics that resulted from the development of non-Euclidean geometry.)

Wolfe, H. E. (1945). *Introduction to Non-Euclidean Geometry.* New York: Holt, Rinehart and Winston. (Chaps. 1, 2, and 4 contain a development similar to that in this text.)

Zage, W. M. (1980). The geometry of binocular visual space. *Mathematics Magazine* 53(5): 289–294.

Readings on the History of Geometry

Barker, S. F. (1984). Non-Euclidean geometry. In *Mathematics: People, Problems, Results*. Edited by D. M. Campbell and J. C. Higgins, Vol. 2, pp. 112–127. Belmont, CA: Wadsworth.

Barker, S. F. (1964). *Philosophy of Mathematics*, pp. 1–55. Englewood Cliffs, NJ: Prentice-Hall.

Bold, B. (1969). *Famous Problems of Geometry and How to Solve Them*. New York: Dover.

Bronowski, J. (1974). The music of the spheres. In *The Ascent of Man*, pp. 155–187. Boston: Little, Brown

Eves, H. (1976). *An Introduction to the History of Mathematics*, 4th ed. New York: Holt, Rinehart and Winston.

Gardner, M. (1966). The persistence (and futility) of efforts to trisect the angle. *Scientific American* 214: 116–122.

Gardner, M. (1981). Euclid's parallel postulate and its modern offspring. *Scientific American* 254: 23–24.

Grabiner, Judith V. (1988). The centrality of mathematics in the history of western thought. *Mathematics Magazine* 61(4): 220–230.

Heath, T. L. (1921). *A History of Greek Mathematics*. Oxford: Clarendon Press.

Heath, T. L. (1956). *The Thirteen Books of Euclid's Elements*, 2d ed. New York: Dover.

Hoffer, W. (1975). A magic ratio recurs throughout history. *Smithsonian* 6(9): 110–124.

Kline, M. (1972). *Mathematical Thought from Ancient to Modern Times*, pp. 3–130, 861–881. New York: Oxford University Press.

Knorr, W. R. (1986). *The Ancient Tradition of Geometric Problems*. Boston: Birkhauser.

Maziarz, E., and Greenwood, T. (1984). Greek mathematical philosophy. In *Mathematics: People, Problems, Results*. Edited by D. M. Campbell and J. C. Higgins. Vol. 1, pp. 18–27. Belmont, CA: Wadsworth.

Mikami, Y. (1974). *The Development of Mathematics in China and Japan*, 2d ed. New York: Chelsea.

Smith, D. E. (1958). *History of Mathematics*, Vol. 1, pp. 1–147. New York: Dover.

Swetz, F. (1984). The evolution of mathematics in ancient China. In *Mathematics: People, Problems, Results*. Edited by D. M. Campbell and J. C. Higgins. Vol. 1, pp. 28–37. Belmont, CA: Wadsworth.

Torretti, Roberto (1978). *Philosophy of Geometry from Riemann to Poincaré*. Dordrect, Holland: D. Reidel Publishing Company.

Suggestions for Viewing

A Non-Euclidean Universe (1978; 25 min). Depicts the Poincaré model of the hyperbolic plane. Produced by the Open University Production Centre, Walton Hall, Milton Keynes MK7 6BH, UK.

3

CHAPTER

Geometric Transformations of the Euclidean Plane

3.1 Gaining Perspective

The presentation of non-Euclidean geometry in Chapter 2 was *synthetic*, that is, figures were studied directly and without use of their algebraic representations. This reflects the manner in which both Euclidean and non-Euclidean geometries were originally developed. However, in the 17th century, French mathematicians Pierre de Fermat (1601–1665) and René Descartes (1596–1650) began using algebraic representations of figures. They realized that by assigning to each point in the plane an ordered pair of real numbers, algebraic techniques could be employed in the study of Euclidean geometry. This study of figures in terms of their algebraic representations by equations is known as *analytic geometry*.

The use of algebraic techniques eventually led to the application of group theory to the study of geometry. This approach led Felix Klein (1849–1925) to give the following definition of geometry in his Erlanger Program of 1872.

Definition 3.1

A *geometry* is the study of those properties of a set α that remain invariant (unchanged) when the elements of α are subjected to the transformations of some transformation group.

Using this definition, Klein was able to give a classification of geometries in terms of subgroups of linear transformations. The Euclidean transformations are the motions required to carry out the superposition of figures. This technique of moving one figure on top of another to verify congruence is based historically on Euclid's Common Notion 4 and was employed in his proofs of Propositions 4 and 8 (commonly known as the SAS and SSS theorems, respectively). In recent times, these transformations and their matrix representations have become basic tools in computer graphics.

In this chapter we use a dual transformation approach to study Euclidean, similarity, and affine geometries. After a brief introduction to the concept of symmetry in this section, we conduct hands-on explorations of specific transformations of the Euclidean plane and investigate symmetries defined by these transformations. Each exploration begins with a list of equipment and materials needed, and in some cases a note indicating that the exploration can be supplemented by using dynamic geometry software (for specific directions, see http://www.stolaf.edu/people/cederj/geotext/info.htm). The explorations assume some basic familiarity with transformations (functions) and standard concepts of Euclidean geometry such as distance, angle, and vector.

In Section 3.5, we set up an analytic model in which geometric terms are carefully interpreted via formal definitions. Within this context, we find matrix representations of all the isometries of the Euclidean plane. Using these matrices we analytically verify that any isometry must be one of the four previously identified and examine properties of each. In another exploration section (Section 3.11) we explore plane tilings with polygons and determine which isometries are in their symmetry groups.

Generalizing the isometries, we then obtain the transformations of similarity geometry and those of affine geometry. With a slight change in the set of points, the next step in this generalization yields the transformations of projective geometry. Before considering projective geometry in Chapter 4, we conclude Chapter 3 by exploring symmetries of Euclidean 3-space in Section 3.14.

An Introduction to Symmetry

For most people the meaning of the term "symmetry" is somewhat vague, even though the term is used frequently in everyday conservation and nontechnical writing. This was true even in the early 1950s when Herman Weyl gave a series of four lectures (later published in the small volume titled *Symmetry*). At the beginning of his first lecture, he interpreted the meanings then commonly ascribed to the term, indicated the variety of nonmathematical subjects to which it is applied, and related these to one of its mathematical uses.

If I Am Not Mistaken the word *symmetry* is used in our everyday language in two meanings. In the one sense symmetry means something like well-proportioned, well-balanced, and symmetry denotes that sort of concordance of several parts by which they integrate into a whole. *Beauty* is bound up with symmetry. Thus Polykleitos, who wrote a book on proportion and whom the ancients praised for the harmonious perfection of his sculptures, uses the word, and Dürer follows him in setting down a canon or proportions for the human figure. In this sense the idea is by no means restricted to spatial objects; the synonym "harmony" points more toward its acoustical and musical than its geometric applications. *Ebenmass* is a good German equivalent for the Greek symmetry; for like this it carries also the connotation of "middle measure," the mean toward which the virtuous should strive in their actions according to Aristotle's Nicomachean Ethics, and which Galen in *De temperamentis* describes as that state of mind which is equally removed from both extremes. . . .

The image of the balance provides a natural link to the second sense in which the word symmetry is used in modern times: [one example is] *bilateral symmetry*, the symmetry of left and right, which is so conspicuous in the structure of the higher animals, especially the human body. Now this bilateral symmetry is strictly geometric and, in contrast to the vague notion of symmetry discussed before, an absolutely precise concept. [Weyl, pp. 3–4]

More recently Ian Stewart and Martin Golubitsky also commented on the lengthy germination of this mathematical concept in their delightful text *Fearful Symmetry: Is God a Geometer?*

> It took humanity roughly two and a half thousand years to attain a precise formulation of the concept of symmetry, counting from the time when the Greek geometers made the first serious mathematical discoveries about that concept, notably the proof that there exist exactly five regular solids. Only *after* that lengthy period of gestation was the concept of symmetry something that scientists and mathematicians could *use* rather than just admire. [Stewart and Golubitsky, pp. 27–28]

Building on this long period of formulation, we can now state the commonly accepted mathematical definition below. This definition describes the two uses of the term *symmetry*. First, the term refers to a transformation that preserves the structure of a point set; and second, it describes a property of the point set whose structure is preserved. Notice that according to this definition a symmetry need not be an isometry. However, if the symmetry of a point set α is a nonidentity isometry, the symmetric set can be said to be congruent to itself under the symmetry.

Definition 3.2
A transformation S is said to be a *symmetry* of the set of points α if S keeps α invariant, that is, $S(\alpha) = \alpha$. If S is not the identity transformation ($S \neq I$), we say that α is *symmetric* or that α has *symmetry*.

For many, the concept of symmetry has become a major theme in geometry. And, as the following quotations indicate, the transformation approach, fundamental to symmetry, has assumed major importance throughout mathematics.

> Mapping [i.e., transformation] is a major theme of contemporary mathematics because it provides a useful and illuminating way to organize relations among shapes and patterns. [Senechal, *On the Shoulders of Giants*, (1999), p. 168.]
> It was only within the last twenty years or so that a definition of mathematics emerged on which most mathematicians now

agree: mathematics is *the science of patterns*. What the mathematician does is examine abstract "patterns"—numerical patterns, patterns of shape, patterns of motion, patterns of behavior, and so on. [Devlin, *Mathematics: The Science of Patterns*, (1994), p. 3]

3.2 Exploring Line and Point Reflections

3.2.1 Equipment and Materials Needed

- Three small mirrors, several pieces of colored paper, a straight edge, and devices/methods for constructing images under line and point reflections.[1]
- Many of these activities can also be carried out using dynamic geometry software. Specific instructions for *Cabri Geometry II* and *Geometer's Sketchpad* can be found at
  http://www.stolaf.edu/people/cederj/geotext/info.htm.

Introduction

This is the first of several exploration sections contained in this chapter. The goal of these explorations is to introduce the concept of symmetry and develop intuitive understanding of isometries by viewing them as symmetry transformations. Each exploration contains a series of activities designed to guide you through hands-on investigations. During your investigations you will be asked to make conjectures, that is, to describe what appears to be happening. In later sections we will find matrix representations for these same transformations and use analytic methods for determining

---

[1]To find images under line reflections, you can use a semitransparent mirror (*Image Reflectors*™ work well and are available from Dale Seymour Publications) or you can fold semitransparent paper and trace.

specific properties of these transformations. In many cases, this analytic approach will verify properties you discovered earlier in the explorations.

3.2.2 Line Reflections

We begin our explorations with what is probably the most readily identifiable symmetry, that known as *bilateral* or *line symmetry*. To give a precise mathematical definition of line symmetry, we need to formalize the idea of a reflection. Intuitively, a *reflection* is a transformation that is created by a mirror and leaves every point on the mirror line invariant; that is, the mirror line is *pointwise invariant*. In practical terms, a semitransparent mirror, paper folding, or dynamic geometry software can be used to carry out a reflection and hence generate a figure with line symmetry.

Definition 3.3

A *(line) reflection with axis m*, denoted R_m, is a transformation that maps each point on m to itself, and maps each point P not on m to a point P' such that m is the perpendicular bisector of segment $\overline{PP'}$. If a point set α ($\alpha \neq m$) is invariant under R_m, we say that α has *line symmetry* and that m is a *line of symmetry* for α.

Activities

Carefully label your drawings to indicate the properties they illustrate.

1. Draw a simple nonsymmetric figure F_0 and a line l. Label both your figure and your line. Then draw all of the following as part of the same illustration. To keep track of things, label each line and figure as indicated.

   a. Draw F_1, the image of F_0 under a reflection in the line l.
   b. Describe how F_1 is related to the original figure F_0. In particular, where is F_1 located relative to F_0 and the line l? Do F_0

and F_1 have the same *orientation*,[2] that is, if you trace a counterclockwise circuit around F_0, will the corresponding circuit around F_1 also go in the counterclockwise direction? Do either the location or orientation of F_1 relative to F_0 appear to depend on the positions of F_0 and the line l? If so, how?

c. Draw F_2, the image of F_1 under a second reflection in l.

d. Describe how the position and orientation of F_2 are related to those of the original figure F_0. Do either the location or orientation of F_2 relative to F_0 appear to depend on the positions of F_0 and the line l? Explain.

e. What types of symmetry does your illustration demonstrate?

2. Draw another simple nonsymmetric figure F_0 and two distinct lines l_1 and l_2. Draw all of the following as part of the same illustration, labeling each figure and line as indicated.

a. Draw F_1, the image of F_0 under a reflection in line l_1.

b. Draw F_2, where F_2 is the image of F_1 under a reflection in line l_2.

c. Describe how F_2 is related to the original figure F_0. Where is it located relative to the original? Does it have the same orientation as the original? Does the relation appear to depend on the relative positions of the lines l_1 and l_2? If so, how?

d. What would happen if you applied to F_0 a sequence of reflections in 3 different lines?

3. Determine if each of the following is possible for $n = 2, 3, 4$. If so create such a figure; if not, explain why not.

a. Create a figure that has exactly n lines of symmetry where the symmetry lines all intersect at the same point.

b. Create a figure that has exactly n lines of symmetry where the symmetry lines are all parallel.

4. Stand two mirrors vertically on a piece of colored paper so that they form an open 'V' with reflecting sides facing each other.

a. Describe what you see in the mirrors.

---

[2]This informal description will be superseded by a formal definition of *orientation* in Section 3.7.

    b. Change the position of the paper and/or of the mirrors so as to make it appear that you have formed a regular polygon[3]. How many sides does your regular polygon have? Which other regular polygons can you form?

    c. For each regular polygon, determine the shape and size of the smallest piece of colored paper necessary to generate the regular polygon using mirrors. Then draw your original shape, the placement of the mirror lines, and the resulting polygon.

    d. Describe the shape of the smallest piece of paper and the angle between the mirrors needed to generate a regular n-gon.

5. Again using mirrors, can you make it appear that you have an infinitely long strip of color? If so, how?

6. Can you make it appear that you have an entire plane of color? If so, how?

7. Does a polygon with at least two distinct line symmetries have to be a regular polygon? Explain.

8. Explain why a figure of finite width and length cannot have two parallel lines of symmetry.

3.2.3　Point Reflections

As typical in mathematics, it is not sufficient to understand only what a single reflection does, but it is also important to understand what happens when several reflections are applied sequentially, that is, when a *composition* of reflections is applied. In the previous activities, your composition of two or more line reflections may have resulted in a symmetry with only one invariant point. One such symmetry is known as a *point reflection*.

---

[3]A polygon is said to be *regular* if all its sides are congruent and all its interior angles are congruent.

Definition 3.4

A *point reflection with center C*, denoted[4] $R_{\underline{C}}$, is a transformation that maps point C to itself and maps every other point P to P' where C is the midpoint of segment $\overline{PP'}$. If the point set α is invariant under $R_{\underline{C}}$, we say that α has *point symmetry* and that C is a *point of symmetry* for α.

Activities

Carefully label your drawings to indicate the properties they illustrate.

9. Draw a simple nonsymmetric figure F_0 and a point C. Then draw the following, labeling each figure and point as indicated.

   a. Draw F_1, the image of F_0 under a point reflection with center C.

   b. Draw F_2, the image of F_1 under a second point reflection with center C.

   c. How is F_2 related to the original figure?

   d. What types of symmetry are demonstrated by your illustration?

10. Draw another simple nonsymmetric figure F_0 and two distinct points, C_1 and C_2. Label your figure and your points.

   a. Draw and label F_1, the image of F_0 under a point reflection with center C_1.

   b. Draw and label F_2, where F_2 is the image of F_1 under a point reflection with center C_2.

   c. Describe how F_2 is related to the original figure. In particular, where is it located relative to the original? Does it have the same orientation as the original? Does the relation appear to depend on the relative positions of the points C_1 and C_2? If so, how?

   d. What would happen if you applied to F_0 a sequence of point reflections in 3 different points?

---

[4]To prevent confusion between a point C and a line c, you may want to underline the center designated in the notation.

11. Can a figure with finite width and length have two distinct points of symmetry? Explain.
12. Another term used to describe a point reflection is the term *half-turn*. Explain why this term is appropriate.
13. Is it possible to have a figure with point symmetry but without line symmetry? with line symmetry but without point symmetry? If it is possible, draw an example; if it isn't possible, explain why it isn't.
14. Explain why the result of applying a sequence, that is, the composition, of two symmetries to a given point set α, is equivalent to applying a single symmetry to α.

3.3   Exploring Rotations and Finite Symmetry Groups*

Equipment and Materials Needed

- A protractor, a scissors, two copies each of an equilateral triangle and a square, and several sheets of semitransparent paper suitable for tracing (or several transparencies with appropriate pens).
- Many of these activities can also be carried out using dynamic geometry software. Specific instructions for *Cabri Geometry II* and *Geometer's Sketchpad* can be found at
  http://www.stolaf.edu/people/cederj/geotext/info.htm.

3.3.1   Rotations

As you may have discovered, the transformations explored in Section 3.2 are not the only symmetries that exist. In fact, the point reflections, or half-turns, are just special cases of "turns" that keep one point invariant and move other points around the invariant point.

Definition 3.5

A *rotation with center C and angle (measure)* θ, denoted $R_{C,\theta}$ is a transformation that maps the point C to itself and maps any other point P to P' where $d(P, C) = d(P', C)$ and $m\angle PCP' = \theta$.[5] If the point set α is invariant under $R_{C,\theta}$, where $R_{C,\theta} \neq I$, we say that α has *rotation symmetry (about C)*. If $\theta = 360°/n$ for a positive integer n, α is also said to have *n-fold rotation symmetry (about C)*.

The following activities ask you to explore individual rotation symmetries and relate them to point and line reflections.

Activities

Be sure to label your drawings to indicate the properties they illustrate.

1. Construct a simple flag and a point C (not on the flag) on one sheet of paper. Then trace your flag and point onto a second sheet of paper. Place one sheet on top of the other so that the flags and points match up exactly. Label the top flag F_0. Keep the papers "pinned" together at point C.

   a. First rotate the bottom (underneath) flag by 120° around the point C.
   b. Then trace the bottom rotated flag onto the top sheet. Label this second flag $F_1 = R_{C,120}(F_0)$.
   c. Continue rotating the bottom flag by 120° around C, tracing and labeling until the bottom flag once again lies under the original top flag.

2. Which symmetries (line, point, rotational) are exhibited by your "multiflag" figure? For each, name the specific points and lines of symmetry.

3. Why can your multiflag figure be said to have *3-fold rotation symmetry*?

4. In an illustration that contains C and the single flag F_0, construct and label lines l and m so that both lines pass through point C

---

[5]Note: If $m\angle PCP' = 0$, then the rotation is the identity transformation.

and so that $m\angle(l, m) = 60°$. (Suggestion: It may work best to put one line on either side of the flag.) Then carry out the reflections described below.

  a. Reflect F_0 in line l to obtain the image flag. Draw this new flag and label it $F_a = R_l(F_0)$.
  b. Then draw and label $F_b = R_m(F_a)$ and $F_c = R_l(F_b)$.
  c. Continue this reflection process, first reflecting in line l and then in line m, drawing and labeling, until the flag once again coincides with the original flag, F_0.

5. Which symmetries are exhibited by your multiflag figure?
6. How is the multiflag figure generated by these reflections related to the figure generated previously by your rotations?
7. How would your results change if you kept the location of your flag F_0 and point C unchanged but changed the location of lines l and m by simultaneously rotating them about C while maintaining the same angle between the lines?

3.3.2 Finite Symmetry Groups

The set of all reflection and rotation symmetries for a given figure can be shown to form a group, that is, a set that not only contains the inverse of each of its elements, but also the composition of any pair of its elements.

Definition 3.6
A nonempty set G of transformations is said to form a *group* under the operation of composition if it satisfies both the following conditions: (1) If $T \in G$, then $T^{-1} \in G$; and (2) if $T_1 \in G$ and $T_2 \in G$, then $T_2 T_1 \in G$. (Note: The order in a composition requires that the transformation on the right be applied first; so in the composition $T_2 T_1$, T_1 is applied first.)

Although groups can contain an infinite number of elements, the symmetry groups explored in this section have only a finite number n and are thus referred to as *finite groups of order n*.

Activities

Be sure to label your drawings to indicate the properties they illustrate.

8. Draw in all lines of symmetry on both an equilateral triangle and a square. *Labeling suggestion*: Label the vertices of both the triangle and square alphabetically in counterclockwise order, using the letters A, B, etc. Then label the line of symmetry through vertex A as l. Continue labeling the symmetry lines counterclockwise around O their point of intersection, using the letters m, n, etc. Notice that vertex B will be located on line n in both cases. Keep these labeled figures unchanged to serve as references.

9. Explain why both the equilateral triangle and the square have rotation symmetry. For which values of n does the triangle have n-fold symmetry? For which values of n does the square have n-fold symmetry?

10. Does either the equilateral triangle or the square have point symmetry? How is point symmetry related to rotation symmetry?

11. Using the notation R_m for a reflection with axis m, and $R_{O,\theta}$ for rotations with center O and angle θ (where counterclockwise is considered as positive), indicate the effect of each transformation as a permutation of the vertices A, B, C, etc. For example, to indicate the effect of $R_{O,120}$ on the triangle labeled as indicated earlier, we can write: $R_{O,120} : A, B, C \rightarrow B, C, A$.

   a. Suggestion: It may be helpful to cut out one copy of each shape and label it on both sides in the same way as your original. You can then use these second shapes to represent the figures after a transformation is applied.

   b. Report your findings in Table 3.1 below, listing rotations first in order of increasing angle size. Then list your reflections alphabetically by axis.

12. Use your entries in Table 3.1 to find the products of all possible pairs of symmetries for the equilateral triangle. Enter your results in the cells of Table 3.2 using the convention that the symmetry used to label the corresponding column is applied first and the symmetry used to label the corresponding row is

TABLE 3.1   Symmetries of Regular n-gons as Permutations of Vertices.

Triangle	Square
$I = R_{O,0} : A, B, C \to A, B, C$	$I = R_{O,0} : A, B, C, D \to$
$R_l : A, B, C \to$	

TABLE 3.2   Symmetry Group of an Equilateral Triangle.

	I	$R_{O,120}$	$R_{O,240}$	R_l	R_m	R_n
I						
$R_{O,120}$						
$R_{O,240}$						
R_l						
R_m						
R_n						

applied last, e.g., $R_{O,120}$ should be entered in the cell in column "R_l" and row "R_m" since $R_m R_l = R_{O,120}$.

13. Using information from Table 3.2, describe the resulting symmetry that appears to be produced by each of the following.

TABLE 3.3 Symmetry Group of a Square.

	I	$R_{O,90}$	$R_{O,180}$	$R_{O,270}$	R_l	R_m	R_n	R_o
I								
$R_{O,90}$								
$R_{O,180}$								
$R_{O,270}$								
R_l								
R_m								
R_n								
R_o								

    a. Two rotations with the same center.

    b. Two reflections with intersecting axes.

    c. A reflection followed by a rotation (where the center of rotation lies on the axis of the reflection).

    d. A rotation followed by a reflection (where the center of rotation lies on the axis of the reflection).

14. In the previous activity you generalized the patterns you observed for compositions of symmetries of an equilateral triangle. Apply these same patterns to compositions of symmetries of a square to fill in the cells in Table 3.3.

15. Rotations from reflections.

    a. Among the symmetries of your equilateral triangle, which pair(s) of reflections can be composed to produce the rotation $R_{O,120}$? $R_{O,240}$?

    b. What is the relation between the axes of the reflections and the center and angle of the resultant rotation?

    c. Use your observation for the equilateral triangle to check the compositions of reflection symmetries recorded in Table 3.3.

16. In Table 3.3, for each entry corresponding to a product of a rotation $R_{O,\theta}$ and a reflection R_p or vice versa, rewrite the rotation as the product of two reflections $R_b R_a$ where one of the axes a and b equals the axis p. (You will need to decide whether you should have $a = p$ or $b = p$.) Then use this technique to check appropriate entries in Table 3.3, thus showing that each such product equals a single reflection.

17. Answer each of the following. You may find it helpful to refer to Tables 3.2 and 3.3.

    a. If R_a and R_b are reflections in intersecting lines, what is the product $R_b R_a$ if $b = a$? If $b \neq a$?
    b. If R_a and R_b are line reflections, does $R_a R_b = R_b R_a$? Explain.
    c. If $R_{C,\theta}$ and $R_{C,\phi}$ are rotations with the same center C, what is the product $R_{C,\phi} R_{C,\theta}$?
    d. If $R_{C,\theta}$ and $R_{C,\phi}$ are rotations with the same center C, does $R_{C,\theta} R_{C,\phi} = R_{C,\phi} R_{C,\theta}$? Explain.

18. Explain why Tables 3.2 and 3.3 are named appropriately, that is, explain why these tables demonstrate that the symmetries of an equilateral triangle and those of a square each form a group.

19. Explain why there are exactly n rotation symmetries and n line symmetries for a regular n-gon.

20. For each of Tables 3.2 and 3.3, show that the subset of rotation symmetries forms a group, that is, a subgroup of the complete group of symmetries.

21. Show that for both the equilateral triangle and the square, the subgroup of rotation symmetries is generated by a single rotation τ; that is, there is a specific rotation such that every rotation is equal to an integer power τ^n.[6] Be sure to name the "generator" symmetry τ and comment on whether or not τ is unique. Note: Such groups are known as *cyclic groups*.

---

[6] For positive integers n, this denotes the composition of τ, with itself n times. For negative integers n, it denotes the composition of τ^{-1} with itself n times. $n = 0$ denotes the identity.

Definition 3.7

A transformation group G is said to be *generated by transformations* τ_i ($G = \langle \tau_1, \tau_2, \ldots, \tau \rangle$) if each element $T \in G$ is a product of powers of the τ_i. If the group is generated by a single transformation τ, it is called *cyclic*.

22. For each of Tables 3.2 and 3.3, show that the symmetry group is generated by two symmetries, that is, show that each symmetry of a triangle (square) can be written as a product of powers of two specified symmetries.[7] Are the two *generating* symmetries for a triangle (square) unique? Explain.
23. Explain why the complete group of symmetries of a regular n-gon can always be generated by two symmetries. Note: Such groups are known as *dihedral groups.*

Definition 3.8

For a positive integer n, the group of all symmetries of a regular n-gon is known as the *dihedral group of order n* and denoted D_n.

24. Use the terminology given in Definitions 3.7 and 3.8 to answer the following:

    a. Which, if any, of your multiflag figures from activities in 3.3.1 has only a cyclic symmetry group of order n (and what is n)?
    b. Which, if any, of your multiflag figures resulting from activities in 3.3.1 has the symmetry group D_n (and what is n)?
    c. For a given positive integer $n \geq 3$, which symmetry types and how many of each type do you expect to be in the dihedral group D_n? Explain.
    d. For a given positive integer $n \geq 3$, what appears to be the relation between the dihedral group D_n and any cyclic subgroups? Explain.
    e. Draw a figure whose only symmetry group is cyclic of order 4.
    f. Cyclic and dihedral groups of finite orders are often referred to as *point groups*. Explain why this term is appropriate.

---

[7] Note that in some cases, you will use the zero power.

25. Mathematicians frequently refer to *the* symmetry group of an equilateral triangle. Why is it appropriate to think of the symmetry groups of all equilateral triangles as the same? Include in your answer a comment on Johnston and Richman's claim that symmetry groups "are scale invariant." [*Numbers and Symmetry: An Introduction to Algebra*, (1997) p. 150]

26. In a previous activity you were asked to explain why the symmetries of an equilateral triangle form a group and why the symmetries of a square form a group. Will this be true for other figures; that is, if α is a point set, will the set of all symmetries of α form a group under composition? Explain.

3.4 Exploring Translations and Frieze Pattern Symmetries*

Equipment and Materials Needed

- A straightedge and several sheets of lightweight paper suitable for tracing (or several transparencies with appropriate pens).
- Many of these activities can also be carried out using dynamic geometry software. Specific instructions for *Cabri Geometry II* and *Geometer's Sketchpad* can be found at
  http://www.stolaf.edu/people/cederj/geotext/info.htm.

3.4.1 Translations

The symmetries explored in Sections 3.2 and 3.3, namely, rotations and line and point reflections, all have invariant points. However, there are also symmetries known as *translations* with no invariant points. A translation can be described intuitively as a "slide," since it slides each point in a given direction through a given distance where the direction and distance are specific to the translation. Because both direction and distance are involved, it is most convenient to designate translations with vectors. So if, for example, the translation

T maps point P to point Q, it will also map any other point X to point Y where $\overrightarrow{XY} = \overrightarrow{PQ}$. Thus, we can use the notation $T_{\overrightarrow{PQ}}$ to unambiguously represent the exact effect of the translation and we refer to this translation as a "translation along line PQ" with "length" equal to the distance $d(P, Q)$.

Definition 3.9

A *translation with vector* $\overrightarrow{PQ}$, denoted $T_{\overrightarrow{PQ}}$, is a transformation that maps any point X to point Y where $\overrightarrow{XY} = \overrightarrow{PQ}$.[8] If a point set α is invariant under a nonidentity translation $T_{\overrightarrow{PQ}}$, we say that α has *translation symmetry* and that line PQ is an *axis of translation symmetry for* α.

3.4.2 Frieze Patterns

If a point set α has translation symmetry under a translation $T = T_{\overrightarrow{PQ}}$ and X is a point in α, then α must also include $X_1 = T(X)$, $X_2 = T(X_1), \ldots$, that is, all points resulting from sliding X in the direction of $\overrightarrow{PQ}$ and through distances that are multiples of the length of $\overrightarrow{PQ}$. Thus, there can be no "last" point in α in the direction of $\overrightarrow{PQ}$, and α necessarily extends infinitely far in this direction. Similarly, since we will consider only point sets invariant under a group of transformations, the point set must also be invariant under T^{-1}, the inverse of the translation T. Thus, α must also extend infinitely in the opposite direction, that is, in the direction of $\overrightarrow{QP}$. As a result α must consist of an infinite number of copies of a basic unit repeated at regular intervals along the line PQ. A point set that satisfies these conditions for one specific translation T is called a *frieze pattern*,[9] since such patterns often occur as motifs around the frieze of buildings. A portion of a frieze pattern reprinted from Audsley's *Designs and patterns from Historic Ornament* (1968) is shown in Figure 3.1.

---

[8]Note: The identity transformation is a translation by definition.
[9]Frieze patterns are also known as one-dimensional or strip patterns.

FIGURE 3.1   A frieze pattern.

Since a frieze pattern is necessarily invariant under all integer powers of a particular translation T, and $T^m \neq T^n$ for unequal integers m and n, any group of symmetries of a given frieze pattern necessarily contains an infinite number of translations. Furthermore, the symmetries of a particular frieze pattern may include symmetries other than translations. In fact, frieze patterns are classified based on the types of nontranslation symmetries they have.

Definition 3.10
A group of transformations that keep a given line c invariant and whose translations form an infinite cyclic subgroup is known as a *frieze group with axis c*. A point set that remains invariant under a frieze group with axis c is called a *frieze pattern with axis c* and denoted $\mathcal{F}_c$. (Note: A frieze group is the symmetry group of the associated frieze pattern.)

3.4.3   Glide Reflections

Some frieze groups contain the reflection R_c as well as translations along the line c. Thus, the frieze group must also contain all products of the reflection with each translation. Since this type of product is a commonly occurring transformation, it has been honored with a name.

Definition 3.11
A *glide reflection with vector* $\overrightarrow{PQ}$, denoted $G_{\overrightarrow{PQ}}$, is the product of a reflection with axis PQ and the nonidentity translation $T_{\overrightarrow{PQ}}$. If a

point set α is invariant under a glide reflection $G_{\overrightarrow{PQ}}$, we say that the line PQ is an axis of *glide symmetry* for α.

Activities

When drawing portions of frieze patterns, include at least two replications of the basic unit. Also label two points P and Q to indicate the vector $\overrightarrow{PQ}$ defining the generating translation $T_{\overrightarrow{PQ}}$. As always, label each drawing to indicate the properties it illustrates.

1. Draw a portion of a frieze pattern $\mathcal{F}_c$ that has no nontranslation symmetries. Suggestion: Start with a very simple nonsymmetric figure and translate it at least once.
2. Examine the frieze pattern partially depicted in Figure 3.1.

   a. Identify and label an axis c. Also label points P and Q in the pattern so that the translation $T_{\overrightarrow{PQ}}$ generates the defining cyclic subgroup of translations.
   b. Will there be other point pairs that could be used in place of P and Q to determine a generating translation for this same pattern? Explain.
   c. Draw an illustration that extends the depicted portion in both directions along its axis.

3. Frieze patterns with point symmetry:

   a. Which points C can be a point of symmetry for a frieze pattern $\mathcal{F}_c$? Be sure to describe the location of the points relative to line c.
   b. If C is a point of symmetry and T is a translational symmetry of $\mathcal{F}_c$, explain why $T(C)$ must be another point of symmetry for $\mathcal{F}_c$.
   c. Draw a portion of a frieze pattern $\mathcal{F}_c$ with a point of symmetry C. Be sure to label C.

4. Explain why a frieze pattern $\mathcal{F}_c$ cannot have rotation symmetry under a rotation $R_{C,\theta}$ for θ other than $0°$ and $180°$ (mod 360).
5. Frieze patterns with reflection symmetry:

    a. Explain why c can be a line of reflection symmetry for $\mathcal{F}_c$.

    b. Which lines other than c can be axes of reflection symmetry for a frieze pattern $\mathcal{F}_c$? How are these lines related to c?

    c. If $p \neq c$ is an axis of reflection symmetry of $\mathcal{F}_c$, and T is a translation symmetry of $\mathcal{F}_c$, explain why $T(p)$ must be another axis of reflection symmetry for $\mathcal{F}_c$.

    d. Draw a portion of a frieze pattern $\mathcal{F}_c$ with reflection symmetry *only* in line c.

    e. Draw a portion of a frieze pattern $\mathcal{F}_c$ with reflection symmetry in line $p \neq c$ but *not* in line c. Be sure to label p.

6. Draw and label a simple nonsymmetric figure F_0 and a line l. Locate and label points P and Q on l.

    a. Draw and label F_1, the image of F_0 under the glide reflection $G_{\overrightarrow{PQ}}$.

    b. Draw F_2, the image of F_1 under the same glide reflection.

    c. Describe how F_1 and F_2 are related to the original figure F_0. In particular, where is each located relative to the original? Do they have the same orientation? Do the relations appear to depend on the relative positions of F_0 and the line l? If so, how?

7. Our definition of a glide reflection indicates that the reflection is applied after the translation. If the order of application is reversed, is the resultant symmetry the same? Explain and illustrate your answer.

8. Demonstrate how a translation $T_{\overrightarrow{PQ}}$ can result from a composition of two glide reflections. Include a specific description of the defining vectors for the glide reflections. Is there more than one way to do this?

9. Frieze patterns with glide symmetry:

    a. Explain why your illustration for Activity 6 can be viewed as part of a frieze pattern $\mathcal{F}_c$. Which line corresponds to c?

    b. Does the frieze pattern $\mathcal{F}_c$ partially depicted in this illustration have any other symmetries? Explain.

10. Explain why the vector designating a translation is not unique. What implications, if any, does this have for possible axes of figures with translation symmetry?
11. Show that the set of all translations that keep line c invariant is necessarily a group.
12. If T is a translation along c that generates a cyclic group G_c, how does the length of T compare to the length of the other translations in G_c?
13. Explain why a cyclic group of translations along c cannot contain *all* translations along line c.

3.5   An Analytic Model of the Euclidean Plane

Before actually describing the analytic model we use, it may be helpful to give some indication of the motivation for choosing this particular model. This discussion will also serve to introduce the terminology and notation that we will use.

The analytic study of Euclidean geometry is based on the premise that each point in the plane can be assigned an ordered pair of real numbers. The usual manner in which this is done is via a Cartesian coordinate system where two perpendicular lines are used as axes. The point of intersection of these axes is assigned the ordered pair (0,0) and other points are assigned ordered pairs as shown in Fig. 3.2. Rather than denote points by ordered pairs (x, y) as is customary in calculus, we will use ordered pairs (x_1, x_2). This choice is motivated by the "symmetrical form" our results will take in this notation.

With this representation of points, lines of the Euclidean plane can be represented by linear equations of the form $a_1x_1 + a_2x_2 + a_3 = 0$ where the a_i are constant real number coefficients. Thus, each ordered triple $[a_1, a_2, a_3]$ where a_1 and a_2 are not both zero, determines the equation of a line. Notice that square brackets are used for coordinates of lines so as to distinguish them from coordinates for points. Unlike points, the coordinates of a line do not uniquely

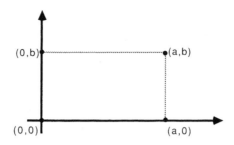

FIGURE 3.2 Assigning point coordinates.

represent a line, since the equations $a_1x_1 + a_2x_2 + a_3 = 0$ and $ka_1x_1 + ka_2x_2 + ka_3 = 0$ represent the same line for every nonzero real number k. There is, however, a one-to-one correspondence between the set of lines and the set of *equivalence classes* of ordered triples of real numbers defined by the following relation:

$$[b_1, b_2, b_3] \sim [a_1, a_2, a_3] \quad \text{if } b_i = ka_i, i = 1, 2, 3, \text{ where}$$
$$k \text{ is a nonzero real number}$$

Using Definition 3.12 we can show that this relation is an equivalence relation (see Exercise 8).

Definition 3.12
A relation "$\sim$" is an *equivalence relation* if it satisfies each of the following:
   a. $a \sim a$
   b. If $a \sim b$, then $b \sim a$.
   c. If $a \sim b$ and $b \sim c$, then $a \sim c$.

Definition 3.13
A set of elements all of which are pairwise related by an equivalence relation is called an *equivalence class*. Any element of an equivalence class is called a *representative* of the equivalence class.

Since there is a one-to-one correspondence between the lines of the Euclidean plane and these equivalence classes, we can interpret lines in terms of these equivalence classes (Table 3.4). The ordered triples $[u_1, u_2, u_3]$ belonging to a particular equivalence class will be called *homogeneous coordinates* of the line. If we consider one of these ordered triples to be a row matrix $u = [u_1, u_2, u_3]$, then the matrix equation of the corresponding line is $uX = 0$ where $X = (x_1, x_2, 1)$ is a column matrix with 1 in its third entry. In particular if $u = [2, -3, 5]$, then $uX = 0$ is the equation $2x_1 - 3x_2 + 5 = 0$. This observation, together with the desire to use similar interpretations for points and lines, suggests that we interpret points in terms of equivalence classes of ordered triples of real numbers (x_1, x_2, x_3), where $x_3 \neq 0$ under the same relation. Again we will refer to elements of these equivalence classes as *homogeneous coordinates* of the point. In the case of points, however, since x_3 is always nonzero, every ordered triple $(x_1, x_2, x_3) \sim (x_1/x_3, x_2/x_3, 1)$, so each equivalence class will have a unique representative of the form $(x_1, x_2, 1)$. In other words, each point in the plane that we are accustomed to denoting with an ordered pair of the form (x_1, x_2) can now be denoted by the corresponding ordered triple of the form $(x_1, x_2, 1)$. For example, instead of referring to a point with coordinates $(1, -3)$ we will now refer to it as a point with coordinates $(1, -3, 1)$.

As indicated before, lines will always be represented by row matrices and points by column matrices. But unlike the conventional algebra usage of uppercase letters for all matrices, here matrices of line coordinates will be represented by lowercase letters.

TABLE 3.4 Analytic Model for the Euclidean Plane.

Undefined Term	Interpretation
Points	Equivalence classes of ordered triples (x_1, x_2, x_3) where $x_3 \neq 0$ (any one of the representatives of an equivalence class will be called coordinates of the point)
Lines	Equivalence classes of ordered triples $[u_1, u_2, u_3]$ where u_1 and u_2 are not both 0 (any one of the representatives of the equivalence class will be called coordinates of the line)
Incident	A point $X(x_1, x_2, x_3)$ is incident with a line $u[u_1, u_2, u_3]$ iff $[u_1, u_2, u_3] \cdot (x_1, x_2, x_3) = 0$, or, in matrix notation, $uX = 0$

Within the context of this analytic model, the operations of matrix algebra take on geometric significance as indicated by the following theorems. In each case the coordinates chosen to represent points will be those in which $x_3 = 1$. The first of these theorems gives a convenient way to determine when three points are *collinear,* that is, on the same line.

Theorem 3.1

Three distinct points $X(x_1, x_2, 1)$, $Y(y_1, y_2, 1)$, and $Z(z_1, z_2, 1)$ are collinear if and only if the determinant

$$\begin{vmatrix} x_1 & y_1 & z_1 \\ x_2 & y_2 & z_2 \\ 1 & 1 & 1 \end{vmatrix} = 0$$

Proof

X, Y, Z are collinear if and only if there is a line $u[u_1, u_2, u_3]$ such that

$$u_1 x_1 + u_2 x_2 + u_3 = 0$$
$$u_1 y_1 + u_2 y_2 + u_3 = 0$$
$$u_1 z_1 + u_2 z_2 + u_3 = 0$$

or

$$[u_1, u_2, u_3] \begin{bmatrix} x_1 & y_1 & z_1 \\ x_2 & y_2 & z_2 \\ 1 & 1 & 1 \end{bmatrix} = [0, 0, 0]$$

But from linear algebra this equation has a nontrivial solution $[u_1, u_2, u_3]$ if and only if

$$\begin{vmatrix} x_1 & y_1 & z_1 \\ x_2 & y_2 & z_2 \\ 1 & 1 & 1 \end{vmatrix} = 0$$

Since this nontrivial solution cannot have both $u_1 = 0$ and $u_2 = 0$ (see Exercise 7), $u[u_1, u_2, u_3]$ is a line containing all three points. ∎

Corollary

If A and B are distinct points, then the equation of the line AB where
$A(a_1, a_2, 1)$ *and* $B(b_1, b_2, 1)$ *can be written*

$$\begin{vmatrix} x_1 & a_1 & b_1 \\ x_2 & a_2 & b_2 \\ 1 & 1 & 1 \end{vmatrix} = 0$$

In the proof of Theorem 3.1 we used the familiar notion that
the equation $u_1 x_1 + u_2 x_2 + u_3 = 0$ determines which points lie on
the line with coordinates $[u_1, u_2, u_3]$, and we refer to this equation as
the *equation of the line u*. We often think of the values of the u_i as
constants. For example, the equation $3x_1 - 4x_2 + 10 = 0$ determines
which points lie on the line with coordinates $[3, -4, 10]$. However, it is
equally useful to regard $u_1 x_1 + u_2 x_2 + u_3 = 0$ as the *equation of the point*
X and use it to determine which lines pass through the point with
coordinates $(x_1, x_2, 1)$. In particular, we can determine which lines
pass through the point with coordinates $(-2, 5, 1)$ by finding ordered
triples $[u_1, u_2, u_3]$ that satisfy the equation $-2u_1 + 5u_2 + u_3 = 0$.

With the previous discussion in mind, we can use line coordinates to determine when three lines are *concurrent*, that is, when all
three lines intersect at a common point. The proof of this theorem
is similar to that of the previous theorem except here special consideration needs to be given to the case where the only nontrivial
solutions are those for which $x_3 = 0$ (see Exercise 12).

Theorem 3.2

Three distinct lines u, v, w are all concurrent or all parallel if and only
if the determinant

$$\begin{vmatrix} u_1 & u_2 & u_3 \\ v_1 & v_2 & v_3 \\ w_1 & w_2 & w_3 \end{vmatrix} = 0$$

Corollary
*The equation of the point of intersection of concurrent lines p and q,
denoted $p \cdot q$, can be written*

$$\begin{vmatrix} u_1 & u_2 & u_3 \\ p_1 & p_2 & p_3 \\ q_1 & q_2 & q_3 \end{vmatrix} = 0$$

In these theorems, it is again important to note that the coordinates
of points appear in columns whereas the coordinates of lines appear
in rows. This convention is used throughout the remainder of the
text.

Just as point coordinates are used to define distance between
points, line coordinates can be used to determine the angle between
lines. Definition 3.14 includes a definition for both distance and angle measure in terms of the ordered triple coordinates we are using.
For angles, this definition makes use of a formula from trigonometry that gives the tangent of the angle between two lines in terms of
slopes of the lines (see Exercise 17).

Definition 3.14
Distance and angle measure:
  a. If $X(x_1, x_2, 1)$ and $Y(y_1, y_2, 1)$ are two points, then the *distance
    between X and Y*, denoted $d(X, Y)$, is defined to be

$$d(X, Y) = \sqrt{(y_1 - x_1)^2 + (y_2 - x_2)^2}$$

  b. If $u[u_1, u_2, u_3]$ and $v[v_1, v_2, v_3]$ are two lines, then the *measure of
    the angle between u and v*, denoted $m\angle(u, v)$, is defined to be

$$m\angle(u, v) = \tan^{-1}\left(\frac{u_1 v_2 - u_2 v_1}{u_1 v_1 + u_2 v_2}\right)$$
where $-90° < m\angle(u, v) < 90°$,   if $u_1 v_1 + u_2 v_2 \neq 0$
$m\angle(u, v) = 90°$,   if $u_1 v_1 + u_2 v_2 = 0$

Note that the definition of the measure of the angle between lines
is independent of the particular set of homogeneous coordinates
used for the lines and that only the first two coordinates of each line
are used. This corresponds to defining the angle between lines u and
v in terms of the angle between lines u' and v' where the latter are

lines through the point $(0, 0, 1)$ and u' is parallel to u and v' is parallel to v (see Exercise 13). In particular, this definition assigns the angle between parallel lines measure 0.

Vectors in the Analytic Model

In addition to working with analytic interpretations for points and lines, we will also make use of an analytic interpretation for vectors. Since we are using point coordinates that are ordered triples, our vectors will have ordered triples as components. Thus, for the points $X(x_1, x_2, 1)$ and $Y(y_1, y_2, 1)$, the vector with initial point X and terminal point Y is $\overrightarrow{XY} = (y_1 - x_1, y_2 - x_2, 0)$.[10] When working with vectors, recall that for vectors $\mathbf{u} = (u_1, u_2, u_3)$ and $\mathbf{v} = (v_1, v_2, v_3)$ and scalar s,

1. $\mathbf{u} = \mathbf{v}$ if and only if their components are equal (i.e., $u_i = v_i$ for $i = 1, 2, 3$).
2. $s\mathbf{u} = (su_1, su_2, su_3)$; and
3. $|\mathbf{v}| = \sqrt{(v_1)^2 + (v_2)^2 + (v_3)^2}$ is the length of vector $\mathbf{v}$.

Exercises

1. Let u be the line with homogeneous coordinates $[-2, 5, 7]$. (a) Find three other sets of coordinates for u. (b) Find an equation for line u. (c) Find coordinates for two distinct points on u.

2. Let P be the point with ordered pair coordinates $(4, -7)$. (a) Find three sets of homogeneous coordinates for P. (b) Find an equation for the point P. (c) Find coordinates for two lines through P.

3. Find homogeneous coordinates for each of the following: (a) the x_1-axis; (b) the x_2-axis; and (c) the line $x_1 = x_2$.

4. Find the general form of the coordinates for lines through the point $(0, 0, 1)$.

---

[10]Note: Since we will be using point coordinates in which the third coordinate is always 1, the third component of our vectors will always be 0.

5. Use the corollary to Theorem 3.1 to find the line containing the points $(10, 2)$ and $(-7, 3)$.

6. Use the corollary to Theorem 3.2 to find the point of intersection of the lines $3x + 4y + 7 = 0$ and $2x - y + 8 = 0$.

7. Show that the nontrivial solution obtained in the proof of Theorem 3.1 cannot have both $u_1 = 0$ and $u_2 = 0$.

8. Show that the following is an equivalence relation: $[u_1, u_2, u_3] \sim [v_1, v_2, v_3]$ if $u_i = kv_i$ for some nonzero k.

9. Prove the corollary to Theorem 3.1.

10. Show algebraically that two distinct lines $u[u_1, u_2, u_3]$ and $v[v_1, v_2, v_3]$ are parallel (do not intersect) if and only if $u_1 = kv_1$, $u_2 = kv_2$, but $u_3 \neq kv_3$ for some nonzero real number k. [*Hint*: Show that the system of equations $u_1x_1 + u_2x_2 + u_3 = 0$ and $v_1x_1 + v_2x_2 + v_3 = 0$ does *not* have a solution if and only if these conditions are true.]

11. Use the result of Exercise 10 to verify that Playfair's axiom is true in this analytic model of the Euclidean plane.

12. Use the result of Exercise 7 to prove Theorem 3.2. (Be sure to see the comment preceding the theorem.)

13. Use the result of Exercise 10 to show that the line parallel to $u[u_1, u_2, u_3]$, which passes through the point $(0, 0, 1)$, has coordinates $[u_1, u_2, 0]$.

14. Using Definition 3.14 find the angles between the following lines: (a) the lines $[-2, 1, 7]$ and $[3, 4, 17]$; (b) the x_1- and x_2-axes; and (c) the lines $x_1 = x_2$ and the x_1-axis.

15. Use the result of Exercise 10 to find the angle between two parallel lines.

16. Let the line u be the x_1-axis and the line v be the line with coordinates $[v_1, v_2, v_3]$. Use Definition 3.14 to show that $\tan(\angle(u, v)) = -(v_1)/(v_2)$. [*Note*: Recall that the *slope* of the line $[v_1, v_2, v_3]$ is given by $-(v_1)/(v_2)$.]

17. The following trigonometry formula gives the tangent of the angle between lines u and v in terms of their slopes m_u and m_v. Use the definition of slope from Exercise 16 to show that this formula is equivalent to the formula used in Definition 3.14:

$$\tan(\angle(u, v)) = \frac{m_v - m_u}{1 + m_u m_v}$$

18. Prove: If P is a point and l is a line, there is a unique line through P perpendicular to l.

19. Use Definition 3.14 to verify the following for vectors $\mathbf{u} = \overrightarrow{OU}$ and $\mathbf{v} = \overrightarrow{OV}$ where $O(0, 0, 1)$; $U(u_1, u_2, 1)$ and $V(v_1, v_2, 1)$.

    a. $|\mathbf{u}| = d(O, U)$, i.e., the length of vector $\mathbf{u}$ is the distance between its initial and terminal points.

    b. $\mathbf{u} \cdot \mathbf{v} = 0$ if and only if $\angle(OU, OV) = 90°$, i.e., the dot product of the vectors $\mathbf{u}$ and $\mathbf{v}$ is 0 if and only if the angle between the lines OU and OV is $90°$.

20. Will the results shown in Exercise 19 be the same if the vectors $\mathbf{u}$ and $\mathbf{v}$ have a common initial point other than O? If they have different initial points? Explain.

3.6 Transformations of the Euclidean Plane

The transformation approach to the study of Euclidean geometry involves identification of appropriate groups of transformations of the Euclidean plane and the investigation of the features preserved by these groups. In this section we introduce the definitions and theorems from linear algebra needed to pursue this approach. Since the analytic model of the Euclidean plane interprets points and lines in terms of equivalence classes of the vector space R^3, we use a special set of transformations, that is, functions whose domain and range are both R^3.

Definition 3.15

Let V be a vector space over R. If $T : V \rightarrow V$ is a transformation, then T is called a *linear transformation of* V if it satisfies both the following conditions: (1) $T(\mathbf{u} + \mathbf{v}) = T(\mathbf{u}) + T(\mathbf{v})$ for all vectors $\mathbf{u}$ and $\mathbf{v}$ in V; and (2) $T(k\mathbf{u}) = kT(\mathbf{u})$ for all vectors $\mathbf{u}$ in V and scalars in R. A linear transformation T is *one-to-one* if whenever $\mathbf{u} \neq \mathbf{v}$, $T(\mathbf{u}) \neq T(\mathbf{v})$.

From these definitions it should be clear that the equivalence classes of R^3 defined by the relation $\mathbf{u} \sim \mathbf{v}$ if and only if $\mathbf{u} = k\mathbf{v}$ are preserved by linear transformations. In other words, if $\mathbf{u} \sim \mathbf{v}$, then $T(\mathbf{u}) \sim T(\mathbf{v})$. So a one-to-one linear transformation of R^3 induces a one-to-one mapping on the set of points of the model for the Euclidean plane. Each of these mappings has a *matrix representation* as indicated by the following summary of results from linear algebra.

Theorem 3.3

T is a one-to-one linear transformation of $R^3 = \{X(x_1, x_2, x_3) : x_i \in R\}$ if and only if $T(X) = AX$ where $A = [a_{ij}]_{3 \times 3}$, $|A| \neq 0$, and $a_{ij} \in R$.

Because we make use of homogeneous coordinates of the form $(x_1, x_2, 1)$ for points, it is important to note the restriction this places on linear transformations and the consequent form of their matrix representation given in the corollary.

Definition 3.16

A one-to-one linear transformation T of R^3 is said to be an *affine transformation (of the Euclidean plane)* if T maps points in the set $V^* = \{X(x_1, x_2, 1)\}$ to points in this same set, that is, if for all $X \in V^*$, $T(X) = X' \in V^*$.

Corollary

T is an affine transformation of the Euclidean plane if and only if $T(X) = AX$ where

$$A = \begin{bmatrix} a_{11} & a_{12} & a_{13} \\ a_{21} & a_{22} & a_{23} \\ 0 & 0 & 1 \end{bmatrix}, \qquad |A| \neq 0 \quad and \quad a_{ij} \in R.$$

Proof

See Exercise 6. ∎

As indicated previously, we need to verify that the set of affine transformations of the Euclidean plane form a group under composition. If T_1 and T_2 are transformations of a vector space V, the *composite* (or *product*) $T_2 T_1$ is the mapping defined by $(T_2 T_1)(\mathbf{u}) = T_2(T_1(\mathbf{u}))$ for all vectors $\mathbf{u}$ in V. Because the composition of functions is *associative*, that is $T_3(T_2T_1) = (T_3T_2)T_1$, we can use the following simplified definition introduced in Section 3.3 and restated below.

Definition 3.6
A nonempty set G of transformations is said to form a *group* under the operation of composition if it satisfies both the following conditions: (1) If $T \in G$ then $T^{-1} \in G$; and (2) if $T_1 \in G$ and $T_2 \in G$, then $T_2T_1 \in G$.

Note that the definition guarantees that any group G contains a transformation T, and therefore by property 1, T^{-1} is in G. Property 2 then tells us that $TT^{-1} = I$ is also in G where I is the *identity* transformation defined by $I(\mathbf{u}) = \mathbf{u}$ for any $\mathbf{u}$ in V. Also note that the order in a composition requires that the transformation on the right be applied first.

An application of results of matrix algebra to the matrix representations given by the corollary to Theorem 3.3 can be used to prove the following theorem (see Exercise 9).

Theorem 3.4
The set of affine transformations of the Euclidean plane is a group.

Even though each of the transformations of this group can be represented by a 3×3 matrix with real number entries and the images of individual points can be computed algebraically, it is important to visualize the geometric action of each transformation as a mapping or moving of all of the points of the Euclidean plane to other points of the plane. Determining the general way in which a transformation moves points, and, in particular, determining which points and lines it leaves unaffected, are essential to understanding this geometric action.

Example 3.1
Let T be the affine transformation with matrix A shown. If X is a point on the line $l[1, -1, 0]$, show that $T(X)$ is also a point on l and

show that $T(P) = P$ where P is the point $P\left(-\frac{2}{3}, -\frac{2}{3}, 1\right)$.

$$A = \begin{bmatrix} 1 & 3 & 2 \\ 3 & 1 & 2 \\ 0 & 0 & 1 \end{bmatrix}$$

Solution
To find the images of points on l, we note that $X(x_1, x_2, 1)$ is on l if and only if $x_1 - x_2 = 0$, that is, if $x_2 = x_1$. Thus we can find the images of any point X on l as follows:

$$\begin{bmatrix} 1 & 3 & 2 \\ 3 & 1 & 2 \\ 0 & 0 & 1 \end{bmatrix} \begin{bmatrix} x_1 \\ x_1 \\ 1 \end{bmatrix} = \begin{bmatrix} 4x_1 + 2 \\ 4x_1 + 2 \\ 1 \end{bmatrix}$$

Since $x_1' = 4x_1 + 2 = x_2'$, it is clear that $T(X) = X'(x_1', x_2', 1)$ is also a point on l. Furthermore, since P is a point on l, we can set $x_1 = x_2 = -\frac{2}{3}$ in the preceding computation to find $T(P)$. With this value of x_1, we get $x_1' = x_2' = 4(-\frac{2}{3}) + 2 = -\frac{2}{3}$. So $T(P) = P$. □

Since the image of P is itself under the transformation T in this example we say that P is an *invariant point* of the transformation. Furthermore, since the images of all points on l are again on l, we say that l is an *invariant line* of T. Note, however, that the points on l other than P are not invariant, so l is not *pointwise invariant*.

Definition 3.17
A property that is unchanged under a transformation is called an *invariant* of the transformation. A property that is invariant under each transformation of a group of transformations is called an *invariant* of the group. An invariant property of a transformation is said to be *preserved* by the transformation.

Essential to the study of any mathematical system is a determination of the transformations that preserve certain features of the system. The following result shows that the affine transformations of the Euclidean plane preserve collinearity; that is, collinearity is one of the invariant properties of this group. Thus these transformations of the points of the Euclidean plane also map lines to lines. We say they *induce* mappings between lines of the Euclidean plane.

Theorem 3.5

An affine transformation of the Euclidean plane preserves collinearity (i.e., the images of collinear points are collinear).

Proof

Let $X'(x_1', x_2', 1)$, $Y'(y_1', y_2', 1)$, and $Z'(z_1', z_2', 1)$ be images of the points X, Y, and Z under a given affine transformation with matrix A. Then combining all our efforts into one matrix equation, we get

$$\begin{bmatrix} x_1' & y_1' & z_1' \\ x_2' & y_2' & z_2' \\ 1 & 1 & 1 \end{bmatrix} = A \begin{bmatrix} x_1 & y_1 & z_1 \\ x_2 & y_2 & z_2 \\ 1 & 1 & 1 \end{bmatrix}$$

and taking determinants of both sides yields

$$\begin{vmatrix} x_1' & y_1' & z_1' \\ x_2' & y_2' & z_2' \\ 1 & 1 & 1 \end{vmatrix} = |A| \begin{vmatrix} x_1 & y_1 & z_1 \\ x_2 & y_2 & z_2 \\ 1 & 1 & 1 \end{vmatrix}$$

Therefore, the result follows by Theorem 3.1. ∎

Note that this theorem also implies that affine transformations preserve incidence. In other words, if the point X is on line u, then X', the image of X, is on u', the image of u.

Just as the image of a point under an affine transformation can be determined by a matrix equation, a matrix equation can be used to determine the image of a line under the *same* transformation. This second equation is related to but *not* identical to the first.

Theorem 3.6

If the image of a point under an affine transformation of the Euclidean plane is given by the matrix equation $X' = AX$ then the image of a line under this same transformation is given by the matrix equation $ku' = uA^{-1}$ for some nonzero scalar k.

Proof

Consider the line $u[u_1, u_2, u_3]$ with equation $u_1 x_1 + u_2 x_2 + u_3 x_3 = 0$; that is, $uX = 0$. Under the affine transformation, u maps to u', X maps to X', and $uX = 0$ if and only if $u'X' = 0$. But $X' = AX$. So substituting $u'AX = 0$ if and only if $uX = 0$. Since this must hold for all points X, $u = ku'A$ for a nonzero scalar k, or $ku' = uA^{-1}$. ∎

The transformation with matrix A is said to have *point equation* $X' = AX$ and *line equation* $ku' = uA^{-1}$. While the use of the point equation is straightforward, the scalar k in the line equation (required because there is no unique set of homogeneous coordinates for a given line) makes the use of the line equation slightly more difficult. It is more important to note that k is *not constant for a given matrix* A. This becomes especially significant when a given line needs to be mapped to a particular line, as in the following example.

Example 3.2

Find the matrix of an affine transformation of the Euclidean plane that maps $[1, -3, 2]$ to $u'[1, 0, -4]$, $v[2, 1, -5]$ to $v'[10, -7, 7]$, and $w[1, -2, 0]$ to $w'[0, 1 - 6]$.

Solution

Since we are told the images of three lines, we will begin with the general form of the line equation of transformation of an affine transformation $ku' = uA^{-1}$. Each line and its image will give a matrix equation, as shown. In these equations we let $B = A^{-1}$ and use three distinct values of k:

$$k_1[1, 0, -4] = [1, -3, 2] \begin{bmatrix} b_{11} & b_{12} & b_{13} \\ b_{21} & b_{22} & b_{23} \\ 0 & 0 & 1 \end{bmatrix}$$

$$k_2[10, -7, 7] = [2, 1, -5] \begin{bmatrix} b_{11} & b_{12} & b_{13} \\ b_{21} & b_{22} & b_{23} \\ 0 & 0 & 1 \end{bmatrix}$$

$$k_3[0, 1, -6] = [1, -2, 0] \begin{bmatrix} b_{11} & b_{12} & b_{13} \\ b_{21} & b_{22} & b_{23} \\ 0 & 0 & 1 \end{bmatrix}$$

The resulting system of nine equations in nine unknown yields the following solutions for the values of k : $k_1 = -2$, $k_2 = 1$, and $k_3 = -1$. The matrix

$$A^{-1} = \begin{bmatrix} 4 & -3 & 6 \\ 2 & -1 & 0 \\ 0 & 0 & 1 \end{bmatrix} \quad \text{and} \quad A = \begin{bmatrix} -\frac{1}{2} & \frac{3}{2} & 3 \\ -1 & 2 & 6 \\ 0 & 0 & 1 \end{bmatrix} \qquad \square$$

Exercises

1. Let T be the affine transformation with matrix

$$A = \begin{bmatrix} 1 & 5 & 0 \\ 0 & 1 & 0 \\ 0 & 0 & 1 \end{bmatrix}$$

(a) Using the technique of Example 3.1, find the images of points on the line $l[1, -2, 3]$. (b) Does T keep any points on l invariant? If so, which one(s)? (c) Use the coordinates of the images of two points on l to find the coordinates of $l' = T(l)$. (d) Sketch both l and l' in the Euclidean plane and describe the geometric action of T.

2. Verify by calculation that the transformation with the matrix in Example 3.2 does indeed map the three lines as desired.

3. Let

$$A = \begin{bmatrix} 1 & 3 & -7 \\ 2 & 5 & 4 \\ 0 & 0 & 1 \end{bmatrix}$$

be the matrix of a transformation, T. (a) Find $P' = T(P)$ and $Q' = T(Q)$ for the points $P(1, 2, 1)$ and $Q(6, 4, 1)$. (b) Find coordinates of the lines PQ and $P'Q'$. (c) Find the matrix of A^{-1} to be used in the line equation of the transformation T. (d) Use this line equation to find the image of the line PQ under T. (Your answer should be the line $P'Q'$.)

4. Find the matrix of an affine transformation that maps $P(0, 0, 1)$ to $P'(1, 5, 1)$, $Q(1, 3, 1)$ to $Q'(3, -7, 1)$, and $R(1, 0, 1)$ to $R'(3, 6, 1)$.

5. Find the matrix of an affine transformation that maps $u[2, -3, 1]$ to $u'[2, 5, 0]$, $v[1, -2, 0]$ to $v'[1, 1, -6]$, and $w[1, 0, 0]$ to $w'[3, 2, -1]$.

6. Prove the corollary of Theorem 3.3.

7. Prove: If A is a matrix of the form given by the corollary of Theorem 3.3, then A^{-1} is also of this form. [*Hint*: Since these are 3×3 matrices with a third row of the form $(0, 0, 1)$ the adjoint method provides an easy way of computing A^{-1}.]

8. Prove: If A and B are matrices of the form described by the corollary to Theorem 3.3, then the matrix product AB is also of this form.

9. Using results of Exercises 7 and 8, prove Theorem 3.4.

10. Find examples of matrices of affine transformations such that $AB \neq BA$. (This example shows that this group does not have the *commutative* property.)

3.7 Isometries

To begin our transformation approach to the study of Euclidean geometry we will single out the subset of affine transformations of the Euclidean plane that preserve distance.

Definition 3.18
An affine transformation of the Euclidean plane is an *isometry* if it preserves distance (i.e., if $d(X, Y) = d(T(X), T(Y))$ for all pairs of points X, Y).

As affine transformations of the Euclidean plane, isometries can be represented by matrices of the form given in the corollary to Theorem 3.3. However, the distance preserving property further restricts the form of their matrix representation.

Theorem 3.7
An isometry has one of the following matrix representations:

$$
\text{(Direct)} \qquad\qquad\qquad \text{(Indirect)}
$$

$$
\begin{bmatrix} a_{11} & a_{12} & a_{13} \\ -a_{12} & a_{11} & a_{23} \\ 0 & 0 & 1 \end{bmatrix} \quad or \quad \begin{bmatrix} a_{11} & a_{12} & a_{13} \\ a_{12} & -a_{11} & a_{23} \\ 0 & 0 & 1 \end{bmatrix}
$$

where $(a_{11})^2 + (a_{12})^2 = 1$.

Proof
Let $X'(x_1', x_2', 1)$ and $Y'(y_1', y_2', 1)$ be the images of the points $X(x_1, x_2, 1)$ and $Y(y_1, y_2, 1)$ under an isometry. Then by the corollary to Theorem 3.3,

$$
\begin{bmatrix} x_1' \\ x_2' \\ 1 \end{bmatrix} = \begin{bmatrix} a_{11} & a_{12} & a_{13} \\ a_{21} & a_{22} & a_{23} \\ 0 & 0 & 1 \end{bmatrix} \begin{bmatrix} x_1 \\ x_2 \\ 1 \end{bmatrix} = \begin{bmatrix} a_{11}x_1 + a_{12}x_2 + a_{13} \\ a_{21}x_1 + a_{22}x_2 + a_{23} \\ 1 \end{bmatrix}
$$

and likewise

$$
\begin{bmatrix} y_1' \\ y_2' \\ 1 \end{bmatrix} = \begin{bmatrix} a_{11}y_1 + a_{12}y_2 + a_{13} \\ a_{21}y_1 + a_{22}y_2 + a_{23} \\ 1 \end{bmatrix}
$$

Because this mapping is an isometry, $d(X', Y') = d(X, Y)$. From the definition of distance this equality yields

$$
\begin{aligned}
[(x_1 - y_1)^2 + (x_2 - y_2)^2]^{1/2} &= [(x_1' - y_1')^2 + (x_2' - y_2')^2]^{1/2} \\
&= [(a_{11}x_1 + a_{12}x_2 - a_{11}y_1 - a_{12}y_2)^2 \\
&\quad + (a_{21}x_1 + a_{22}x_2 - a_{21}y_1 - a_{22}y_2)^2]^{1/2} \\
&= [(a_{11}^2 + a_{21}^2)(x_1 - y_1)^2 \\
&\quad + 2(a_{11}a_{12} + a_{21}a_{22})(x_1 - y_1)(x_2 - y_2) \\
&\quad + (a_{12}^2 + a_{22}^2)(x_2 - y_2)^2]^{1/2}
\end{aligned}
$$

Since this equality must hold for all points X and Y, and therefore for all ordered pairs of real numbers (x_1, x_2) and (y_1, y_2), we can square the first and last of these expressions and then equate the coefficients of like terms. This gives the following equations:

(a) $a_{11}^2 + a_{21}^2 = 1$
(b) $a_{12}^2 + a_{22}^2 = 1$
(c) $a_{11}a_{12} + a_{21}a_{22} = 0$
(d) $a_{11}a_{12} = -a_{21}a_{22}$

To solve these equations, we consider two cases.

Case 1: $a_{11} \neq 0$. Equation (d) implies $a_{12} = -(a_{21}a_{22})/a_{11}$. Substituting this into (b) gives

$$
\frac{a_{21}^2 a_{22}^2}{a_{11}^2} + a_{22}^2 = 1 \quad \text{or} \quad (a_{11}^2 + a_{21}^2)a_{22}^2 = a_{11}^2.
$$

But by (a) this becomes $a_{22} = \pm a_{11}$. If $a_{22} = a_{11}$, then Equation (d) implies $a_{21} = -a_{12}$. If $a_{22} = -a_{11}$, then Equation (d) implies $a_{21} = a_{12}$. These results yield the two forms of the matrix given earlier.

Case 2: $a_{11} = 0$. Again in this case the equations yield the same two forms of the matrix (see Exercise 3). ∎

The determinant of the first isometry matrix is $(a_{11})^2 + (a_{12})^2 = 1$, while the determinant of the second matrix is $-(a_{11})^2 - (a_{12})^2 = -1$. This observation gives a convenient way to distinguish the two types of isometries and justifies the labels given in the statement of Theorem 3.7.

Definition 3.19

If the determinant of the matrix of an isometry is $+1$, the isometry is said to be a *direct isometry*. If the determinant is -1, the isometry is said to be an *indirect isometry*.

A relatively straightforward argument demonstrates that the isometries form a group. However, since there are direct and indirect isometries, it is necessary to verify that the inverse of each type is an isometry. It is also necessary to demonstrate that the composite $T_2 T_1$ is an isometry where T_1 and T_2 are both direct, both indirect, direct and indirect, and finally indirect and direct isometries, respectively. The result of these computations are summarized in the following theorem and corollary.

Theorem 3.8

The set of isometries forms a group, of which the set of direct isometries is a subgroup.

Corollary

The product of two direct or two indirect isometries is a direct isometry. The product of a direct and an indirect isometry in either order is an indirect isometry.

Having identified the set of isometries as a group of transformations, we can study Euclidean geometry by determining which properties of sets of points in the Euclidean plane are preserved by this group. The following definition formalizes Euclid's use of "superposition."

Definition 3.20

Two sets of points α and β are *congruent*, denoted $\alpha \simeq \beta$, if β is the image of α under an isometry.

Two specific sets of points whose congruence is invariably studied in any presentation of Euclidean geometry are those figures known as segments and triangles. Before considering these particular figures, it is necessary to accept the following definitions.

Definition 3.21

P is *between* Q and R if P, Q, and R are three distinct collinear points and $d(Q, P) + d(P, R) = d(Q, R)$. The set of points consisting of Q and R together with all points P between Q and R is called the *segment* with *endpoints* Q and R and is denoted $\overline{QR}$. The *measure* of $\overline{QR}$, denoted by $m(QR)$, is $d(Q, R)$.

Definition 3.22

If P, Q, and R are three noncollinear points, the *triangle PQR*, denoted by $\triangle PQR$, is the set of segments $\overline{PQ}$, $\overline{QR}$, and $\overline{RP}$. These segments are called the *sides* of the triangle. $\angle PQR$, $\angle QRP$, and $\angle RPQ$ are called the *angles* of the triangle.

Using Definition 3.21 and the definition of an isometry it is relatively easy to verify that congruent segments have the same measure (see Exercise 5).

Theorem 3.9

If $\overline{PQ} \simeq \overline{P'Q'}$, then $m(PQ) = m(P'Q')$.

In the case of congruent triangles, we are interested in knowing not only if the corresponding sides of the triangles have the same measure but also how the measures of corresponding angles compare. As the following theorem indicates, the angle measure is unchanged under a direct isometry, but under an indirect isometry the sign of the angle measure is changed. For this reason, we say that indirect isometries *reverse orientation*.

Theorem 3.10

Let u' and v' be the images of lines u and v under an isometry. If the isometry is direct then $m\angle(u', v') = m\angle(u, v)$. If the isometry is indirect then $m\angle(u', v') = -m\angle(u, v)$.

Proof

Let $u[u_1, u_2, u_3]$ and $v[v_1, v_2, v_3]$ be two lines and $u'[u'_1, u'_2, u'_3]$ and $v'[v'_1, v'_2, v'_3]$ their images. The theorem will be proved by showing that $\tan(\angle(u', v')) = \pm\tan(\angle(u, v))$. Using the line equation of an isometry we have $k_1 u' = uA^{-1}$, $k_2 v' = vA^{-1}$ where k_1 and k_2 are nonzero scalars and A is the matrix of an isometry. If we let $B = A^{-1}$, then B is also the matrix of an isometry since the isometries form a group. Thus matrix B has one of the two forms given in Theorem 3.7. In both cases the coordinates of u' and v' can be determined by direct calculation and substituted into the expression for $\tan(\angle(u', v'))$. Simplification of the resulting expressions yields the results given in the theorem (see Exercise 7). ∎

The previous two theorems lead to the following result.

Theorem 3.11
If $\triangle PQR \simeq \triangle P'Q'R'$ then $m(PQ) = m(P'Q')$, $m(QR) = m(Q'R')$, $m(RP) = m(R'P')$, $m\angle PQR = \pm m\angle P'Q'R'$, $m(QRP) = \pm m\angle Q'R'P'$, and $m\angle RPQ = \pm m\angle R'P'Q'$.

Definition 3.23
Triangles $\triangle PQR$ and $\triangle P'Q'R$ have the *same (opposite) orientation* if the measures of corresponding pairs of angles all have the same (opposite) sign.

To show that the converse of Theorem 3.11 is also valid, it is most convenient to first investigate and classify the isometries. This will be done in the next two sections where we will also show that the isometries are the transformations investigated in Section 3.2 through 3.4. For convenience, the definitions of these transformations are repeated below.[11]

Definition 3.3
A *(line) reflection with axis m*, denoted R_m, is a transformation that maps each point on m to itself and maps each point P not on m to a point P' such that m is the perpendicular bisector of segment $\overline{PP'}$ (Fig. 3.3). If a point set α ($\alpha \neq m$) is invariant under R_m, we say that α has *line symmetry* and that m is a *line of symmetry* for α.

---

[11] Note: The numbers assigned to these definitions are those used earlier.

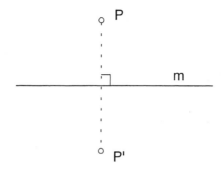

FIGURE 3.3 Line reflection with axis m.

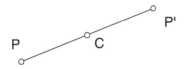

FIGURE 3.4 Point reflection with center C.

Definition 3.4

A *point reflection with center C*, denoted[12] $R_{\underline{C}}$, is a transformation that maps the maps the point C to itself and maps every other point P to P' where C is the midpoint of segment $\overline{PP'}$ (Fig. 3.4). If the point set α is invariant under R_C, we say that α has *point symmetry* and that C is a *point of symmetry* for α.

Definition 3.5

A *rotation with center C and angle (measure)* θ, denoted $R_{C,\theta}$, is a transformation that maps the point C to itself and maps any other point P to P' where $d(P, C) = d(P', C)$ and $m\angle PCP' = \theta$ (Fig 3.5).[13] If the point set α is invariant under $R_{C,\theta}$, where $R_{C,\theta} \neq I$, we say that α has *rotation symmetry (about C)*. If $\theta = 360°/n$ for a positive integer n, α is also said to have *n-fold rotation symmetry (about C)*.

---

[12]To prevent confusion between a point C and a line c, you may want to underline the center designated in the notation.
[13]Note: If $m\angle PCP' = 0$, the rotation is the identity transformation I.

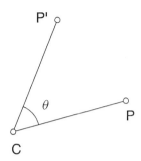

FIGURE 3.5   Rotation with center C and angle θ.

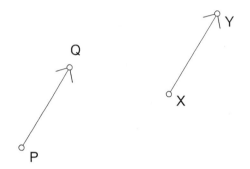

FIGURE 3.6   Translation with vector $\overrightarrow{PQ}$.

Definition 3.9

A *translation with vector* $\overrightarrow{PQ}$, denoted $T_{\overrightarrow{PQ}}$, is a transformation that maps any point X to point Y where $\overrightarrow{XY} = \overrightarrow{PQ}$ (Fig. 3.6).[14] If a point set α is invariant under a nonidentity translation $T_{\overrightarrow{PQ}}$, we say that α has *translation symmetry* and that line PQ is an *axis of translation symmetry for* α.

Definition 3.11

A *glide reflection with vector* $\overrightarrow{PQ}$, denoted $G_{\overrightarrow{PQ}}$, is the product of a reflection with axis PQ and the nonidentity translation $T_{\overrightarrow{PQ}}$ (Fig. 3.7).

---

[14]Note: The identity transformation is a translation by definition.

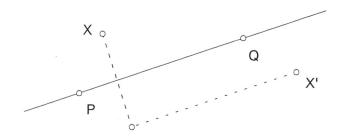

FIGURE 3.7   Glide reflection with vector $\overrightarrow{PQ}$.

If a point set α is invariant under a glide reflection $G_{\overrightarrow{PQ}}$, we say that the line PQ is an axis of *glide symmetry* for α.

Exercises

1. Find both a direct isometry and an indirect isometry that map $X(0, 0, 1)$ and $Y(2, 0, 1)$ to $X'(1, 1, 1)$ and $Y'(3, 1, 1)$. What happens to the point $Z(1, -1, 1)$ under each of these isometries?

2. Prove that the distance function given in Definition 3.14 satisfies properties (a)–(c) in the following definition. (It is also possible to verify that the distance function satisfies property (d) and is therefore a metric on V^*.)

Definition of metric
A function $d(P, Q)$ on a set S is a *metric* if for all points P, Q and R in S: (a) $d(P, Q)$ is a real number; (b) $d(P, Q) = d(Q, P)$; (c) $d(P, Q) \geq 0$ and $d(P, Q) = 0$ if and only if $P = Q$; (d) $d(P, R) \leq d(P, Q) + d(Q, R)$.

3. Prove case 2 of Theorem 3.7.

4. Prove Theorem 3.8 and its corollary. (Note: $G' \subset G$ is a subgroup of G if G' is also a group.)

5. Prove Theorem 3.9.

6. Show that the congruence relation as given in Definition 3.20 is an equivalence relation (see Definition 3.12).

7. Carry out the algebraic computations needed to complete the proof of Theorem 3.10 for both direct and indirect isometries.

8. Prove: If $\alpha \simeq \beta$ and $T(\alpha) = \alpha'$, $T(\beta) = \beta'$ where T is an isometry, then $\alpha' \simeq \beta'$.

3.8 Direct Isometries

In Section 3.7, we described isometries as being either direct or indirect. In this section we will investigate and further classify the direct isometries based on the number of points that remain invariant under the isometry. Knowing which points and lines are invariant is important in understanding the geometric action of any transformation.

Theorem 3.12
A nonidentity direct isometry with matrix $A = \left[a_{i,j}\right]$ has
  a. exactly one invariant point if $a_{11} \neq 1$; and
  b. no invariant points if $a_{11} = 1$.

Proof
The point $X(x_1, x_2, 1)$ is an invariant point of the isometry if and only if $AX = X$; that is,

$$\begin{bmatrix} a_{11} & a_{12} & a_{13} \\ -a_{12} & a_{11} & a_{23} \\ 0 & 0 & 1 \end{bmatrix} \begin{bmatrix} x_1 \\ x_2 \\ 1 \end{bmatrix} = \begin{bmatrix} x_1 \\ x_2 \\ 1 \end{bmatrix}$$

or

$$(a_{11} - 1)x_1 + a_{12}x_2 + a_{13} = 0 \tag{3.1}$$

and

$$-a_{12}x_1 + (a_{11} - 1)x_2 + a_{23} = 0 \tag{3.2}$$

Case 1: $a_{11} \neq 1$. In this case, Equation 3.1 yields

$$x_1 = \frac{-a_{12}x_2 - a_{13}}{a_{11} - 1}$$

and Equation 3.2 yields

$$-a_{12}\left[\frac{-a_{12}x_2 - a_{13}}{a_{11} - 1}\right] + (a_{11} - 1)x_2 + a_{23} = 0,$$

or, solving for x_2,

$$x_2 = \frac{-a_{12}a_{13} - a_{23}(a_{11} - 1)}{a_{12}^2 + (a_{11} - 1)^2}$$

giving a unique solution.

Case 2: $a_{11} = 1$. Then $a_{12} = 0$, since $a_{11}^2 + a_{12}^2 = +1$. So

$$AX = \begin{bmatrix} 1 & 0 & a_{13} \\ 0 & 1 & a_{23} \\ 0 & 0 & 1 \end{bmatrix} \begin{bmatrix} x_1 \\ x_2 \\ 1 \end{bmatrix} = \begin{bmatrix} x_1 + a_{13} \\ x_2 + a_{23} \\ 1 \end{bmatrix}$$

Thus, there are no invariant points unless $a_{13} = a_{23} = 0$, in which case $A = I$. ∎

Using the categorization of Theorem 3.12, we will show that the direct isometries are either (a) rotations or (b) translations, that is, the familiar transformations that you have encountered in previous mathematics classes and/or in Sections 3.2 through 3.4. We begin the process by showing that nonidentity translations have 3×3 matrix representations placing them in category (b) and then note that any direct isometry in this category is necessarily a translation. Using a similar process, we will then show that the transformations in category (a) are rotations. In both cases, the process will lead to either a specific matrix representation for the transformation or a relationship that will yield the matrix representation. Our use of 3×3 matrices is unlike the 2×2 matrix representations for rotations frequently used elsewhere. But the increased matrix size makes possible the representation within a single matrix of translations and of rotations centered at points other than the origin O.

Theorem 3.13

I. A translation is a direct isometry. II. Conversely, any direct isometry with no invariant points is a translation.

* *A translation $T_{\overrightarrow{PQ}}$ with $\overrightarrow{PQ} = (a, b, 0)$ has matrix representation*

$$\begin{bmatrix} 1 & 0 & a \\ 0 & 1 & b \\ 0 & 0 & 1 \end{bmatrix}$$

Corollary

A nonidentity translation has no invariant points.

The verification of this theorem and its corollary, as well as the next two theorems, involves calculations using vectors and matrices (see Exercises 9 through 11).

Theorem 3.14

The set of translations forms a group.

Theorem 3.15

Given a point X and a point Y, there is a unique translation mapping X to Y.

Using the matrix representation, several characteristic properties of translations can be identified. These properties should confirm the frequently used description of a translation as *sliding points along fixed lines.*

Theorem 3.16

If a translation maps a line u to a line v, then u and v are either identical or parallel.

Proof

If A is the matrix of the translation, then $kv = uA^{-1}$, since v is the image of u. So

$$k[v_1, v_2, v_3] = [u_1, u_2, u_3] \begin{bmatrix} 1 & 0 & -a \\ 0 & 1 & -b \\ 0 & 0 & 1 \end{bmatrix} \qquad (3.3)$$

$$= [u_1, u_2, -au_1 - bu_2 + u_3]. \qquad (3.4)$$

Since $kv_1 = u_1$ and $kv_2 = u_2$ the conclusion follows (see Exercise 10 in Section 3.5). ∎

The proof of the following theorem demonstrates the interplay between synthetic and analytic methods and offers a nice application of many of the analytic techniques we have developed.

Theorem 3.17

If a translation maps P to P'(P ≠ P'), then the line PP' as well as all lines parallel to PP' are invariant. No other lines are invariant.

Proof

Let P be a point with coordinates $(p_1, p_2, 1)$. Since T is a translation with a matrix of the form given in Theorem 3.13, $P' = T(P)$ has coordinates $(p_1 + a, p_2 + b, 1)$, so the equation of line PP' is given by

$$\begin{vmatrix} x_1 & p_1 & p_1 + a \\ x_2 & p_2 & p_2 + b \\ 1 & 1 & 1 \end{vmatrix} = 0$$

Evaluating this equation yields $[-b, a, p_1 b - p_2 a]$ as the line coordinates for PP'. So the lines parallel to PP', as well as PP', all have coordinates of the form $[-b, a, c]$. Applying the line equation of this translation gives

$$[-b, a, c] \begin{bmatrix} 1 & 0 & -a \\ 0 & 1 & -b \\ 0 & 0 & 1 \end{bmatrix} = [-b, a, c]$$

so these lines are indeed invariant under this translation.

To verify the second statement of the theorem, we will use an indirect proof. Assume a line l not parallel to PP' is also invariant under the translation. Then l and PP' intersect at a point, Q. So Q is on two invariant lines, l and PP'. Since isometries preserve incidence, $Q' = T(Q)$ must also be on both l and PP' implying that $Q = Q'$. This would mean that Q is an invariant point of the translation. However, since this translation is not the identity $(P \neq P')$, we have a contradiction. It follows that no lines in addition to those parallel to PP' are invariant. ■

Theorem 3.18

If u and v are parallel lines, then there is a translation mapping u to v.

Proof

Let X be a point on u, X' a point on v. Then by Theorem 3.15 there is a translation mapping X to X'. But this translation also maps line

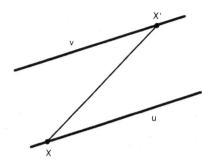

FIGURE 3.8 Translating u to the parallel line v.

u to a line u' through X' (Fig. 3.8). Since u' is parallel to u (Theorem 3.16), it follows that $u' = v$. ∎

Using the preceding properties of translations it is possible to determine synthetically the image of any other point under a translation T that maps P to P'. If Q is any other point, its image Q' can be found as follows.

Case 1: Q is not on PP' (Fig. 3.9a). Q' will be the point at which the line through P' parallel to PQ and the line through Q parallel to PP' intersect.

Case 2: Q is on PP' (Fig. 3.9b). First find R' for some R not on PP' and then use R and R' in place of P and P' in case 1.

Rotations also have matrix representations which we will use to analyze their effects. However, for rotations, it is most convenient to first find and use the matrix representation for a rotation with center $O = O(0, 0, 1)$. We can then find matrix representations for rotations with other centers by using a translation and its inverse as indicated in Theorem 3.19.

Theorem 3.19

I. A rotation is a direct isometry. II. Conversely, any direct isometry with an invariant point is a rotation.

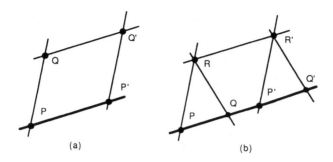

FIGURE 3.9 Finding $Q' = T_{\overrightarrow{PP'}}(Q)$.

a. *A rotation $R_{O,\theta}$ centered at $O(0,0,1)$ has matrix representation*

$$\begin{bmatrix} \cos\theta & -\sin\theta & 0 \\ \sin\theta & \cos\theta & 0 \\ 0 & 0 & 1 \end{bmatrix}$$

b. *The matrix representation of a rotation centered at $C \neq O$, can be obtained from the relation below where $T = T_{\overrightarrow{OC}}$:*

$$R_{C,\theta} = TR_{O,\theta}T^{-1}$$

Proof

Part I: Since our points have coordinates $(x_1, x_2, 1)$ the matrix of a rotation is necessarily 3×3 with third row $(0\,0\,1)$. If the rotation is the identity transformation, that is, if $\theta = 0 (\mathrm{mod}\,360)$, its matrix is the identity and therefore the rotation is clearly a direct isometry (Theorem 3.7). If $\theta \neq 0$, we first consider the case where the center $C = O(0,0,1)$. Since O is invariant, the matrix is of the form

$$A = \begin{bmatrix} a_{11} & a_{12} & 0 \\ a_{21} & a_{22} & 0 \\ 0 & 0 & 1 \end{bmatrix}$$

To find the entries a_{ij} we note that the rotation $R_{O,\theta}$ maps points $X(1,0,1)$ and $Y(0,1,1)$ to $X'(\cos\theta, \sin\theta, 1)$ and $Y'(-\sin\theta, \cos\theta, 1)$, respectively. But $AX = X'$ where $X'(a_{11}, a_{21}, 1)$, and $AY = Y'$ where $Y'(a_{12}, a_{22}, 1)$. It follows that $a_{11} = \cos\theta$, $a_{21} = \sin\theta$, $a_{12} = -\sin\theta$, and $a_{22} = \cos\theta$. To show that this matrix actually represents the rotation $R_{O,\theta}$, we first note that by Theorem 3.7, the transformation with matrix A is necessarily an isometry, so it follows that the image

$P' = AP$ of any point $P \neq O$ satisfies the distance relation $d(O, P) = d(O', P') = d(O, P')$. Thus, it remains to show that $\angle POP' = \theta$ for each point P and image P'. Using $P(p_1, p_2, 1)$, $P' = AP$ has coordinates $P'(p_1 \cos\theta - p_2 \sin\theta, \ p_1 \sin\theta + p_2 \cos\theta, 1)$. It follows that lines $u = OP$ and $v = OP'$ have coordinates: $u[-p_2, p_1, 0]$ and $v[-p_1 \sin\theta - p_2 \cos\theta, \ p_1 \cos\theta - p_2 \sin\theta, 0]$. Substituting these into the expression for $\tan(\angle(u, v))$ in Definition 3.14, we get

$$\tan(\angle(u, v)) = \frac{u_1 v_2 - v_1 u_2}{u_1 v_1 + u_2 v_2}$$

$$= \frac{-p_2(p_1 \cos\theta - p_2 \sin\theta) - p_1(-p_1 \sin\theta - p_2 \cos\theta)}{p_2 p_1 \sin\theta + p_2^2 \cos\theta + p_1^2 \cos\theta - p_1 p_2 \sin\theta}$$

$$= \frac{\sin\theta(p_1^2 + p_2^2)}{\cos\theta(p_1^2 + p_2^2)} = \frac{\sin\theta}{\cos\theta} = \tan\theta$$

So it follows that $m\angle POP' = \theta$ for any point $P \neq O$. Thus, $R_{O,\theta}$ does have matrix representation A and is therefore a direct isometry.

To verify that $R_{C,\theta}$ is a direct isometry when $C \neq O$, we first note that this rotation can be written as a product involving three direct isometries, namely the translations $T = T_{\overrightarrow{OC}}$ and T^{-1} and $R_{O,\theta}$:

$$R_{C,\theta} = T R_{O,\theta} T^{-1}$$

That this product yields the desired rotation follows from noting that: (1) $R_{C,\theta}(C) = T R_{O,\theta} T^{-1}(C) = T R_{O,\theta}(O) = T(O) = C$; (2) since all three transformations are isometries, their product necessarily preserves distances; and (3) since translations map lines to parallel lines, the angle change carried out by $R_{O,\theta}$ is unchanged by the translations. Thus, since the rotation $R_{C,\theta}$ is a product of direct isometries, it is also a direct isometry (Theorem 3.8).

Part II: Now assume that $\mathcal{T}$ is a direct isometry with an invariant point C. As before, we will first assume that $C = O$. Using Theorem 3.7 and noting that O must remain invariant yields the following matrix representation of $\mathcal{T}$:

$$A = \begin{bmatrix} a_{11} & a_{12} & 0 \\ -a_{12} & a_{11} & 0 \\ 0 & 0 & 1 \end{bmatrix}$$

Since we are working with an isometry, $a_{11}^2 + a_{12}^2 = 1$. So we let θ be the angle where $a_{11} = \cos\theta$ and $a_{12} = -\sin\theta$. Substituting these into the matrix A gives the matrix for $R_{O,\theta}$, that is, the direct isometry is a rotation. In the case where the direct isometry's invariant point $C \neq O$, we note that as in Part I, its matrix representation can be obtained using the matrix product involving $A_{O,\theta}$, the matrix obtained when $C = O$, and A_T, a matrix of a translation; namely, $A = A_T A_{O,\theta} A_T^{-1}$. The resultant matrix is that of a rotation with center C. ∎

Corollary
A nonidentity rotation has exactly one invariant point.

Using the matrix representation for a rotation centered at O and the relation in part (b) of Theorem 3.19, we can verify that for each point C, the rotations with center C form a group and, furthermore, show that there is a rotation mapping any line to any other intersecting line.

Theorem 3.20
The set of all rotations with a given center C forms a group.

Theorem 3.21
If lines u and v intersect at a point C with $m\angle(u, v) = \theta$ then $R_{C,\theta}$ will map u to v.

We conclude our consideration of direct isometries with two important results. The first of these notes that on the basis of Theorems 3.12, 3.13, and 3.19, translations and rotations are the *only* direct isometries. Furthermore, these two types of isometries are all that is needed to prove the converse of Theorem 3.11 for triangles that have the same orientation.

Theorem 3.22
A direct isometry is either a translation or a rotation.

Theorem 3.23
If $\triangle PQR$ and $\triangle P'Q'R'$ are two triangles with $m(PQ) = m(P'Q')$, $m(QR) = m(Q'R')$, $m(RP) = m(R'P')$, $m\angle PQR = m\angle P'Q'R'$,

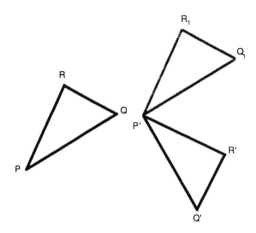

FIGURE 3.10 Mapping $\triangle PQR$ to $\triangle P'Q'R'$.

$m\angle QPR = m\angle Q'R'P'$ and $m\angle RPQ = m\angle R'P'Q'$, then there is a direct isometry mapping $\triangle PQR$ to $\triangle P'Q'R'$ so $\triangle PQR \simeq \triangle P'Q'R'$.

Proof

To show the congruence of the two triangles, it is sufficient to show that there is an isometry mapping $\triangle PQR$ to $\triangle P'Q'R'$ (Definition 3.20). In the following paragraph we will outline a procedure for obtaining such an isometry.

Let T be a translation mapping P to P'. T will also map points Q and R to points Q_1 and R_1 as indicated in Figure 3.10. Let $\theta = m\angle Q_1 P'Q'$. Then the rotation with center P' and angle θ will map the points P' and Q_1 to P' and Q', respectively, since $d(P', Q_1) = d(P, Q) = d(P', Q')$. Furthermore, since $m\angle Q_1 P'R_1 = m\angle QPR = m\angle Q'P'R'$ and $d(P', R_1) = d(P, R) = d(P', R')$, this rotation will also map point R_1 to R'. Therefore, the isometry consisting of the composite $R_{P', \theta} T$ will map $\triangle PQR$ to $\triangle P'Q'R'$. ■

Exercises

1. Let T be the translation mapping $X(1, -2, 1)$ to $X'(3, 4, 1)$. (a) Find the matrix of T and the image of line $u[2, 3, -1]$ under T. (b) Verify that lines u and $T(u)$ are parallel.

2. Find the matrix of a translation that maps $u[1, -2, 5]$ to $v[2, -4, 7]$.

3. Find the invariant lines of the translation with matrix
$$\begin{bmatrix} 1 & 0 & -3 \\ 0 & 1 & 7 \\ 0 & 0 & 1 \end{bmatrix}$$

4. Prove: If l is a line, the set of all translations that keep l invariant forms a group.

5. a. Verify that the following matrix is a matrix of a rotation:
$$\begin{bmatrix} \frac{3}{5} & \frac{4}{5} & 2 \\ -\frac{4}{5} & \frac{3}{5} & 1 \\ 0 & 0 & 1 \end{bmatrix}$$

   b. What is the angle of this rotation?

   c. What is the center of this rotation?

6. Verify that $TR_{0,\theta}T^{-1}$ is a rotation with center C and angle θ where O is the point with coordinates $(0, 0, 1)$ and T is a translation mapping O to C.

7. (a) Find the point of intersection of lines $u[2, 0, 3]$ and $v[1, 1, 5]$. (b) Find $m\angle(u, v)$. (c) Find a rotation that maps line u to line v. (Be sure the check your answer.)

8. (a) Describe synthetically how to find the center and angle of a rotation that maps a given point P to a given point P'. (Note that there is an infinite number of possible rotations.) (b) Use the answer to part (a) to find the matrix of a rotation that maps $P(2, 0, 1)$ to $P'(1, -3, 1)$. Verify that the rotation works.

9. Prove Theorem 3.13 and its corollary.

10. Prove Theorem 3.14.

11. Prove Theorem 3.15.

12. Give an analytic proof of the second statement in Theorem 3.17. (No other lines are invariant.)

13. (a) Demonstrate by diagramming an example that the product of two rotations with different centers can be a translation. (b) Show how one particular triangle is mapped under the two rotations you used in part (a).

14. Use the relation in part (b) of Theorem 3.19 to find the matrix representation of $R_{C,\theta}$ with $C(c_1, c_2, 1)$.

15. Show that $R_{C,\theta}R_{C,\phi} = R_{C,\theta+\phi}$. [*Hint*: You may want to explain why it is sufficient to show this for the case where $C = O$ and then use matrices to do so.]

16. Prove that any direct isometry can be expressed as the product of a rotation with center $O(0, 0, 1)$ and a translation (the wording indicates that the rotation is to be used first and the translation second).

17. (a) Find a direct isometry that maps $P(1, 0, 1)$ and $Q(5, 3, 1)$ to $P'(3, -2, 1)$ and $Q'(0, 2, 1)$, respectively. (b) Is the isometry you found a rotation or a translation? Why?

18. (a) Use the procedure outlined in the proof of Theorem 3.23 to verify that $\triangle PQR$ and $\triangle P'Q'R'$ are congruent where P, Q, R, P', Q', and R' have the following coordinates; $P(2, 8, 1)$, $Q(4, 4, 1)$, $R(10, 7, 1)$, $P'(7, -2, 1)$, $Q'(11, -4, 1)$, and $R'(14, 2, 1)$. (b) Verify that the isometry you found in part (a) is a rotation. What is its center?

19. Prove: If $C \neq D$ and $R_{C,\theta}$ and $R_{D,\phi}$ are two nonidentity rotations, then the product $R_{D,\phi}R_{C,\theta}$ is (a) a rotation with angle $\theta + \phi$ if $\theta + \phi \neq 0$ (mod 360) and (b) a translation if $\theta + \phi = 0$ (mod 360).

20. Prove: If T is a direct isometry such that $T^2 = I$, where I is the identity, then $T = I$ or T is a rotation with an angle of $180°$.

21. Prove: (a) If a line is invariant under a nonidentity rotation with center C, then the line is incident with C. [*Hint*: Assume $C = O(0, 0, 1)$.] (b) If a nonidentity rotation with center C has an invariant line, then the angle of the rotation is $180°$.

3.9 Indirect Isometries

We will show in this section that, as in the case of direct isometries, there are two types of indirect isometries: those that have invariant points (reflections) and those that do not (glide reflections). But unlike a direct isometry with an invariant point, an indirect isometry with an invariant point actually keeps every point on some line invariant. Such a line is said to be *pointwise invariant*. The adjective "pointwise" is important, since a line can be invariant without any points on it being invariant. For example, under the translation $T_{\overrightarrow{PQ}}$

$(P \neq Q)$ the line PQ is invariant but none of the points on PQ are invariant.

Theorem 3.24

I. *A (line) reflection is an indirect isometry.* II. *Conversely, any indirect isometry with a pointwise invariant line is a (line) reflection.*

a. *A reflection with axis $x[0, 1, 0]$ has matrix representation*

$$\begin{bmatrix} 1 & 0 & 0 \\ 0 & -1 & 0 \\ 0 & 0 & 1 \end{bmatrix}$$

b. *The matrix representation of a reflection with axis $m \neq x$ can be obtained from the relation below where S is a direct isometry that maps line x to line m $(S(x) = m)$.*

$$R_m = S R_x S^{-1}$$

Proof

Part I: As in the proof of Part I of Theorem 3.19, the matrix of a reflection is necessarily 3×3 with third row $(0\,0\,1)$. We will first assume that the axis of the reflection is the line $x[0, 1, 0]$, that is, the x- or x_1-axis in the usual Cartesian coordinate system. In this case all points on x have coordinates of the form $X(x_1, 0, 1)$. Then since the reflection keeps each such point invariant, we must have $A X = X$ for all $x_1 \in R$, that is,

$$\begin{bmatrix} a_{11} & a_{12} & a_{13} \\ a_{21} & a_{22} & a_{23} \\ 0 & 0 & 1 \end{bmatrix} \begin{bmatrix} x_1 \\ 0 \\ 1 \end{bmatrix} = \begin{bmatrix} x_1 \\ 0 \\ 1 \end{bmatrix}$$

So $a_{11}x_1 + a_{13} = x_1$ and $a_{21}x_1 + a_{23} = 0$. Since this must hold for all $x_1 \in R$, it follows that $a_{11} = 1$ and $a_{13} = a_{21} = a_{23} = 0$. To find the entries a_{12} and a_{22}, we note that the reflection R_x must map point $Y(0, 1, 1)$ to $Y'(0, -1, 1)$. But $A Y = Y'$ where $Y'(a_{12}, a_{22}, 1)$. It follows that $a_{12} = 0$, $a_{22} = -1$. To show that this matrix actually represents R_x, let $P(p_1, p_2, 1)$ be a point not on x; thus, $p_2 \neq 0$. Then $P' = AP$ has coordinates $P'(p_1, -p_2, 1)$ and straightforward calculations show that segment $\overline{PP'}$ is perpendicular to x and that its midpoint $M(p_1, 0, 1)$ is on x. Thus, A is indeed the matrix representation of R_x and so R_x is an indirect isometry as claimed.

To verify that R_m is an indirect isometry when $m \neq x$ we claim that this reflection can be written as the following product involving the indirect isometry R_x and direct isometries S and S^{-1} where S maps x to m (see Theorems 3.18 and 3.21):

$$R_m = S R_x S^{-1}$$

To show that this product yields the desired reflection, we note that if M is a point on m, then $S^{-1}(M) = X$ is a point on x. So $S R_x S^{-1}(M) = S R_x(X) = S(X) = M$. So each such point M on m is invariant. In addition, since all isometries preserve distance, their product necessarily does so; and since the direct isometry preserves angles and their orientation, the angle change carried out by R_x is unchanged by S. Thus, $S R_x S^{-1}$ is the reflection R_m, and R_m is an indirect isometry (see Corollary to Theorem 3.8).

Part II: Now assume that T is an indirect isometry with a point-wise invariant line m. As before we will first assume that $m = x$. Using Theorem 3.7 and noting that the point $O(0, 0, 1)$ must remain invariant yields the following matrix representation for T:

$$A = \begin{bmatrix} a_{11} & a_{12} & 0 \\ a_{12} & -a_{11} & 0 \\ 0 & 0 & 1 \end{bmatrix}$$

Imposing the condition that all points $X(x_1, 0, 1)$ must also remain invariant leads, as it did in Part I, to the conclusion that $a_{11} = 1$ and $a_{12} = 0$. Thus, $A = A_x$ is the matrix for R_x and hence T is necessarily a reflection. For an indirect isometry T with pointwise invariant line $m \neq x$, we note that its matrix representation A can be found using $A = A_S A_x A_S^{-1}$ where A_x is the matrix for R_x and A_S is a matrix of a direct isometry S where $S(x) = m$. The resultant matrix A is the matrix of a reflection with axis m. ∎

Using results from this theorem, we can demonstrate a property which we will use extensively in future proofs; namely that a reflection is its own inverse.

Corollary
For a reflection R_m, $R_m = R_m^{-1}$.

According to the definition, a reflection with axis m keeps all points on m invariant and thus line m invariant. But does R_m have any other invariant points? Any other invariant lines? The answers to these questions are given by the next two theorems. The proofs of these and the remaining theorems about reflections will be given for the case where the axis $m = x[0, 1, 0]$. As outlined in the proof of Theorem 3.25, these results can then be extended to reflections with other axes by using the relation $R_m = S R_x S^{-1}$ where S is a direct isometry mapping x to m.

Theorem 3.25

The only invariant points under the reflection R_m are those on m.

Proof

Let P be a point with coordinates $(p_1, p_2, 1)$. Then $P' = R_x(P)$ has coordinates $(p_1, -p_2, 1)$ so the invariant points of R_x are precisely those for which $p_2 = -p_2$ or $p_2 = 0$. These are the points on $x[0, 1, 0]$. Using this result for the reflection R_x, it is then possible to verify that the only invariant points of $R_m = S R_x S^{-1}$ are those on line m (see Exercise 1). ∎

Theorem 3.26

Every line perpendicular to m is invariant under R_m, and conversely any line invariant under R_m is either m or a line perpendicular to m.

Proof

As noted earlier, we will assume that $m = x$. Let u be a line perpendicular to x. Since x has coordinates $[0, 1, 0]$ it follows from Definition 3.14 that u has coordinates $[u_1, 0, u_3]$. If u' is the image of u under the reflection, then $ku' = u(R_x)^{-1} = uR_x$ or, in matrix notation,

$$ku' = [u_1, 0, u_3] \begin{bmatrix} 1 & 0 & 0 \\ 0 & -1 & 0 \\ 0 & 0 & 1 \end{bmatrix} = [u_1, 0, u_3]$$

So $u' = u$ is invariant.

Now assume $u[u_1, u_2, u_3]$ is an invariant line under R_x. Then

$$k[u_1, u_2, u_3] = [u_1, u_2, u_3] \begin{bmatrix} 1 & 0 & 0 \\ 0 & -1 & 0 \\ 0 & 0 & 1 \end{bmatrix}$$

So $ku_1 = u_1$, $ku_2 = -u_2$, and $ku_3 = u_3$. If u_1 or $u_3 \neq 0$, it follows that $k = 1$ and hence $u_2 = 0$. Thus, u has coordinates $[u_1, 0, u_3]$ and so is perpendicular to x. If $u_1 = u_3 = 0$, then $u_2 \neq 0$, and so $u = x[0, 1, 0]$. ∎

Using reflections along with direct isometries it is now possible to verify the converse of Theorem 3.11 for triangles with opposite orientation (see Exercise 4).

Theorem 3.27
If $\triangle PQR$ and $\triangle P'Q'R'$ are two triangles with

$$m(PQ) = m(P'Q'), \quad m(QR) = m(Q'R'), \quad m(RP) = m(R'P'),$$

and also

$$m\angle PQR = -m\angle P'Q'R', \quad m\angle QRP = -m\angle Q'R'P',$$

and $m\angle RPQ = -m\angle R'P'Q'$, then there is an indirect isometry mapping $\triangle PQR$ to $\triangle P'Q'R'$ so $\triangle PQR \simeq \triangle P'Q'R'$.

The previously described properties of reflections also lead to the remarkable fact that the direct isometries used in the proof of the preceding theorem are themselves products of two reflections with appropriately chosen axes.

Theorem 3.28
An isometry T is a product of two reflections if and only if it is a translation or a rotation. The exact relationships are spelled out below.
I. *T is a product of two reflections.*
   Case A: $T = R_n R_m$ where m and n are parallel lines intersecting a common perpendicular at M and N, respectively.
   Then $T = T_{\overrightarrow{PP'}}$ where $\overrightarrow{PP'} = 2\overrightarrow{MN}$.
   Case B: $T = R_n R_m$ where lines m and n intersect at a point C.
   Then $T = R_{C,\theta}$ where $\theta = 2\angle(m, n)$.

II. T *is a translation or a rotation.*

 Case A: T *is the translation* $T_{\overrightarrow{PP'}}$.

 Then $T = R_n R_m$ *where m and n are two lines intersecting a common*

 perpendicular at M and N respectively, with $\overrightarrow{MN} = \frac{1}{2} \overrightarrow{PP'}$.

 Case B: T *is the rotation* $R_{C,\phi}$.

 Then $T = R_n R_m$ *where m and n are two lines through C with* $\angle(m, n) = \frac{1}{2} \phi$.

Proof

Case I-A: We shall assume that $m = x$. Then m is the line with coordinates $[0, 1, 0]$ and the matrix representation of R_m is that given for R_x by Theorem 3.24. The parallel line n must have coordinates of the form $[0, 1, n_3]$. Using $p[1, 0, 0]$ as the common perpendicular gives points of intersection $M(0, 0, 1)$ and $N(0, -n_3, 1)$, respectively. To find the matrix representation of R_n, we will use the translation $T = T_{\overrightarrow{MN}}$. The matrix of T is

$$T = \begin{bmatrix} 1 & 0 & 0 \\ 0 & 1 & -n_3 \\ 0 & 0 & 1 \end{bmatrix}$$

So $R_n = T R_m T^{-1}$ has matrix representation

$$\begin{bmatrix} 1 & 0 & 0 \\ 0 & 1 & -n_3 \\ 0 & 0 & 1 \end{bmatrix} \begin{bmatrix} 1 & 0 & 0 \\ 0 & -1 & 0 \\ 0 & 0 & 1 \end{bmatrix} \begin{bmatrix} 1 & 0 & 0 \\ 0 & 1 & n_3 \\ 0 & 0 & 1 \end{bmatrix} = \begin{bmatrix} 1 & 0 & 0 \\ 0 & -1 & -2n_3 \\ 0 & 0 & 1 \end{bmatrix}$$

 Thus, $R_n R_m$ has matrix representation

$$\begin{bmatrix} 1 & 0 & 0 \\ 0 & -1 & -2n_3 \\ 0 & 0 & 1 \end{bmatrix} \begin{bmatrix} 1 & 0 & 0 \\ 0 & -1 & 0 \\ 0 & 0 & 1 \end{bmatrix} = \begin{bmatrix} 1 & 0 & 0 \\ 0 & 1 & -2n_3 \\ 0 & 0 & 1 \end{bmatrix}$$

which is a translation matrix. Using this matrix to find $T(P) = P'$:

$$P' = \begin{bmatrix} 1 & 0 & 0 \\ 0 & 1 & -2n_3 \\ 0 & 0 & 1 \end{bmatrix} \begin{bmatrix} p_1 \\ p_2 \\ 1 \end{bmatrix} = \begin{bmatrix} p_1 \\ p_2 - 2n_3 \\ 1 \end{bmatrix}$$

Therefore, $\overrightarrow{PP'} = (0, -2n_3, 0) = 2(0, -n_3, 0) = 2\overrightarrow{MN}$. Thus, T is the translation $T_{\overrightarrow{PP'}}$.

Case I-B: The proof is similar to that for I-A except in this case it is necessary to use a rotation to map m to n (see Exercise 6).

Case II-A: The proof is similar to that given below for II-B (see Exercise 7).

Case II-B: We shall assume that $\phi = 2\theta$ and that $C = O(0, 0, 1)$. Then $R_{C,\phi} = R_{C,2\theta}$ has matrix representation

$$
R_{C,2\theta} =
\begin{bmatrix}
\cos(2\theta) & -\sin(2\theta) & 0 \\
\sin(2\theta) & \cos(2\theta) & 0 \\
0 & 0 & 1
\end{bmatrix}
$$

We will use $m = x[0, 1, 0]$ as one of the two lines through C. According to Theorem 3.21, to find n such that $\angle(m, n) = \theta$, we can find the image of m under the rotation $R_{C,\theta}$ by using the product $m R_{C,\theta}^{-1}$:

$$
n = [0, 1, 0]
\begin{bmatrix}
\cos\theta & \sin\theta & 0 \\
-\sin\theta & \cos\theta & 0 \\
0 & 0 & 1
\end{bmatrix}
= [-\sin\theta, \cos\theta, 0]
$$

Note that the point $C = 0(0, 0, 1)$ is on n. To find the matrix representations for R_m and R_n, note that $R_m = R_x$ and that $R_n = R_{C,\theta} R_m R_{C,-\theta}$, thus R_n has matrix representation

$$
\begin{bmatrix}
\cos\theta & -\sin\theta & 0 \\
\sin\theta & \cos\theta & 0 \\
0 & 0 & 1
\end{bmatrix}
\begin{bmatrix}
1 & 0 & 0 \\
0 & -1 & 0 \\
0 & 0 & 1
\end{bmatrix}
\begin{bmatrix}
\cos\theta & \sin\theta & 0 \\
-\sin\theta & \cos\theta & 0 \\
0 & 0 & 1
\end{bmatrix}
$$
$$
=
\begin{bmatrix}
\cos^2\theta - \sin^2\theta & 2(\sin\theta)(\cos\theta) & 0 \\
2(\sin\theta)(\cos\theta) & \sin^2\theta - \cos^2\theta & 0 \\
0 & 0 & 1
\end{bmatrix}
$$
$$
=
\begin{bmatrix}
\cos(2\theta) & \sin(2\theta) & 0 \\
\sin(2\theta) & -\cos(2\theta) & 0 \\
0 & 0 & 1
\end{bmatrix}
$$

And finally, using matrix representations, we see that $R_n R_m = R_{C,2\theta}$:

$$
\begin{bmatrix}
\cos(2\theta) & \sin(2\theta) & 0 \\
\sin(2\theta) & -\cos(2\theta) & 0 \\
0 & 0 & 1
\end{bmatrix}
\begin{bmatrix}
1 & 0 & 0 \\
0 & -1 & 0 \\
0 & 0 & 1
\end{bmatrix}
=
\begin{bmatrix}
\cos(2\theta) & -\sin(2\theta) & 0 \\
\sin(2\theta) & \cos(2\theta) & 0 \\
0 & 0 & 1
\end{bmatrix}
$$

■

Corollary 1
A direct isometry is the product of two reflections.

Corollary 2
$R_n R_m = R_{n'} R_{m'}$ *if and only if m, n, m', and n' are all parallel (intersecting a common perpendicular at M, N, M', and N', respectively) and* $\overrightarrow{MN} = \overrightarrow{M'N'}$ *or are all concurrent and* $m\angle(m, n) = m\angle(m', n')$.

Corollary 3
A glide reflection is an indirect isometry.

Corollary 1 not only summarizes Theorem 3.28 but also suggests the following question: Are all indirect isometries also products of reflections? By Theorem 3.24 reflections are indirect isometries, and Corollary 3 to Theorem 3.28 assures us that glide reflections are indirect isometries. So to answer this question, we need to determine if there are additional indirect isometries. The following theorem provides the key for doing so.

Theorem 3.29
An indirect isometry is the product of one or three reflections.

Proof
The proof follows easily after noting that any indirect isometry can be expressed as a product of a direct isometry and R_x (see Exercise 9). ∎

The next theorem demonstrates that the indirect isometries are either reflections or glide reflections. The proof of this result makes extensive use of Corollary 2 to Theorem 3.28.

Theorem 3.30
An indirect isometry is either a reflection or a glide reflection.

Proof
By Theorem 3.29 we need only consider indirect isometries that can be written as the product $R_c R_b R_a$. We will examine this product for each of several cases.

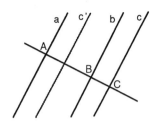

FIGURE 3.11   Proof 3.30, case 1.

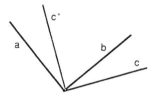

FIGURE 3.12   Proof 3.30, case 2.

Case 1: a, b and c are all parallel, intersecting a common perpendicular at A, B and C, respectively (Fig. 3.11). Let $C' = T_{\overrightarrow{BC}}(A)$ and c' be the line through C' parallel to a. Then $\overrightarrow{AC'} = \overrightarrow{BC}$ and hence, by Corollary 2 of Theorem 3.28, $R_c R_b = R_{c'} R_a$. So $R_c R_b R_a = R_{c'} R_a R_a = R_{c'}$.

Case 2: a, b, c are concurrent (Fig. 3.12) The proof is similar to that in case 1 except here the line c' must be chosen so that c' is a line through the intersection of a and b (denoted $a \cdot b$) and $m\angle(a, c') = m\angle(b, c)$.

Case 3: Each pair of the lines a, b, c intersects in distinct ordinary points (Fig. 3.13). Let b' be incident with $b \cdot c$ and perpendicular to a at point B. Let c' be a line incident with $b \cdot c$ such that $m\angle(b', c') = m\angle(b, c)$. Then $R_c R_b R_a = R_{c'} R_{b'} R_a$ where b' is perpendicular to a. Let a' be a line incident with $B = a \cdot b'$ and perpendicular to c' at point C and let b'' be a line incident with $a \cdot b'$ such that $m\angle(a, b') = m\angle(a', b'')$. Then $R_{c'} R_{b'} R_a = R_{c'} R_{b''} R_{a'}$ where a' is perpendicular to c'. Since b' is perpendicular to a, it follows that b'' is perpendicular to a'. So b'' and c' are parallel and both perpendicular to a' at points

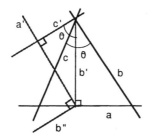

FIGURE 3.13   Proof 3.30, case 3.

B and C, respectively. Therefore, $R_{c'}R_{b''} = T_{\overrightarrow{BD}}$ where $\overrightarrow{BD} = 2\overrightarrow{BC}$. Thus, the product $R_{c'}R_{b''}R_{a'}$ is a glide reflection with axis a'.

Case 4: Exactly two of the lines are parallel. The proof for this case is analogous to the preceding ones. ■

We have now shown that there are exactly two types of indirect isometries, namely reflections and glide reflections. However, un-like rotations and translations, the two indirect isometries are not easily distinguished based on the form of their matrix representa-tions. But by multiplying an indirect isometry matrix by itself, we can immediately determine whether or not the product yields the identity. If so, the isometry is a reflection (see Corollary to Theo-rem 3.24); if not, the isometry is a glide reflection (see Exercise 3). Another distinction between the two types of indirect isometries in-volves the existence of invariant points. That reflections keep a line pointwise invariant has already been noted. Glide reflections, on the other hand, have an invariant line but no invariant points (see Exercise 16).

Theorem 3.31

A glide reflection has one invariant line but no invariant points.

With the results of this section we can now completely categorize the isometries and show that the isometry mapping a triangle to a congruent triangle is unique (see Exercises 17–19).

Theorem 3.32

Every isometry is either a rotation, a translation, a reflection, or a glide reflection; and therefore every isometry can be written as the product of at most three reflections.

Corollary

An isometry with three noncollinear invariant points is the identity.

Theorem 3.33

If $\triangle PQR \simeq \triangle P'Q'R'$, then there is a unique isometry mapping $\triangle PQR$ onto $\triangle P'Q'R'$ where P maps to P', Q to Q', and R to R'.

Exercises

1. If S is a direct isometry mapping line x to line m, show that the *only* invariant points of $R_m = SR_xS^{-1}$ are the points on m.

2. (a) Find the matrix of R_m where m is the line $x_2 = (\sqrt{3}/3)x_1$. (b) Use this matrix to find P', the image of the point $P(3, 7, 1)$ under this reflection. (c) Verify that m is the perpendicular bisector of $\overline{PP'}$.

3. Show that the product of a glide reflection with itself is a nonidentity translation.

4. Outline a proof of Theorem 3.27 similar to the outline given for the proof of Theorem 3.23 in Section 3.8.

5. Find a product of a translation, a rotation, and a reflection that maps $\triangle PQR$ to $\triangle P'Q'R'$ were $P(-2, 5, 1)$ $Q(-2, 7, 1)$, $R(-5, 5, 1)$, $P'(4, 3, 1)$, $Q'(6, 3, 1)$, and $R'(4, 0, 1)$.

6. Prove part I-B of Theorem 3.28.

7. Prove part II-A of Theorem 3.28.

8. Let R_a and R_b be reflections with axes a and b where $a \neq b$. Prove: $R_aR_b = R_bR_a$ if and only if a and b are perpendicular. [*Hint:* Use Theorem 3.28.]

9. Prove Theorem 3.29.

10. Show by diagramming an example, that the product of two distinct glide reflections can be a translation. (Be sure to indicate how a triangle is mapped under the glide reflections.)

11. Identify the following matrices as matrices of reflections or glide reflections. In each case find the axis.

$$(a) \begin{bmatrix} 0 & 1 & -1 \\ 1 & 0 & 1 \\ 0 & 0 & 1 \end{bmatrix} \qquad (b) \begin{bmatrix} 0 & 1 & 3 \\ 1 & 0 & 1 \\ 0 & 0 & 1 \end{bmatrix}$$

$$(c) \quad \frac{1}{25} \begin{bmatrix} -7 & -24 & -64 \\ -24 & 7 & -48 \\ 0 & 0 & 25 \end{bmatrix}$$

12. Show that if l and m are two parallel lines and n is the image of line l under a glide reflection with axis m, then l and n are also parallel.

13. Let P' be the image of P under a glide reflection with axis m. Show that m bisects the segment $\overline{PP'}$.

14. (a) Find the matrix of a glide reflection which maps $\overline{PQ}$ to $\overline{P'Q'}$ where $P(4, -2, 1)$, $Q(7, 2, 1)$, $P'(-3, -4, 1)$, and $Q'(0, 0, 1)$. [*Hint:* Use the result of Exercise 13.] (b) Is this glide reflection unique? Why? (c) Is there a unique glide reflection mapping P to P'? Why?

15. Prove: If line a intersects parallel lines b and c, then $R_c R_b R_a$ is a glide reflection. (This is part of case 4 in the proof of Theorem 3.30.)

16. Prove Theorem 3.31.

17. Prove Theorem 3.32.

18. Prove the corollary to Theorem 3.32.

19. Prove Theorem 3.33. [*Hint:* Assume there are two different isometries and use the corollary to Theorem 3.32 to obtain a contradiction.]

3.10 Frieze and Wallpaper Patterns

With our classification of isometries and the ability to express any isometry as a product of reflections, we now have the tools necessary to identify and compare *frieze patterns*. As indicated in Section 3.4, frieze patterns are "border" patterns made up of a single motif repeated over and over. The frieze pattern shown in that section and in Figure 3.14 is reprinted from Audsley's (1968) *Design and Patterns from Historic Ornament*. In practice, such patterns obviously are of finite length or cycle and are bounded. However, the mathematical

FIGURE 3.14 A frieze pattern.

versions extend infinitely far in both directions and are characterized as being invariant under some "shortest" translation. In fact, each frieze pattern is invariant under a group of symmetries known as a *frieze group*. The precise definition of frieze group and frieze pattern is repeated below:

Definition 3.10
A group of transformations that keep a given line c invariant and whose translations form an infinite cyclic subgroup[15] is a *frieze group with axis c* and denoted $\mathcal{G}_c$. A point set that remains invariant under a frieze group with axis c is called a *frieze pattern with axis c* and denoted $\mathcal{F}_c$. (*Note*: A frieze group is the symmetry group of the associated frieze pattern.)

3.10.1   Classifying Frieze Patterns

We will assume that all frieze patterns have the same axis c. Then our task is the identification and classification of all possible frieze patterns $\mathcal{F}$. As often the case in mathematics, frieze patterns are distinguished on the basis of their structure. This means we disregard the motif used in the frieze pattern and concentrate instead on comparing the associated frieze groups; that is, we will consider frieze patterns to be equivalent if their symmetry groups are isomorphic. In effect, we are disregarding design and scale and concentrating instead on the underlying construction.

---

[15]That is, a group of an infinite number of distinct translations where each translation $T = \tau^n$ for some integer n and translation τ. τ is said to "generate the group."

As we will see, every frieze group is generated by a small finite set of transformations. So to compare frieze groups, it is sufficient to compare their generating transformations. Since each frieze group contains a "shortest" translation τ that "generates" all the other translations in the frieze group, we will assume that each frieze group $\mathcal{F}$ has the same generating translation τ. However, frieze groups can also contain symmetries other than translations. And it is on the basis of these other symmetries that frieze groups are classified.

Because the structure of an individual frieze pattern is dependent on the length of τ, it follows that all symmetries in the associated frieze group must preserve distance and are therefore isometries. So we begin looking for frieze groups by identifying finitely generated groups of isometries that keep a line c invariant and include a single generating translation τ. Once we have determined all permissible non-translational isometries, we consider groups generated by combinations of these with τ. By determining which point and line reflections belong to each frieze group, we can find the points and lines of symmetry of the associated frieze pattern. To avoid confusion between point and line reflections, we will use the term "half-turn" and the symbol H_P to designate the point reflection with center P. The choice of P and other points relevant to the investigation of a specific frieze group $\mathcal{G}$ will be based on the algorithm in Table 3.5.

The exercises below and the following commentary justify the classification of frieze groups with axis c given in Table 3.6. This classification makes use of the reference points described in Table 3.5

TABLE 3.5   Reference Points in Frieze Patterns $\mathcal{F}_c$ with Frieze Group $\mathcal{G}$.

$$P = \begin{cases} \text{the center of a half-turn} & \text{if } \mathcal{G} \text{ contains half-turns, otherwise} \\ \text{the intersection of } p \text{ and } c & \text{if } \mathcal{G} \text{ contains a reflection in } p, \\ & p \perp c, \text{ otherwise} \\ \text{a chosen point on } c \end{cases}$$

$P_n = \tau^n(P)$ Note $P_0 = P$

$M_0 = $ the midpoint of $\overline{P_0 P_1}$

$M_n = \tau^n(M)$ Note: M_n is the midpoint of $\overline{P_n P_{n+1}}$
(Fig. 3.15)

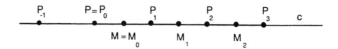

FIGURE 3.15 Location of reference points.

TABLE 3.6 Classification of Frieze Groups.

A.	*Containing only direct isometries*
	$\mathcal{G}_1 = \langle \tau \rangle$
	$\mathcal{G}_2 = \langle \tau, H_P \rangle$
B.	Containing reflections but no half-turns
	$\mathcal{G}_3 = \langle \tau, R_c \rangle$
	$\mathcal{G}_4 = \langle \tau, R_p \rangle$
C.	*Others containing indirect isometries*
	$\mathcal{G}_5 = \langle \tau, H_P, R_c \rangle$
	$\mathcal{G}_6 = \langle \tau, H_P, R_q \rangle$, line $q \neq p$, $q \perp c$
	$\mathcal{G}_7 = \langle \sigma \rangle$, σ is a glide reflection, $\sigma^2 = \tau$.

and notation such as $G = \langle \tau_1, \tau_2, R_c \rangle$ to indicate which symmetries generate the group. In this particular case, there are three generators, namely, two translations and a line reflection, that is, each element $T \in G$ is a product of powers of τ_1, τ_2, and R_c.

Exercises

In these exercises you are to assume that (1) k and n are always integers, (2) the groups $\mathcal{G}_i$ are the groups defined in Table 3.6, and (3) τ is the "shortest" generating translation of $\mathcal{G}_i$.

1. Prove that the only nontranslation symmetries in a frieze group with axis c are half-turns with centers on c, the reflection R_c, reflections in lines perpendicular to c, and glide reflections with axis c.

2. Explain why the group $\mathcal{G}_1$ (see Table 3.6) contains only translations.

3. Explain why the frieze pattern $\mathcal{F}_1$ associated with $\mathcal{G}_1$ has no points or lines of symmetry nor any axes of glide symmetry.

4. Show that if A, B are points on c, then $H_B H_A$ is a translation along c.

5. Explain why $\mathcal{G}_2$ contains only symmetries of the form τ^n and $\tau^n H_P$. [*Hint:* Explain why $H_P \tau = \tau H_P$.]

6. Prove that $\tau^n H_P$ is a half-turn.

7. Verify that the center of the half-turn $\tau^{2k} H_P$ is P_k, while the center of $\tau^{2k+1} H_P$ is M_k.

8. Explain why the frieze pattern $\mathcal{F}_2$ associated with $\mathcal{G}_2$ has no lines of symmetry or axes of glide symmetry, but does have points of symmetry. Where are these points of symmetry?

9. Show that if the half-turn H_C (where $C \neq P$) is a symmetry in a frieze group with axis c then either $C = P_k$, or $C = M_k$ for some k. [*Hint:* Explain why $H_C H_P(P) = P_n$ for some n and apply H_C to both sides of this equation.]

10. Use the previous results to explain why $\mathcal{G}_1$ and $\mathcal{G}_2$ are the only frieze groups containing no indirect isometries.

11. Explain why a frieze group that contains no half-turns cannot contain both reflections R_c and R_p.

12. Prove: If T is a translation along c, then $R_c T = T R_c$.

13. Explain why $\mathcal{G}_3$ contains only symmetries of the form τ^n and $\tau^n R_c$.

14. Explain why the frieze pattern $\mathcal{F}_3$ associated with $\mathcal{G}_3$ has c as a line of symmetry but no points of symmetry.

15. Prove: If T is a translation along c and p is a line perpendicular to c, then $R_p T = T^{-1} R_p$.

16. Explain why $\mathcal{G}_4$ contains only symmetries of the form τ^n and $\tau^n R_p$.

17. Prove that $\tau^n R_p$ is a reflection in a line perpendicular to c.

18. Verify that the axis of $\tau^{2k} R_p$ is perpendicular to c at P_k and the axis of $\tau^{2k+1} R_p$ is perpendicular to c at M_k.

19. Explain why the frieze pattern $\mathcal{F}_4$ associated with $\mathcal{G}_4$ has a line perpendicular to c as a line of symmetry but no point of symmetry.

20. Prove: If R_q is an element of a frieze group $\mathcal{G}$ with axis c where $q \neq p$ is a line perpendicular to c at point Q, then Q is either P_k or M_k for some k. [*Hint:* Show that $R_q R_p = \tau^n$ and so $R_q R_p(P) = P_n$ for some n, and apply R_q to both sides of the second equation.]

21. Explain why $\mathcal{G}_3$ and $\mathcal{G}_4$ are the only frieze groups containing reflections but no half-turns. [*Hint:* Use the results of previous exercises.]

22. Name the frieze groups for each of the frieze patterns in Figure 3.16.

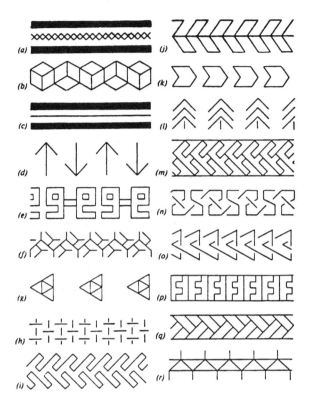

FIGURE 3.16 Examples of frieze patterns.

The exercises above investigated four of the seven possible frieze groups—those consisting of only direct isometries and those containing reflections, but no half-turns. The procedure for obtaining the three remaining frieze groups (two generated by both half-turns and reflections and one generated by only a glide reflection) is similar to that used above. We will settle for a brief description of each of these three frieze groups and their associated frieze patterns. A more comprehensive description is given in Martin [1982b, Chapter 10].

$\mathcal{G}_5 = \langle \tau, H_P, R_c \rangle$: Since $H_P R_c = R_p R_c R_c = R_p$, the reflection R_p is in $\mathcal{G}_5$. $\mathcal{G}_5$ also includes elements of the form $\tau^n R_c$, which are glide reflections mapping P to P_n. Other elements are $\tau^{2k} R_p$ and $\tau^{2k+1} R_p$, reflections in lines perpendicular to c at P_k and M_k, respectively. The associated frieze pattern $\mathcal{F}_5$ has a point of symmetry. It also has the axis c and a line perpendicular to c as lines of symmetry.

TABLE 3.7 Frieze Patterns and Their Symmetries.

| | | Type of Symmetry | | |
| | | Center | Perpendicular | Glide |
Frieze Patterns	Point	Line	Line	Reflection
$\mathcal{F}_1$ LLLLLLL				
$\mathcal{F}_2$ NNNNNNN	X			
$\mathcal{F}_3$ DDDDDDD		X		X
$\mathcal{F}_4$ VVVVVVV			X	
$\mathcal{F}_5$ HHHHHHH	X	X	X	X
$\mathcal{F}_6$ ΛVΛVΛVΛ	X		X	X
$\mathcal{F}_7$ LΓLΓLΓL				X

$\mathcal{G}_6 = \langle \tau, H_P, R_q \rangle$: To obtain a frieze group different from $\mathcal{G}_5$, R_q must be a reflection in a line perpendicular to c at a point Q distinct from the points P_k and M_k. As Martin shows, the point Q must be the midpoint of $\overline{PM_k}$ for some k. The associated frieze pattern has a point of symmetry where the line of symmetry is perpendicular to the center.

$\mathcal{G}_7 = \langle \sigma \rangle$: $\mathcal{G}_7$ is generated by the glide reflection σ where $\sigma^2 = \tau$. Since $\mathcal{G}_7$ contains no reflections or half-turns, the associated frieze pattern, $\mathcal{F}_7$ has no point of symmetry and no line of symmetry. Unlike $\mathcal{G}_1$ it does remain invariant under a glide reflection.

The frieze patterns associated with all seven frieze groups along with their types symmetry are displayed in Table 3.7. An example of each is shown in Figure 3.16 (reprinted from Martin, p. 84).

3.10.2 An Introduction to Wallpaper Patterns

Just as frieze patterns remain invariant under a group generated by one translation, there are *wallpaper patterns* that remain invariant under a group generated by two independent translations, that is, translations along nonparallel lines. The symmetry group defining a particular wallpaper pattern must also contain a finite subgroup of isometries known as a *point group*.[16] A consideration of the possible

---

[16]That is, there is a specific point P invariant under each isometry in the group.

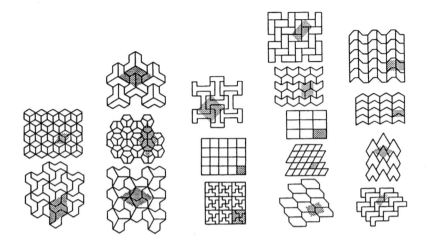

FIGURE 3.17 Examples of wallpaper patterns.

rotations in these point subgroups demonstrates that n-fold rotation symmetries are restricted to $n = 2, 3, 4, 6$ (see Exercise 23). Since the classification of wallpaper patterns according to their symmetry groups is a two-dimensional version of the procedure used by crystallographers to classify crystals, this limitation on n has become known as the *crystallographic restriction*. This restriction leads to the conclusion that there are exactly 17 possible wallpaper patterns as depicted by samples in Fig. 3.17 where these can be categorized according to the largest n for which they have n-fold rotation symmetry as listed in Table 3.8. More detailed information on these patterns and their classification is available in Martin [1982b, Chapter 11] and in Schattschneider [1978].

TABLE 3.8 Wallpaper Patterns.

Number of Patterns	Largest n for n-Fold Symmetry
5	$n = 2$
3	$n = 3$
3	$n = 4$
2	$n = 6$
4	None

Exercises

23. *Derivation of the crystallographic restriction:*

   a. Use the following procedure to explain why a pattern cannot have n-fold symmetry for $n > 6$.

   Assume there is such a pattern with n-fold symmetry and let $\theta = 360°/n$. Let P be a center of n-fold symmetry in such a pattern and let $Q = \tau(P)$ where τ is the generating translation of shortest length. (1) Explain why $Q' = R_{P,\theta}(Q)$ is also a center of n-fold symmetry; (2) compare the distance between Q and Q' with that between P and Q; and (3) show that $T_{\overrightarrow{QQ'}}$ is yet another symmetry of the pattern.

   b. Use the following similar procedure to explain why a pattern cannot have 5-fold symmetry.

   Assume there is such a pattern with 5-fold symmetry and let $\theta = 360°/5 = 72°$. Let P be a center of 5-fold symmetry in such a pattern and let $Q = \tau(P)$ where τ is the generating translation of shortest length. (1) Explain why $Q' = R_{P,\theta}(Q)$ and $P' = R_{Q,-\theta}(P)$ are also centers of 5-fold symmetry; (2) compare the distance between P' and Q' with that between P and Q; and (3) show that $T_{\overrightarrow{P'Q'}}$ is yet another symmetry of the pattern.

24. For each pattern shown in Figure 3.17 determine the largest n for which the pattern has n-fold symmetry. Note that there are 4 patterns without n-fold symmetry for any n.

3.11 Exploring Plane Tilings*

Equipment and Materials Needed

- Patterns for an equilateral triangle, a square, a regular pentagon, and a regular hexagon (all with the same edge length).
- Many of these activities can also be carried out using dynamic geometry software. Specific instructions for *Cabri Geometry II* and *Geometer's Sketchpad* can be found at
  `http://www.stolaf.edu/people/cederj/geotext/info.htm`.

Introduction

Whereas the examination of frieze and wallpaper patterns often begins with a consideration of possible symmetry groups and then investigates "designs" induced by the groups from a given motif, the usual procedure for tilings begins with a determination of the tile shapes that can be used to cover the plane and then considers the symmetries of the resultant tiling. Since the study of tilings begins with "concrete" tiles, the initial study of tiling is best done with hands-on exploration and provides another way to illustrate isometries and symmetry groups.

Definition 3.24

A *tiling*, or *tessellation*, of the plane is a covering of the plane with congruent copies of one or more *prototiles* so there are no gaps or overlaps (except at edges). Copies of the prototiles are called *tiles* and a point at which three or more tiles meet is called a *vertex* of the tiling.

Definition 3.25

If all the tiles in a tiling are copies of one prototile, the tiling is *monohedral*; if the tiles in a tiling are copies of exactly two different prototiles, the tiling is *dihedral*. If a monohedral tiling has a regular polygon as its prototile, the tiling is called *regular*. If a tiling has two or more distinct regular polygons as its prototiles, and if at each vertex in the tiling a circuit can be made that will encounter the same sequence of polygon types, the tiling is called *semiregular*.

Tilings or Patterns?

As indicated by the definitions, the prototiles for tilings are often polygons and the least complicated tilings use a single regular polygon as a prototile. However, with increasing complexity of the prototiles, the distinction between tilings and patterns becomes less clear. Although the term *tiling* has a commonly accepted definition as given above, the term *pattern* does not. In fact, as Grünbaum and Shephard indicate in *Tilings and Patterns*, "There seems to be not a single instance in the [mathematical] literature of a meaningful definition of 'pattern' that is, in any sense, useful." (pp. 4–5) Instead they use the informal description of patterns as "designs repeating some motif in a more or less systematic manner." (p. 1)

The beginning of a mathematical theory of tilings and patterns is generally considered to be the enumeration of the crystallographic groups in the late 19th century (p. 261). But without the crystallographic restrictions leading to wallpaper patterns, there are numerous other possible plane patterns. And as of 1987, Grünbaum and Shephard indicate that there is no known characterization of the possible symmetry groups of patterns (p. 218).

3.11.1   Regular Tilings of the Euclidean Plane

We will begin the study of tilings of the Euclidean plane by investigating those that are regular, that is, consist of congruent copies of a single regular polygon.

Activities

1. Show that the measures of each interior angle in a regular n_i-gon, that is, a regular polygon with n_i sides, is given by

$$\text{For regular } n_i\text{-gons:} \qquad A = 180\left(1 - \frac{2}{n_i}\right) \qquad (A)$$

2. For a regular n-gon to serve as a prototile for a regular tiling of the plane, it is necessary that there be some positive integer k such that exactly k copies of the n-gon fit around a point in the plane without gaps or overlaps. Use the formula found above to determine all possible values of n for which this is true. For each value of n you find, name the corresponding value of k.

3. For each value of n for which there is a possible regular tiling, carry out the following activities. Label each construction using a title that indicates the value of n.

   a. Use a regular n-gon as a prototile together with isometries of the Euclidean plane to create a two-dimensional tiling "patch," that is, a region covered with several adjacent strips of tiles where each strip contains at least three tiles. Color your tiling with as few colors (or shadings) as possible so that adjacent tiles have different colors.

b. List a minimal set of isometries that could be used (with repetition) to create a complete regular tiling of the plane with this n-gon. For each isometry you list, give an exact description, indicating a defining vector for translations, a center and angle for rotations, etc. Be sure to include labels on your construction for any points, lines, etc. used in the description of your isometries.

c. Choose and label a point P in the center of one of your tiles in the tiling. List all the symmetries that keep P invariant. Give specific descriptions of each and show that the set of all these symmetries constitutes a finite group.

d. Show that your tiling also has point symmetry groups where the *symmetry point* is not in the center of a tile. Describe the location of such possible symmetry points, and compare these groups with the group you found in the previous activity.

4. The following problem[17] relates the frieze groups of Section 3.10 to symmetry groups of tilings:

a. For each of the seven frieze groups, find a monohedral tiling with this group as its symmetry group.

b. Determine for which frieze groups it is possible to require that the prototile in a monohedral tiling have as its symmetry group: (i) a cyclic group of order 2; (ii) a dihedral group of order 2; (iii) a dihedral group of order 4; (iv) a cyclic group of order 3.

---

[17]This problem is based on a problem in Grünbaum and Shephard (p. 45).

3.11.2 Semiregular Tilings of the Euclidean Plane

A *semiregular tiling* uses two or more distinct regular polygons as prototiles with the same arrangement of polygon shapes at each vertex. To represent semiregular tilings, it is customary to use ordered tuple notation to list the values of n for each n-gon surrounding a vertex; so, for example, the label $(3, 4, 6, 4)$ represents a semiregular tiling where each vertex is surrounded by a triangle, two squares, and a hexagon. It also indicates that a circuit around any vertex in this tiling can be found that begins with a triangle and continues by encountering, in order, a square, a hexagon, and a square. As you may have already realized, there are several possible ordered tuples that can be used to represent the same semiregular tiling depending on the n-gon with which the circuit begins. To eliminate some of this ambiguity, it is customary to begin the ordered tuple with the smallest value of n; furthermore, we will avoid concerns about orientation, that is, we will not distinguish between circuits made in clockwise or counterclockwise directions. The activities below lead to a determination of ordered tuples that represent actual semiregular tilings.

Activities

5. Use Equation (A) from Activity 1 to show that the requirement that k regular n_i-gons $(i = 1, \ldots, k)$ fit together around a vertex without gaps or overlaps leads to

$$\text{For } k \text{ regular } n_i\text{-gons} \qquad \frac{(k-2)}{2} = \frac{1}{n_1} + \frac{1}{n_2} + \cdots + \frac{1}{n_k} \quad (B)$$
$$\text{to surround a vertex:}$$

6. Verify that the ordered 4-tuple $(3, 4, 6, 4)$ satisfies Equation (B) and construct a tiling "patch" containing at least 3 vertices surrounded by the indicated regular polygons.

7. In a semiregular tiling, show that the smallest possible value of k in Equation (B) is 3 while the largest possible value is 5.

8. If $k = 3$ explain why $3 \leq n_1 \leq 5$ (recall that n_1 is the smallest of the n_i.).

9. What must be true about the values of n_1 for $k = 4$? $k = 5$?
10. For each value of k $(k = 3, 4, 5)$, find as many k-tuples as you can containing values of n_i that satisfy Equation (B). Note: For each value of k, you must list values for n_i $i = 1, 2, \ldots, k$ where at least two values of n_i must differ.
11. One of the $k = 4$ solutions you found for Equation (B) should consist of two "3's" and two "6's". How many different semiregular tilings appear to be possible for this solution and what *ordered* 4-tuples represent these solutions? Explain.
12. Which other solutions found above actually represent more than one possible semiregular tiling?
13. Make a complete list of all *ordered* k-tuple solutions to Equation (B) that represent distinct possible semiregular tilings. (Note: There should be three 5-tuples, six 4-tuples and nine 3-tuples.)
14. Draw an equilateral triangle; and by considering the tiling around each of its vertices, demonstrate that a semiregular tiling represented by $(3, x, y)$ is impossible unless $x = y$. Which ordered 3-tuples does this eliminate from the list you just created?
15. Using reasoning similar to that in Activity 14, determine which ordered 3-tuples of the type $(x, 5, y)$ represent impossible semiregular tilings.
16. Now explain why semiregular tilings represented by the ordered tuples (3,3,4,12), (3,4,3,12), (3,3,6,6), and (3,4,4,6) are also impossible. [*Hint:* Draw an equilateral triangle, $\triangle ABC$, and consider how the n-gons represented by the last 3 entries in these ordered tuples could be placed around each of its 3 vertices.]
17. List the eight remaining ordered k-tuples and illustrate tile "patches" for at least three of these eight. (Note: Each of the remaining eight ordered tuples represents a possible semiregular tiling.)

3.11.3 Regular Tilings of the Hyperbolic Plane

The determination of all possible regular and semiregular tiling of the Euclidean plane is based on one of the most important theorems of Euclidean geometry, namely that the angle sum of any triangle is 180°. As you have seen, this theorem is not true in the non-Euclidean geometries and numerous significant differences of these geometries from Euclidean geometry can be traced directly to the variance in triangle angle sums. The activities below show how tiling the hyperbolic plane reflects this difference. Those interested in further exploration of tiling in the Poincaré model of the hyperbolic plane or in the spherical model of the elliptic plane should consult Singer, *Geometry: Plane and Fancy* (1997).

Activities

18. Modify Equation (A) from Activity 1 to determine an upper bound for the measure of individual angles in a regular n-gon in the hyperbolic plane.
19. In the hyperbolic plane, what is the smallest number of congruent equilateral triangles, that is, regular 3-gons, that can be used to surround a point without gaps or overlaps? Is there a largest possible number? Explain.
20. What do your conclusions in the previous two items tell you about the number of different possible tilings of the hyperbolic plane with equilateral triangles?
21. What is the smallest number of regular 4-gons that can be used to surround a point in the hyperbolic plane?
22. Earlier you found that the only regular n-gons that can be used to generate a regular tiling of the Euclidean plane are those for $n = 3, 4, 6$. Does this same restriction hold in the hyperbolic plane? Explain.

3.11.4 Periodic versus Aperiodic Tilings

The previous activities are only a brief introduction to the vast topic of tilings. Tilings can involve prototiles that vary vastly from convex polygons, demonstrating that there can be a wide variation in prototile shapes. Moreover, it is not necessary that tilings exhibit the "periodicity" found in those examined so far. A tiling is said to be *periodic* if one of its symmetries is a translation. Since translations are used to create tilings from each of the patches generated in the previous activities in this section, translations are among the symmetries of these tilings. Strange as it seems, there are also tilings for which there are *no* translation symmetries.

Definition 3.26
A tiling is *periodic* if there is at least one nonidentity translation that keeps the tiling invariant. A tiling that is not periodic is said to be *aperiodic*.

An aperiodic tiling of great current interest among mathematicians and scientists is that known as a *Penrose* tiling. In the 1970s while trying to tile the Euclidean plane with regular pentagons, Roger Penrose discovered that by using tiles that were copies of two different rhombus-shaped prototiles and by specifying a set of rules for matching marks placed on these tiles, he could generate an aperiodic tiling. Remarkably these tilings exhibit 5-fold symmetry, a symmetry thought not to be possible in a plane tiling, and they appear to be related to the puzzling arrangement of atoms in materials known as quasi-crystals. Further introductory information on Penrose tiling is available in Gardner's *Penrose Tiles to Trapdoor Ciphers*, (1989). A comprehensive treatment of tilings of all types is contained in the definitive work in this area, Grünbaum and Shephard, *Tilings and Patterns* (1987).

3.11.5 Escher-type Tilings (Optional)

The Dutch graphic artist M.C. Escher produced a large number of fanciful tilings. "Escher-type" tilings can be created by starting with regular tilings of the plane and altering the basic shapes using isometries. Although there are several very nice software programs designed specifically to create these patterns, the patterns can also be created with paper and pencil or with dynamic geometry software.[18] Below you will find directions for creating prototiles for these tilings from regular polygons.[19] Both the paper and pencil and dynamic software techniques provide wonderful examples of the use of isometries.

Activities

If you are using paper and pencil to carry out the following activities you may find it helpful to (1) trace replacement paths onto a second set of paper; (2) place the second sheet under the first and apply to this second sheet the required slide, turn, or flip; and (3) trace the resulting path back onto the original paper. "Hide" objects as required by erasing them.

23. *Creating a prototile from a square using translations*

   a. Construct a square[20] with side length measuring approximately 2 inches. Label your square $ABCD$ in counterclockwise order.

   b. Create a new path from A to B that consists of a curve or at least two noncollinear segments. Then hide segment $\overline{AB}$ (Do not hide points A and B.).

   c. Use the translation $T_{\overrightarrow{AD}}$ to translate your new path to create a congruent new path from D to C. Then hide segment $\overline{CD}$ (but not points C and D).

   d. Before continuing, make a second copy of the current construction for use in Activity 25.

   e. If desired, you can similarly replace segment $\overline{AD}$ and translate it to create a "parallel" path replacing segment $\overline{BC}$.

   f. Once you have a prototile shape you like, color it and hide the point labels.

   g. Use your prototile to generate a tiling patch.

---

[18]A list of tiling software and directions for dynamic geometry software can be found at `http://www.stolaf.edu/people/cederj/geotext/info.htm`.

[19]More detailed directions are available in Ranucci, E.R., and Teeters, J.E. Creating Escher-Type Drawings, *Mathematics Teacher*, April '74, Vol. 64 No. 4.

[20]This procedure can also be used on tilings of parallelograms or hexagons.

h. Find a minimal set of isometries that could be used to generate a complete tiling with your prototile.

24. *Creating a prototile from an equilateral triangle using rotations*

a. In a new sketch, construct equilateral triangle $\triangle ABC$ with approximately 2 inch sides. Again, label your triangle in counterclockwise order.

b. Construct a path from A to B that consists of a curve or at least two noncollinear segments.

c. Before continuing, make a copy of your triangle for use in Activity 26.

d. Hide segment $\overline{AB}$ and rotate your path about point A to create an image path joining A with C. Hide segment $\overline{AC}$.

e. Now construct M, the midpoint of segment $\overline{BC}$.

f. Construct a path from B to M that consists of a curve or at least two noncollinear segments and rotate this about point M to create a path from M to C.

g. Hide segment $\overline{BC}$ and all point labels, and color your prototile.

h. Use your prototile to generate a tiling patch.

i. Find a minimal set of isometries that could be used to generate a complete tiling with your prototile.

25. *Creating a prototile from a square using reflections*

a. Begin with the single modified square[21] saved in Activity 23.

b. Construct segment $\overline{BD}$. If either of your paths from A to B or from C to D cross segment $\overline{BD}$, you'll need to modify them so they do not cross.

c. Now reflect the paths from A to B and C to D in line BD, creating paths from B to C and A to D.

d. Hide segments $\overline{AD}$, $\overline{BC}$, and $\overline{BD}$ and the labels for all your points, and color your prototile.

e. Use your prototile to generate a tiling patch.

f. Find a minimal set of isometries that could be used to generate a complete tiling with your prototile.

26. *Creating a prototile from an equilateral triangle using glide reflections*

---

[21] This procedure can also be used on rhombi.

a. Begin with the single modified equilateral triangle[22] saved in Activity 24.

b. Construct D, the midpoint of side $\overline{AB}$ and E, the midpoint of side $\overline{AC}$.

c. Apply the glide reflection $G_{\overrightarrow{DE}}$ to the path joining A and B to create a path joining A and C.

d. Hide segments $\overline{AB}$ and $\overline{AC}$ as well as unneeded intermediate constructions

e. If desired, modify side $\overline{BC}$ as follows: Construct F, the midpoint of segment $\overline{BC}$, and connect C and F with a new path. Rotate this new path around F to create a path from F to B. Then hide segment $\overline{BC}$ and the point labels and color your prototile.

f. Use your prototile to generate a tiling patch.

g. Find a minimal set of isometries that could be used to generate a complete tiling with your prototile.

3.12 Similarity Transformations

In previous sections of Chapter 3, we studied Euclidean geometry by exploring the invariant properties of the Euclidean plane under the group of distance preserving transformations known as isometries. In this section we will determine which properties of the Euclidean plane remain invariant under affine transformations that preserve ratios of distance. The geometry determined by these transformations is called *similarity geometry*.

Definition 3.27
A *similarity with ratio r* is an affine transformation T of the Euclidean plane such that for each pair of points P and Q, $d(T(P), T(Q)) = rd(P, Q)$ for some nonzero real number $r > 0$.

---

[22]This procedure can also be used on isosceles triangles.

Clearly, every isometry is a similarity with ratio ± 1, and thus isometries have all the properties of similarities, The converse is not true. However, since similarities are affine transformations of V^* they also have 3×3 matrix representations with corresponding point and line equations $X' = AX$ and $ku' = uA^{-1}$, respectively (see Section 3.6). The matrix form of a similarity can be obtained by a method analogous to that used in the proof of Theorem 3.7. As in the case of isometries, there are direct and indirect similarities and the set of all similarities forms a group.

Theorem 3.34
A similarity with ratio r has one of the following matrix representations:

$$
\begin{array}{cc}
\text{(Direct)} & \text{(Indirect)} \\
\begin{bmatrix} a_{11} & a_{12} & a_{13} \\ -a_{12} & a_{11} & a_{23} \\ 0 & 0 & 1 \end{bmatrix} & \begin{bmatrix} a_{11} & a_{12} & a_{13} \\ a_{12} & -a_{11} & a_{23} \\ 0 & 0 & 1 \end{bmatrix}
\end{array}
$$

where $a_{11}^2 + a_{12}^2 = r^2$.

Theorem 3.35
The set of similarities forms a group of which the set of isometries is a subgroup.

Figures that correspond to each other under a similarity are said to be *similar*. The verification that similar triangles do indeed have angles of the same measure and sides of proportional measure is nearly a replication of the proofs of comparable theorems for congruent triangles (see Section 3.7).

Definition 3.28
Two sets of points α and β are *similar*, denoted $\alpha \sim \beta$, if β is the image of α under a similarity.

Theorem 3.36
Let u' and v' be the images of lines u and v under a similarity. If the similarity is direct then $m\angle(u'v') = m\angle(u, v)$. If the similarity is indirect then $m\angle(u', v') = -m\angle(u, v)$.

Theorem 3.37
If $\triangle PQR \sim \triangle P'Q'R'$, then there exists an $r > 0$ such that $m(P'Q') = r(m(PQ))$, $m(Q'R') = r(m(QR))$, $m(R'P') = r(m(RP))$, $m\angle P'Q'R' = \pm m(\angle PQR)$, $m\angle Q'R'P' = \pm m\angle QRP$, and $m\angle R'P'Q' = \pm m\angle RPQ$.

To verify the converse of this last theorem, it is necessary to determine more about the behavior of similarities. Fortunately, we need only consider one particular type of similarity.

Definition 3.29
A dilation with center C and ratio r, denoted $D_{C,r}$ is a direct similarity with invariant point C that maps any point P to a point P' such that $\overrightarrow{CP'} = r\overrightarrow{CP}$ (see Fig. 3.18) for some nonzero real number r. Dilations are also called dilatations or central similarities.

Notice that unlike the definition of a similarity, the definition of a dilation includes the case where $r < 0$. If $r < 0$, the direction of $\overrightarrow{CP'}$ is opposite that of $\overrightarrow{CP}$, but it is always the case that $d(C, P') = |r|\, d(C, P)$. Thus, the dilation $D_{C,r}$ is a similarity with ratio $|r|$. Using this definition, the invariant points and lines of a dilation can be determined (see Exercise 9) and the matrix representation can be found.

Theorem 3.38
Under a dilation $D_{C,r}$, the point C and each line incident with C are invariant.

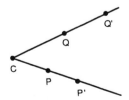

FIGURE 3.18 Dilation with center C mapping P to P'.

Theorem 3.39

A *dilation with vector* $O(0, 0, 1)$ *and ratio* r *has matrix representation*

$$\begin{bmatrix} r & 0 & 0 \\ 0 & r & 0 \\ 0 & 0 & 1 \end{bmatrix}$$

A *dilation with center* $C(c_1, c_2, 1)$ *has matrix representation*

$$\begin{bmatrix} r & 0 & c_1(1-r) \\ 0 & r & c_2(1-r) \\ 0 & 0 & 1 \end{bmatrix}$$

Proof

(Outline) For the first case, the requirement that a direct similarity with matrix $A = [a_{ij}]$ keep $O(0, 0, 1)$ invariant implies that $a_{13} = a_{23} = 0$. The requirement that $\overrightarrow{OX'} = r\overrightarrow{OX}$ implies that any point $X(x, 0, 1)$ on the line $[0, 1, 0]$ must map to a point $X'(rx, 0, 1)$. This yields $a_{12} = 0$ and $a_{11} = r$.

The second case can be verified after noting that $D_{C,r} = TD_{O,r}T^{-1}$ where T is the translation mapping O to C. ∎

Using this matrix representation we can now determine the effect of a dilation on lines that are not incident with the dilation's center.

Theorem 3.40

If $D_{C,r}$ is a dilation with $r \neq 1$ and m is a line not incident with C, then $D_{C,r}(m) = m'$ is a distinct line parallel to m.

Proof

The line equation of this dilation requires the matrix of $(D_{C,r})^{-1}$. Since this transformation is also a dilation with center C and ratio $r' = 1/r$ (see Exercise 11), its matrix representation is given by Theorem 3.39.

Using this matrix in the line equation of the dilation, we can find m', the image of the line $m[m_1, m_2, m_3]$, as follows:

$$[m_1, m_2, m_3] \begin{bmatrix} r' & 0 & c_1(1-r') \\ 0 & r' & c_2(1-r') \\ 0 & 0 & 1 \end{bmatrix} = [r'm_1, r'm_2, m_3']$$

where $m_3' = m_1 c_1(1-r') + m_2 c_2(1-r') + m_3$.

Clearly, m' is equal to m if and only if $m_3' = r'm_3$, that is, if and only if

$$m_1 c_1(1-r') + m_2 c_2(1-r') + m_3 = r'm_3$$

or

$$m_1 c_1(1-r') + m_2 c_2(1-r') + m_3(1-r') = 0$$

or

$$m_1 c_1 + m_2 c_2 + m_3 = 0 \quad \text{since } r' \neq 1;$$

but this is exactly the condition that makes m incident with C. Thus, if m is not incident with C, m' is necessarily a distinct line parallel to m. ∎

Given the center C, points P and P' (P' on line CP), it is now possible to construct the image of any other point under a dilation $D_{C,r}$ that maps P to P'. This construction demonstrates that a dilation is uniquely determined by its center together with a point and its image.

Case 1: Q is not on CP (Fig. 3.19). Q' will be the point of intersection of line CQ and the line through P' parallel to PQ.

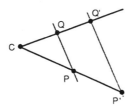

FIGURE 3.19 Finding Q', the image of Q, case 1.

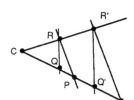

FIGURE 3.20 Finding Q', the image of Q, case 2.

Case 2: Q is on CP (Fig. 3.20). We can find the image of a point R not on CP as before and then use R and R' in place of P and P' in case 1.

The matrix representation of dilations can be used to characterize the similarities in terms of dilations and isometries (see Exercise 13).

Theorem 3.41
Every similarity can be expressed as the product of a dilation and an isometry.

With this characterization, it is possible to outline a proof of the converse of Theorem 3.37 similar to the outline given for Theorem 3.23 (see Exercise 15).

Theorem 3.42
If $\triangle PQR$ and $\triangle P'Q'R'$ are two triangles with $m(P'Q') = r(m(PQ))$, $m(Q'R') = r(m(QR))$, $m(R'P') = r(m(RP))$, and also $m\angle P'Q'R' = \pm m\angle PQR$, $m\angle Q'R'P' = \pm m\angle QRP$, and $m\angle R'P'Q' = \pm m\angle RPQ$, then there is a similarity mapping $\triangle PQR$ to $\triangle P'Q'R'$.

Another major result that follows directly from the proof of Theorem 3.41 has to with the increased freedom allowed by similarities. Whereas an isometry can always be found to map a point P to an arbitrary image point P', it is not possible to use an isometry to map a pair of points P and Q to a second arbitrary pair of points P' and Q' (why not?). Such a mapping *can* be accomplished with a similarity (see Exercise 17).

Theorem 3.43
There exist two similarities, one direct and one indirect, that map a pair of distinct points P and Q to a pair of corresponding points P' and Q'.

Exercises

1. Show that similarities preserve betweenness (see Definition 3.21).

2. Prove: If a similarity maps $\overline{PQ}$ and $\overline{RS}$ to $\overline{P'Q'}$ and $\overline{R'S'}$, respectively, and $d(P, Q) = s(d(R, S))$, then $d(P'Q') = s(d(R', S'))$. (This proves that similarities preserve ratios of distance.)

3. Prove Theorem 3.34.

4. Prove Theorem 3.35.

5. Prove Theorem 3.36.

6. Prove Theorem 3.37.

7. Let C, P, and P' be points with coordinates, $C(3, -2, 1)$, $P(1, 0, 1)$, and $P'(7, -6, 1)$. (a) Show that these three points are collinear. (b) Find the matrix of a dilation with center C that maps P to P'. (c) Find the image of lines $m[1, 1, -1]$ and $n[1, 1, 1]$ under this dilation.

8. Show that a rotation with angle $180°$ is a dilation.

9. Prove Theorem 3.38.

10. Complete the proof of Theorem 3.39 outlined in the text.

11. Show $(D_{C,r})^{-1} = D_{C,1/r}$

12. Prove that the *only* invariant point under a nonidentity dilation with center C is C itself, and the only invariant lines under such a dilation are lines through C.

13. Prove Theorem 3.41

14. Using the product of a translation, rotation, and dilation find a transformation that maps $\triangle PQR$ to $\triangle P'Q'R'$ where $P(3, 6, 1)$, $Q(-2, 5, 1)$, $R(-3, -1, 1)$, $P'(0, 0, 1)$, $Q'(2, -10, 1)$, $R'(14, -12, 1)$. [*Hint*: translate P to P' first.]

15. Outline a proof of Theorem 3.42.

16. Find matrices of two different similarities both of which map $P(1, 2, 1)$ and $Q(0, 0, 1)$ to $P'(2, 4, 1)$ and $Q'(-4, 2, 1)$, respectively. What is the image of $R(1, 1, 1)$ under each?

17. Prove Theorem 3.43.

3.13 Affine Transformations

In Section 3.12, similarities were shown to be generalizations of isometries. In this section we will continue this process of generalizing the isometries by considering the unrestricted set of affine transformations of the Euclidean plane. For convenience, we will restate the definition of affine transformations (see Definition 3.16 for earlier version.). The geometry determined by these transformations is called *affine geometry*.

Definition 3.30
A one-to-one linear transformation T of R^3 is said to be an *affine transformation (of the Euclidean plane)*, or more concisely an *affinity*, if T maps points in the set $V^* = \{X(x_1, x_2, 1)\}$ to points in this same set, that is, if for all $X \in V^*$, $T(X) = X' \in V^*$.

In other words, the affinities are the transformations described in Section 3.6. There we discovered that affinities map points according to the matrix equation $X' = AX$ where

$$A = \begin{bmatrix} a_{11} & a_{12} & a_{13} \\ a_{21} & a_{22} & a_{23} \\ 0 & 0 & 1 \end{bmatrix} \quad \text{and} \quad |A| \neq 0.$$

We also noted that affinities preserve collinearity and map lines according to the matrix equations $ku' = uA^{-1}$. Theorem 3.4 can be reworded to state that the set of affinities form a group and Theorem 3.35 in Section 3.12 implies that the set of similarities forms a subgroup of the group of affinities.

Since similarities and isometries are specific types of affinities, any properties invariant under affinities are also invariant under similarities and isometries. One of the most important of these invariant properties is parallelism.

Theorem 3.44
If T is an affinity and m and n are parallel lines, then $T(m)$ is parallel to $T(n)$.

Proof

Assume $m[m_1, m_2, m_3]$ and $n[n_1, n_2, n_3]$ are parallel lines. Then there is a nonzero real number t such that $n_1 = tm_1$ and $n_2 = tm_2$. We can find $T(m)$, the image of line m under the affinity T with matrix A, using the line equation $k_1 m' = mB$ where $B = A^{-1}$. Specifically,

$$k_1 m' = [m_1, m_2, m_3] \begin{bmatrix} b_{11} & b_{12} & b_{13} \\ b_{21} & b_{22} & b_{23} \\ 0 & 0 & 1 \end{bmatrix}$$

or

$$[m_1', m_2', m_3'] = \frac{1}{k_1}[m_1 b_{11} + m_2 b_{21}, m_1 b_{12} + m_2 b_{22}, m_1 b_{13} + m_2 b_{23} + m_3]$$

Similarly,

$$[n_1', n_2', n_3'] = \frac{1}{k_2}[n_1 b_{11} + n_2 b_{21}, n_1 b_{12} + n_2 b_{22}, n_1 b_{13} + n_2 b_{23} + n_3]$$

Then, substituting $n_1 = tm_1$ and $n_2 = tm_2$ yields

$$n' = \frac{1}{k_2}[tm_1 b_{11} + tm_2 b_{21}, tm_1 b_{12} + tm_2 b_{22}, n_1 b_{13} + n_2 b_{23} + n_3]$$

or

$$n_i' = \frac{t}{k_2}(m_1 b_{1i} + m_2 b_{2i}) = \frac{tk_1}{k_2}m_i' \quad \text{for } i = 1, 2.$$

Thus, m' and n' are parallel. ∎

Clearly, general affinities do not preserve distance as do isometries, nor do they preserve ratios of distances as do similarities. However, they do preserve a more general ratio of distances known as a *segment division ratio*. This is verified by the proof of the next theorem (see Exercise 1).

Theorem 3.45

If T is an affinity and P, Q, and R are three distinct collinear points such that

$$\frac{d(Q, P)}{d(Q, R)} = k,$$

then

$$\frac{d(T(Q), T(P))}{d(T(Q), T(R))} = k.$$

We can use this theorem along with Definition 3.21 to show that affinities preserve betweenness of points. It then follows that affinities also preserve segments and their midpoints.

Theorem 3.46
If T is an affinity and P, Q, and R are three collinear points with P between Q and R, then T(P) is between T(Q) and T(R).

Proof
Since P is between Q and R, $d(Q, P) + d(P, R) = d(Q, R)$. Dividing each term of this equation by $d(Q, R)$ and letting $d(Q, P)/d(Q, R) = k$, gives $d(P, R)/d(Q, R) = 1 - k$. By Theorem 3.45, $d(Q', P')/d(Q', R') = k$ and $d(P', R')/d(Q', R') = 1 - k$ where $P' = T(P)$, and so on. Substitution then yields $d(P', R')/d(Q', R') = 1 - d(Q', P')/d(Q', R')$ or $d(Q', P') + d(P', R') = d(Q', R')$, so P' is between Q' and R'. ∎

Corollary
If T is an affinity and M is the midpoint of the segment with endpoints Q and R, then T(M) is the midpoint of the segment with endpoints T(Q) and T(R).

Proof
Merely let $k = \frac{1}{2}$ in the proof of Theorem 3.46. ∎

We can gain an intuitive understanding of the effect of affinities by considering two specific types known by the suggestive names of *shears* and *strains*.

Definition 3.31
A *shear with axis m*, denoted S_m, is an affinity that keeps m pointwise invariant and maps every other point P to a point P' so that the line PP' is parallel to m (Fig. 3.21).

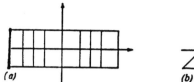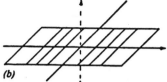

FIGURE 3.21 A shear with axis $x[0, 1, 0]$.

Theorem 3.47

The matrix representation of a shear with axis $x[0, 1, 0]$ is

$$\begin{bmatrix} 1 & j & 0 \\ 0 & 1 & 0 \\ 0 & 0 & 1 \end{bmatrix}$$

In general the matrix representation of a shear S_m can be found using $S_m = SS_xS^{-1}$ where S is a direct isometry mapping x to m, that is, $S(x) = m$.

Proof

Since S_x keeps each point on the line $x[0, 1, 0]$ invariant, the following equation must be true for all real numbers x_1:

$$\begin{bmatrix} a_{11} & a_{12} & a_{13} \\ a_{21} & a_{22} & a_{23} \\ 0 & 0 & 1 \end{bmatrix}\begin{bmatrix} x_1 \\ 0 \\ 1 \end{bmatrix} = \begin{bmatrix} x_1 \\ 0 \\ 1 \end{bmatrix}$$

Therefore, $a_{11}x_1 + a_{13} = x_1$ and $a_{21}x_1 + a_{23} = 0$, yielding $a_{11} = 1$, $a_{13} = 0$, $a_{21} = 0$, and $a_{23} = 0$. If $P(p_1, p_2, 1)$ is a point not on line $x[0, 1, 0]$ (so $p_2 \neq 0$), P must map to a point P' on the line through P parallel to line x. This line has coordinates $u[0, 1, -p_2]$, so P' must have coordinates $P'(p_1', p_2, 1)$ leading to the following equation

$$\begin{bmatrix} 1 & a_{12} & 0 \\ 0 & a_{22} & 0 \\ 0 & 0 & 1 \end{bmatrix}\begin{bmatrix} p_1 \\ p_2 \\ 1 \end{bmatrix} = \begin{bmatrix} p_1' \\ p_2 \\ 1 \end{bmatrix}$$

so $a_{22}p_2 = p_2$. Since $p_2 \neq 0$, this implies that $a_{22} = 1$. Therefore, the matrix does have the form given in the statement of the theorem.

The verification of the second part of the theorem is analogous to that used to prove similar results in previous theorems. ∎

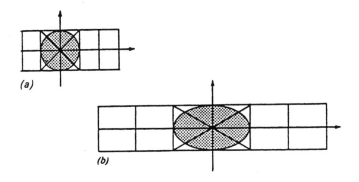

FIGURE 3.22 A strain with axis $y[1, 0, 0]$.

Strains are also defined in terms of a pointwise invariant line and the procedure used to determine their matrix representation is similar to that just used to find the matrix of a shear (see Exercise 4).

Definition 3.32
A *strain with axis* m, denoted T_m, keeps m pointwise invariant and maps every other point P to a point P' so that the line PP' is perpendicular to m (Fig. 3.22).

Theorem 3.48
The matrix representation of a strain with axis $x[0, 1, 0]$ is

$$\begin{bmatrix} 1 & 0 & 0 \\ 0 & k & 0 \\ 0 & 0 & 1 \end{bmatrix}$$

In general, the matrix representation of strain T_m can be found using $T_m = ST_xS^{-1}$ where S is a direct isometry mapping x to m, that is, $S(x) = m$.

Using shears and strains along with similarities, it is possible to obtain any affinity. In particular, we can obtain any affinity as a product of a shear S_x, a strain T_x, and a direct similarity.

Theorem 3.49
Any affinity can be written as the product of a shear, a strain, and a direct similarity.

Proof

We can verify this theorem by merely demonstrating that the following product does indeed yield the matrix of a general affinity as indicated:

$$\begin{bmatrix} a_{11} & a_{12} & a_{13} \\ a_{21} & a_{22} & a_{23} \\ 0 & 0 & 1 \end{bmatrix} = \begin{bmatrix} a_{11} & -a_{21} & a_{13} \\ a_{21} & a_{11} & a_{23} \\ 0 & 0 & 1 \end{bmatrix} \begin{bmatrix} 1 & 0 & 0 \\ 0 & k & 0 \\ 0 & 0 & 1 \end{bmatrix} \begin{bmatrix} 1 & j & 0 \\ 0 & 1 & 0 \\ 0 & 0 & 1 \end{bmatrix}$$

where

$$j = \frac{(a_{11}a_{12} + a_{21}a_{22})}{(a_{11}^2 + a_{21}^2)} \quad \text{and} \quad k = \frac{(a_{11}a_{22} - a_{12}a_{21})}{(a_{11}^2 + a_{21}^2)}. \quad \blacksquare$$

As indicated in the previous section, the more general the transformations become, the more freedom they allow. Whereas isometries exist that map a point P to a point P', and similarities exist that map a pair of points P and Q to a pair of points P and Q', the next theorem shows that affinities exist that map three noncollinear points P, Q, R to three noncollinear points P', Q', R'.

Theorem 3.50

Given two triangles, $\triangle PQR$ and $\triangle P'Q'R'$, there is an affinity mapping $\triangle PQR$ to $\triangle P'Q'R'$.

Proof

We can show that there is an affinity mapping P, Q, and R to P', Q', and R', respectively, by finding a matrix A such that $P' = AP$, $Q' = AQ$, and $R' = AR$. This involves six equations in six unknowns. However, in actual practice we can simplify the determination of the matrix A as follows: First find the matrix of the affinity S that maps $O(0, 0, 1)$, $X(1, 0, 1)$, and $U(1, 1, 1)$ to P, Q, and R, respectively. Then find the matrix of the affinity T, which maps O, X, and U to P', Q', and R'. The affinity TS^{-1} will map P, Q, and R to P', Q', and R'. Since affinities preserve betweenness, TS^{-1} also maps the segments $\overline{PQ}$, $\overline{QR}$, and $\overline{RP}$ to $\overline{P'Q'}$, $\overline{Q'R'}$, and $\overline{R'P'}$, and therefore $\triangle PQR$ to $\triangle P'Q'R'$. $\quad \blacksquare$

In addition to segments and triangles, affinities also preserve other geometric figures. Since isometries preserve distance and each of the conic sections (circles, ellipses, parabolas, and hyberbolas) can be characterized in terms of distances, it is obvious that isometries preserve each of the conic sections, for example, the image of a circle under an isometry is a circle. To explore the invariance of conic sections under more general linear transformations, it is convenient to note that all conic sections can be written via matrix equations (see Exercise 10).

Theorem 3.51
Any conic section can be written algebraically as

$$c_{11}x_1^2 + c_{22}x_2^2 + 2c_{13}x_1 + 2c_{23}x_2 + 2c_{12}x_1x_2 + c_{33} = 0$$

or, in matrix notation, as

$$[x_1, x_2, 1] \begin{bmatrix} c_{11} & c_{12} & c_{13} \\ c_{12} & c_{22} & c_{23} \\ c_{13} & c_{23} & c_{33} \end{bmatrix} \begin{bmatrix} x_1 \\ x_2 \\ 1 \end{bmatrix} = 0 \quad or \quad X^t C X = 0.$$

The symmetric matrix $C = [c_{ij}]$ is called the matrix of the conic section. The conic section is nondegenerate (i.e., it is not a line, pair of lines, point, or the empty set if and only if $|C| \neq 0$). Furthermore, a conic section is an ellipse, hyperbola, or parabola if $(c_{12})^2 - c_{11}c_{22} < 0$, $(c_{12})^2 - c_{11}c_{22} > 0$, or $(c_{12})^2 - c_{11}c_{22} = 0$ (but c_{11} and c_{22} are not *both* zero), respectively. Thus, there are three distinct types of conic sections where circles ($c_{11} = c_{22}$) are considered to be special cases of ellipses.

Using matrix notation, it is relatively easy to determine the matrix of the image of a conic section under an affinity. The entries in this second matrix show that affinities preserve types of conic sections.

Theorem 3.52
The image of a conic section under an affinity is a conic section of the same type. Furthermore, if A is the matrix of an affinity, then the matrix of the image conic section is $C' = (A^{-1})^t C A^{-1}$.

Proof
Under the affinity, X is mapped to $X' = AX$. Solving for X gives $X = A^{-1}X'$. Substituting this into the matrix equation $X^t C X = 0$

yields $(A^{-1}X')^t C(A^{-1}X') = 0$ or $X'^t((A^{-1})^t CA^{-1})X' = 0$. This latter equation is the equation of a conic section with symmetric matrix $C' = (A^{-1})^t CA^{-1}$, where $|C'| = 0$ if and only if $|C| = 0$. To show that the type of conic section is preserved requires a straightforward but somewhat tedious calculation. ∎

Exercises

1. Prove Theorem 3.45 for the case where P, Q, and R have coordinates $P(x, 0, 1)$, $Q(0, 0, 1)$, $R(y, 0, 1)$.

2. Find the matrix of a shear with axis $x_1 = x_2$.

3. Find the matrix of a strain with axis $x_1 = 5$.

4. Prove Theorem 3.48. [*Hint*: See the proof of Theorem 3.47.]

5. Show that a dilation with center O is the product of strains with axes $x[0, 1, 0]$ and $y[1, 0, 0]$

6. Find the matrix of an affinity mapping $P(1, -1, 1)$, $Q(2, 1, 1)$, and $R(3, 0, 1)$ to $P'(0, 1, 1)$, $Q'(1, 2, 1)$, and $R'(0, 3, 1)$, respectively. [*Hint*: Use the method described in the proof of Theorem 3.50.]

7. Show that the only affinity with three noncollinear invariant points is the identity. [*Hint*: First assume the invariant points are $O(0, 0, 1)$ $X(1, 0, 1)$, and $U(1, 1, 1)$.]

8. Use Exercise 7 to show that there is a *unique* affinity mapping any three noncollinear points to any three noncollinear points. [*Hint*: Assume S and T are two such affinities and consider the affinity ST^{-1}.]

9. Show that affinities preserve parallelograms.

10. Verify that the standard equation for a conic section given in Theorem 3.51 is equivalent to the given matrix equation.

11. Let $A = \begin{bmatrix} 3 & -2 & 4 \\ 2 & -1 & -2 \\ 0 & 0 & 1 \end{bmatrix}$. Find the image of the parabola $y = 6x^2$ under the affinity with matrix A. Verify that the image is also a parabola.

12. Show that the image of a circle under a similarity is again a circle. (Note: In general, affinities can map circles to noncircular ellipses.)

Exercises 13 and 14 require the use of the following linear algebra formula for the area of a triangle with vertices $P(p_1, p_2, 1)$ $Q(q_1, q_2, 1)$, and $R(r_1, r_2, 1)$ where *abs* denotes *absolute value*.

$$\text{area}(\triangle PQR) = \frac{1}{2} \text{ abs} \left(\det \begin{bmatrix} p_1 & q_1 & r_1 \\ p_2 & q_2 & r_2 \\ 1 & 1 & 1 \end{bmatrix} \right)$$

13. Prove: If T is an affinity with matrix A, and T maps $\triangle PQR$ to $\triangle P'Q'R'$, then

$$\text{area}(\triangle P'Q'R') = k(\text{area}(\triangle PQR))$$

where $k = \text{abs}(\det(A))$. (Note: When $k = 1$, the affinity is called an *equiareal* transformation.)

14. Using Exercise 13 show that the area of a triangle is preserved under isometries and shears.

3.14 Exploring 3-D Isometries

Equipment and Materials Needed

- A polygon set (containing at least 20 triangles, 6 squares, 12 pentagons, and 3 hexagons where all the polygons have the same edge length) and a means of attaching the polygons to each other. Paper polygons and tape will work, or you can use a commercially prepared set.[23]
- Two patterns for creating tetrahedra and several skewers.[24]
- (Optional) Play dough for creating 3-D objects.

Introduction

This section generalizes the explorations of Sections 3.2 and 3.3 to isometries of R^3 and finds matrix representations for some of

---

[23] *Polydrons*[TM] work well and are available from Dale Seymour Publications.
[24] Bamboo kebob skewers work well and are available in many food stores.

these isometries. The transition from considering transformations of 2-space to considering transformations of 3-space increases the difficulty of the analysis substantially.[25] To ease into this 2-D to 3-D transition, we will start by exploring the 3-D analogues of polygons known as *regular polyhedra* or *Platonic solids*. Then, just as we studied finite symmetry groups of R^2 by considering symmetries of equilateral triangles and squares (see Section 3.3), we will study symmetry groups of R^3 by considering symmetries of a regular tetrahedron. Excellent sources for more information on these concepts are Chapters 16 and 17 in George E. Martin, *Transformation Geometry: An Introduction to Symmetry* (1982) and Chapter 6 in Clayton Dodge, *Euclidean Geometry and Transformations* (1972).

3.14.1 Regular Polyhedra

To begin our study, we first need a precise definition of regular polyhedron.

Definition 3.33

A *polyhedron* (plural *polyhedra*) is a solid with plane faces and straight edges where every edge joins two vertices and is adjacent to two faces. A polyhedron is said to be *convex* if, when any face is extended to form a plane, the remainder of the polyhedron lies entirely on one side of the plane.

Definition 3.34

A *regular polyhedron* is a convex polyhedron, all of whose faces are made of congruent regular polygons with n sides (n-gons) for a fixed n and all of whose vertices are surrounded by the same number of these n-gons.

As you will discover, there are exactly five regular polyhedra. These five solids have fascinated mathematicians and others throughout

---

[25]For a summary of some of the studies on people's perception of, and difficulty with, various types of symmetry, see Section 1.4 in Washburn and Crowe, *Symmetries of Culture* (1988).

the ages and have played a role in the history of subjects ranging from philosophy to astronomy. Plato associated four of them with the elements fire, air, water, and earth, and the fifth with the universe; Kepler even proposed a model of planetary motion based on the five polyhedra.[26]

The determination of the number and types of possible regular polyhedra can be carried out in a manner analogous to that used to determine all possible regular tilings of the plane. The following activities guide you through (1) a determination of possible regular polyhedra; (2) an exploration of isometries of R^3 and their effects on a regular tetrahedron; and (3) the derivation of matrices for some of these isometries.

Much of this exploration will be based on generalizations of ideas encountered in our investigations of isometries of R^2. Here, however, each isometry is a transformation of R^3, so it is appropriate to restate the definition of *isometry* with specific reference to R^3. In doing so, we will include the preservation of angle measures as part of the definition.

Definition 3.35
An affine transformation of Euclidean space (i.e., of the point set $\{(x_1, x_2, x_3, 1)\}$, is an *isometry of R^3* if it preserves distance and the absolute value of angle measure.

Activities

1. Place a point P on a sheet of paper as a reference. Then begin drawing adjacent, non-overlapping congruent regular n-gons, each with a vertex at P so as to "nearly" surround P leaving a gap between the "last" one and the "first" one. Then cut out (or fold under) the unfilled gap and tape the first and last edges of your n-gons together to form a "3-D corner," or "cone" that could hold something.

---

[26] An easy-to-read introduction to Kepler's ideas is contained in Section 1.3 of Davies, while Senechal and Fleck contains a comprehensive exploration of polyhedra.

a. Why do you need more than 2 regular polygons to form such a 3-D corner?
b. What must be true about the sum of the vertex angles of the regular polygons placed around the point to create a 3-D corner?
c. What is the largest possible value of n for which congruent regular n-gons can be used to create a 3-D corner? Explain.
d. For each value of n greater than 2 and less than or equal to the value found in part c, determine the maximum number of regular n-gons that can be used to create a 3-D corner.

2. Use the results of Activity 1 to explain why there are only 5 possible regular polyhedra.
3. Construct each of the 5 possible regular polyhedra, thus demonstrating their existence. Then fill in Table 3.9 giving the face shape, the number of faces around each vertex (k), the total number of faces (f), the total number of edges (e), and the total number of vertices (v).
4. Verify that each of your regular polyhedron satisfy Euler's formula for convex polyhedron, namely, $f - e + v = 2$.
5. The pyramid-shaped regular polyhedron with faces consisting of 4 equilateral triangles is known as a (regular) tetrahedron.

TABLE 3.9   The Regular Polyhedra.

Face Shape	Number of Faces at a Vertex (k)	Total Number of Faces (f)	Total Number of Edges (e)	Total Number of Vertices (v)

a. Label the vertices of a regular tetrahedron with the letters
A–D. If you are making a tetrahedron from a flat pattern, it
is easiest to label it before putting it together. (Suggestion:
Place the same letter in the corner of each of the triangles
surrounding a vertex so that you will be able to see the vertex
label from any direction.)

b. Explain why a tetrahedron can be said to have two different
orientations. These are described as right-hand and left-hand
orientations and can be detected by applying the so-called
"right-hand rule." Which is yours?

c. Now label a second regular tetrahedron so it has the same orientation as your first one. (Note: In some of the explorations
that follow, you will want to keep one of your tetrahedra
"fixed" to serve as a "before" version and observe the effects
of the isometries on the second one.)

3.14.2 Isometries of Space

In two dimensions, figures have a point of symmetry C if they are invariant under a point reflection with center C, and they have a line of
symmetry l if they are invariant under a reflection with axis l. These
isometries of R^2 are known as *point reflections* and *line reflections*, respectively, and the following activities explore transformations of R^3
analogous to these and other transformations of R^2.

6. R_π, *a plane reflection with axis* π, is an isometry of R^3 that leaves
   each point of the plane π invariant and maps any other point P
   to a point P' so that π is perpendicular to $\overline{PP'}$, intersecting the
   segment at its midpoint. If a point set α ($\alpha \neq \pi$) is invariant
   under R_π, we say that α has *plane symmetry* and that π is a *plane
   of symmetry* for α.

   a. Explain why plane reflections of R^3 can be considered as
   generalizations of line reflections of R^2.

   b. Assume that $l' = R_\pi(l)$ for a line l. Describe the location of
   line l' relative to l and π if l is parallel to π. If l intersects π.

c. Does the regular tetrahedron have any planes of symmetry? If so, give the number of these symmetry planes and describe their locations; if not, explain why not.

7. R_c, a *line reflection with center c*, is an isometry of R^3 that leaves each point of the line c invariant and maps any other point P to a point P' so that c is perpendicular to $\overline{PP'}$, intersecting the segment at its midpoint. If a point set α ($\alpha \neq c$) is invariant under R_c, we say that α has *line symmetry* and that c is a *line of symmetry* for α.

a. Explain why line reflections of R^3 can be considered as generalizations of point reflections of R^2.
b. Assume that $l' = R_c(l)$ is the image of a line l. Describe the location of l' relative to both c and l. Be sure to consider cases where c and l intersect, where they are parallel, and where they are skew.
c. Does the regular tetrahedron have any lines of symmetry? If so, give the number of these symmetry lines and describe their location; if not, explain why not.

8. R_C, a *point reflection with center C*, also known as a *central inversion*, is an isometry of R^3 that leaves the point C invariant and maps any other point P to a point P' so that C is the midpoint of segment $\overline{PP'}$. If a point set α ($\alpha \neq C$) is invariant under R_C, we say that α has *point symmetry* and that C is a *point of symmetry* for α.

a. How does the effect of this mapping compare to that of a point reflection in R^2?
b. Assume that $l' = R_C(l)$ is the image of a line l. Describe the location of l' relative to both C and l. Be sure to consider cases where C lies on l and where it doesn't.
c. Does the regular tetrahedron have any points of symmetry? If so, describe the number of symmetry points and the location of each; if not, explain why not.

9. (Optional) Use play dough to construct each of the following:

a. An object with plane, but not line or point, symmetry.
b. An object with line, but not plane or point, symmetry.

c. An object with point, but not line or plane, symmetry.

10. $R_{c,\theta}$, a *rotation with center c and directed angle* θ, is an isometry of R^3 that leaves each point on line c invariant and maps any other point P to point P', where P' is in the plane through P perpendicular to line c at C and $m\angle PCP' = \theta$. If a point set α is invariant under a rotation $R_{c,\theta}$ where $\theta = \frac{360}{k}$ for some integer k, the center line is said to be an *axis of k-fold symmetry for* α.

a. Explain why a line reflection can also be considered a rotation about a line. Be sure to describe both the center and angle of the rotation.

b. Why can a line of symmetry also be called an axis of k-fold symmetry? What is the value of k in this case?

c. (Optional) Use play dough to construct an object with exactly one axis of 3-fold symmetry.

11. What are the axes of k-fold symmetry of a regular tetrahedron? For each, be sure to specify both the axis and the value of k.

12. Each isometry of R^2 can be generated using a product, that is, a succession, of three or fewer line reflections. Similarly, each isometry of R^3 can be generated using a product of plane reflections. For each of the four isometries described above, determine how the isometry could be generated using a product of plane reflections. Include in your answer the number of plane reflections needed and a description of the relative location of the planes.

13. Four other isometries of R^3 are described below. Observe the effect of an isometry of each type on your tetrahedron. For each type, determine whether the isometry changes orientation of the tetrahedron and how the isometry can be expressed as a product of reflections in planes.

a. A *translation* with vector $\overrightarrow{PQ}$ where P and Q are points in 3-space.

b. A *glide reflection* (the product of a reflection in a plane π followed by a translation with vector in the plane π).

c. A *screw displacement* (a rotation with center c followed by a translation with vector on line c).

d. A *rotatory reflection* (a reflection in a plane π followed by a rotation with center c, where c is about a line perpendicular to the plane π).

3.14.3 Symmetries of Regular Tetrahedra

In R^2 a symmetry of an equilateral triangle is completely determined by its effect on the vertices of the triangle; and in particular, a symmetry can be identified as a specific permutation of the triangle vertices. Similarly, symmetries of a regular tetrahedron can be identified as permutations of the vertices of the tetrahedron.

Activities

14. Use the idea above to predict the number of symmetries of a regular tetrahedron.
15. Which of the above isometries of R^3 can be symmetries of a regular tetrahedron?
16. Of the symmetries of a regular tetrahedron, how many of each type are there? [*Hint:* Determine the planes of symmetry, the lines of k-fold symmetry, etc., and note that there are axes of k-fold symmetry for at least two different values of k.]
17. Now try making a complete list of all of the symmetries of a regular tetrahedron by indicating the permutation each performs on the 4 vertices of the tetrahedron. A standard way to do this is to indicate the results of the permutation with an ordered 4-tuple, for example, $(BACD)$ where this listing indicates that B maps to A, A maps to C, C maps to D and D maps to B.
18. (Optional) Create a group table for the symmetries of a regular tetrahedron similar to Table 3.2 for an equilateral triangle.

3.14.4 Matrix Format of Isometries of R^3

By generalizing the format and properties of matrices of affine transformations of R^2, we can find matrix representations of affine transformations of R^3. The following activities are intended to guide you through a determination of some of these matrices. Note that whereas points in R^2 have been represented with ordered triples $(x_1, x_2, 1)$, points in R^3 are represented by ordered 4-tuples of the form $(x_1, x_2, x_3, 1)$.

Activities

19. Assume that an affine transformation T of R^3 keeps $O(0, 0, 0, 1)$ invariant.

   a. Which entries in the 4×4 matrix representation of T are then automatically determined and what are their numerical values?

   b. If you are given all the entries in the matrix representation of T, how can you determine the coordinates for the images of $X(1, 0, 0, 1)$? of $Y(0, 1, 0, 1)$? of $Z(0, 0, 1, 1)$?

   c. If you know the coordinates of the images of $X(1, 0, 0, 1)$ and $Y(0, 1, 0, 1)$ and $Z(0, 0, 1, 1)$ under the transformation T, how can you find a matrix representation for T?

Matrices of "Point Symmetries" of R^3

Using information found in the previous activity it is possible to find matrices for the following "point symmetries," that is, symmetries that keep one point (in this case $O(0, 0, 0, 1)$) invariant.

20. Find 4×4 matrices for each of the following:

   a. Plane reflections in each of the three "coordinate planes," that is, the x, y-plane $(x_3 = 0)$, the y, z-plane $(x_1 = 0)$ and the x, z-plane $(x_2 = 0)$.

   b. Line reflections in the x-axis, the y-axis, and the z-axis.

   c. The point reflection with center at the origin, that is, $O(0, 0, 0, 1)$.

   d. The rotation about the x-axis with angle measure $45°$.

21. Using the distance formula, it is possible to show that the tetrahedron with vertices $A(1, 1, 1, 1)$, $B(-1, 1, -1, 1)$, $C(1, -1, -1, 1)$, and $D(-1 - 1, 1, 1)$ is a regular tetrahedron.

    a. Use your matrices from the previous activity to check to see if any of the coordinate planes is a plane of symmetry of this tetrahedron.
    b. Use your matrices from the previous activity to check to see if any of the coordinate axes is an axis of symmetry for this tetrahedron.
    c. Similarly determine if the origin $O(0, 0, 0, 1)$ is a point of symmetry for this tetrahedron.

Matrices of "Space Symmetries" of R^3

By finding matrices of translations and using these in combination with matrices of "point symmetries" like those found in Activity 20, it is possible to find the matrix of any symmetry of R^3.

22. Find 4×4 matrices for each of the following:

    a. The translation with vector $\overrightarrow{OS}$ where $O(0,0,0,1)$ and $S(1,2,3,1)$.
    b. The plane reflection with axis $x_3 = 1$.
    c. The point reflection with center $C(1, 2, 3, 1)$.

3.15   Suggestions for Further Reading

The following list contains a wealth of resources both for the topics formally covered in Chapter 3 as well as for those encountered in the chapter's geometric explorations.

Caldwell, J. H. (1966). Chapter 11: The plane symmetry groups. In *Topics in Recreational Mathematics*. Cambridge, U.K.: Cambridge University Press.

Coxford, A. F., and Usiskin, Z. P. (1971). *Geometry: A Transformation Approach*. River Forest, IL: Laidlow Brothers. (Uses transformations in presentation of the standard topics of elementary Euclidean geometry.)

Cromwell, P. R. (1997). *Polyhedra*. Cambridge, U.K.: Cambridge University Press.

Crowe, D. (1986). *HiMAP Module 4: Symmetry, Rigid Motions, and Patterns.* Arlington, MA: COMAP.

Davis, D. M. (1993). *The Nature and Power of Mathematics.* Princeton, NJ: Princeton University Press.

Devlin, K. (1994). *Mathematics: The Science of Patterns.* New York: Scientific American Library.

Dodge, C. W. (1972). *Euclidean Geometry and Transformations.* Reading, MA: Addison-Wesley. (Chapters 2 and 3 contain an elementary presentation of isometries and similarities and include applications.)

Eccles, F. M. (1971). *An Introduction to Transformational Geometry.* Menlo Park, CA. Addison-Wesley. (Intended to introduce secondary-school students to transformations following a traditional geometry course.)

Farmer, D. W. (1996). *Groups and Symmetry*, Vol. 5, Mathematical World. AMS. (A beginning undergraduate guide to discovery of groups and symmetry.)

Faulkner, J. E. (1975). Paper folding as a technique in visualizing a certain class of transformations. *Mathematics Teacher* 68: 376–377.

Gans, D. (1969). *Transformations and Geometries.* New York: Appleton-Century-Crofts. (A detailed presentation of the transformations introduced in this chapter followed by a presentation of the more general projective and topological transformations.)

Gardner, M. (1975). On tessellating the plane with convex polygon tiles. *Scientific American* 233(1):112–117.

Gardner, M. (1978). The art of M. C. Escher. In *Mathematical Carnival*, pp. 89–102. New York: Alfred A. Knopf.

Gardner, M. (1989). *Penrose Tiles to Trapdoor Ciphers.* New York: W. H. Freeman & Co.

Grünbaum, B., and Shepard, G. C. (1987). *Tilings and Patterns.* New York: W. H. Freeman. (The authoritative source on the subject of tilings and polyhedra.)

Haak, S. (1976). Transformation geometry and the artwork of M. C. Escher. *Mathematics Teacher* 69:647–652.

Iaglom, I. M. (1962). *Geometric Transformations*, Vols. 1, 2, 3. New York: Random House. (Numerous problems of elementary Euclidean geometry are solved through transformations.)

Jeger, M. (1969). *Transformation Geometry.* London: Allen and Unwin. (Numerous diagrams are included in this easy-to-understand presentation of isometries, similarities, and affinities.

Johnson, D. A. (1973). *Paper Folding for the Mathematics Class.* Reston, VA: NCTM.

Johnston, B. L., and Richman, F. (1997). *Numbers and Symmetry: An Introduction to Algebra*. New York: CRC Press. (Nice introductory chapter on symmetries and another on wallpaper patterns.)

Jones, O. (1986). *The Grammar of Ornament*. Ware England: Omega Books. (Wonderful collection of ornamental patterns and designs from different civilizations.)

King, J., and Schattschneider, D. (1997). *Geometry Turned On! Dynamic Software in Learning, Teaching and Research*, MAA Notes 41. MAA. (A collection of articles by people at the forefront of dynamic geometry.)

Lockwood, E. H., and Macmillan, R. H. (1978). *Geometric Symmetry*. Cambridge: Cambridge University Press. (Great source of information about frieze, wallpaper, and space patterns.)

MacGillavry, C. H. (1976). *Symmetry Aspects of M.C. Escher's Periodic Drawings*, 2d ed. Utrecht: Bohn, Scheltema & Holkema.

Martin, G. E. (1982b). *Transformation Geometry: An Introduction to Symmetry*. New York: Springer-Verlag. (Introduces isometries and applies them to ornamental groups and tessellations.)

Maxwell, E. A. (1975). *Geometry by Transformations*. Cambridge: Cambridge University Press. (A secondary-school–level introduction of isometries and similarities including their matrix representations.)

O'Daffer, P. G., and Clemens, S. R. (1976). *Geometry: An Investigative Approach*. Menlo Park, CA: Addison-Wesley.

Olson, A. T. (1975). *Mathematics Through Paper Folding*. Reston, VA: NCTM.

Radin, C. (1995). Symmetry and Tilings. *Notices of the AMS*, 42(1). pp. 26–31.

Ranucci, E. R. (1974). Master of tessellations: M. C. Escher, 1898–1972. *Mathematics Teacher* 67:299–306.

Ranucci, E. R., and Teeters, J. E. (1977). *Creating Escher-Type Drawings*. Palo Alto, CA: Creative Publications (Straightforward, easy to follow directions.)

Robertson, J. (1986). Geometric constructions using hinged mirrors. *Mathematics Teacher* 79: 380–386.

Rosen, J. (1975). *Symmetry Discovered: Concepts and Application in Nature and Science*. Cambridge: Cambridge University Press.

Schattschneider, D. (1978). The plane symmetry groups: Their recognition and notation. *The American Mathematical Monthly*, 85:439–450.

Schattschneider, D. (1990). *M. C. Escher: Visions of Symmetry*. New York: W. H. Freeman and Company. (Contains all of Escher's notebook patterns with extensive commentary by the Escher expert.)

Senechal, M., and Fleck, G. (eds.) (1988). *Shaping Space: A Polyhedral Approach*. Cambridge MA: Birkhäuser Boston.

Singer, D. (1997). *Geometry: Plane and Fancy.* New York: Springer-Verlag (Contains information about tessellations in non-Euclidean geometry.)

Steen, L.A. (Ed.) (1990). *On the Shoulders of Giants: New Approaches to Numeracy.* Washington DC: National Academy Press.

Stewart, I., and Golubitsky, M. (1993). *Fearful Symmetry: Is God A Geometer?* London: Penguin Books. (Analyzes the role of "symmetry breaking" in a wide range of natural patterns.)

Teeters, J. C. (1974). How to draw tessellations of the Escher type. *Mathematics Teacher* 67: 307–310.

Washburn, D., and Crowe, D. (1988). *Symmetries of Culture; Theory and Practice of Plane Patterns Analysis.* Seattle: University of Washington Press. (Careful and nontechnical presentation of pattern analysis with examples from numerous cultures.)

Watson, A. (1990). The mathematics of symmetry. *New Scientist* 17, October 1990: 45–50. (Survey article describing the group concept, its history and its application in mathematics, chemistry, and physics.)

Weyl, H. (1989). *Symmetry.* Princeton: Princeton University Press. (Original copyright in 1952. This classic explores symmetry as a geometrical concept and as an underlying principle in art and nature.)

Suggestions for Viewing

Adventures in Perception (1973, 22 min). An especially effective presentation of the work of M. C. Escher. Produced by Hans Van Gelder, Film Producktie, N. V., The Netherlands. Available from Phoenix/B.F.A. Films, 468 Park Ave. S., New York, NY 10016 (800) 221–1274.

Dihedral Kaleidoscopes (1971; 13 min). Uses pair of intersecting mirrors (dihedral kaleidoscopes) to demonstrate several regular figures and their stellations and tilings of the plane. Produced by the College Geometry Project at the University of Minnesota. Available from International Film Bureau, 332 South Michigan Ave., Chicago, IL 60604.

Isometries (1971; 26 min). Demonstrates that every plane isometry is a translation, rotation, reflection, or glide reflection and that each is the product of at most three reflections. Produced by the College Geometry Project at the University of Minnesota. Available from International Film Bureau, 332 South Michigan Ave., Chicago, IL 60604.

Similarity (1990; 25 min). A Project Mathematics video, produced by and available from California Institute of Technology, Caltech 1–70, Pasadena, CA 91125.

Symmetries of the Cube (1971; 13.5 min). Uses mirrors to exhibit the symmetries of a square as a prelude to the analogous generation of the cube by reflections. Produced by the College Geometry Project at the University of Minnesota, Available from International Film Bureau, 332 South Michigan Ave., Chicago, IL 60604.

Three-Dimensional Symmetry (1995; 17 min). Shows how transformations create symmetries in two and three dimensions. Computer animation is used to show the relationships found in symmetrical objects. Available from Key Curriculum Press, Berkeley, CA.

The Fantastic World of M. C. Escher (1994; 50 min). Explores the man, his inspirations, and the mathematical principles found in so much of his art through first-person accounts by Escher's friends and mathematicians, computer animated recreations of his work, and a look at his sources of inspiration. Published by Film 7 International, Rome, Italy. Available from Atlas Video.

Suggested Software

The Geometry Center (`http://www.geom.umn.edu/`) is a great source of downloadable geometry software. In particular, you may want the following:

Geomview—A 3D object viewer.

Kali—A 2D symmetry pattern editor.

Kaleido Tile—Creates tilings of the sphere, plane, or hyperbolic space.

KaleidoMania!—A tool for dynamically creating symmetric designs and exploring the mathematics of symmetry. Available from Key Curriculum Press (`http://www.keypress.com/`).

4 Projective Geometry

4.1 Gaining Perspective

From the analytic viewpoint of Klein's definition of geometry, projective geometry is the logical generalization of the affine geometry introduced in Chapter 3. Just as we were able to generalize the isometries of the Euclidean plane to similarities, and these in turn to affinities, we will now be able to generalize affinities to *collineations*, the transformations that define projective geometry. There is, however, one new ingredient required in this last generalization. The set of points contained in the Euclidean plane must be enlarged to include points on one additional line, a line often referred to as the *ideal* line. Rather than complicating the geometry, these new ideal points simplify projective geometry and give it the highly desirable property of duality.

The historical development of projective geometry, however, was synthetic, rather than analytic, in nature. The origins of this geometry can be traced to the attempts of Renaissance painters to achieve realistic representations of three-dimensional objects on two-dimensional canvas. These painters, influenced by Plato's thesis that nature is mathematically designed, sought and found mathematical relations that could be used to achieve perspective. This interplay of mathematics and art, the importance of Plato's thesis, and the influence of the church make the origins of projective geometry a fascinating episode in the history of mathematics. This history is detailed in the sources given at the end of this chapter. These readings should explain the connection between the *ideal* points referred to at the beginning of this section and the *vanishing* points used in paintings.

The relevance of projective geometry to achieving realistic planar representations of three-dimensional objects is currently making the study of projective geometry a prerequisite to the study of computer graphics. The value of this prerequisite is enhanced, since computer graphics uses the analytic representations of points and lines by homogeneous coordinates and the representation of transformations by matrices developed in projective geometry.

On the other hand, computer-based dynamic geometry software can enhance the presentation and understanding of concepts of plane projective geometry covered in this chapter. Such software facilitates efficient and accurate constructions of the point and line configurations involved in definitions, theorems and proofs. And using computer tools to "paint" lines with different colors and to "drag" initial objects so that intersection points are within view can change an apparent tangle of lines into an enlightening visual aid. (For specific instructions for using the dynamic geometry software programs *Cabri Geometry II* and *Geometer's Sketchpad* to carry out selected exercises, see http://www.stolaf.edu/people/cederj/geotext/info.htm.)

4.2 The Axiomatic System and Duality

Before introducing an analytic model for plane projective geometry, it is necessary to develop an axiomatic system for this geometry. The axiom system we will consider contains six axioms; however, we will call any system satisfying the first four of these axioms a *projective plane.*[1] It is these first four axioms we will consider as we begin our synthetic treatment of plane projective geometry. Just as in the axiom systems of Chapter 1, the undefined terms for this system are "point," "line," and "incident"; points are said to be *collinear* if they are incident with the same line. The term "complete quadrangle" used in Axiom 4.4 will be explained in Definition 4.2.

Axioms for a Projective Plane

Axiom 4.1
Any two distinct points are incident with exactly one line.

Axiom 4.2
Any two distinct lines are incident with at least one point.

Axiom 4.3
There exist at least four points, no three of which are collinear.

Axiom 4.4
The three diagonal points of a complete quadrangle are never collinear.

Note that although the first axiom is characteristic of Euclidean geometry, the second axiom, guaranteeing that pairs of lines intersect, is not; that is, there do not exist parallel lines in this geometry. Also notice that Axioms 4.1 and 4.2 are nearly dual statements. (Recall that the dual of a statement is obtained by replacing each occurrence of the word "point" by the word "line" and vice versa.) The dual of Axiom 4.1 would read: "Any two distinct lines are incident with exactly one point." A proof of this statement follows trivially from Axioms 4.1 and 4.2 (see Exercise 1), and thus the duals of both axioms are theorems of this axiomatic system.

---

[1]In general, a *projective plane* is a system that satisfies Axioms 4.1–4.3 and an axiom that guarantees that every line contains at least three points.

FIGURE 4.1 A triangle.

A careful reading will show that Axioms 4.1 and 4.2 do *not* assert the existence of either points or lines. However, Axiom 4.3 and its dual assure us that points and lines do exist in the projective plane.

Theorem 4.1 (Dual of Axiom 4.3)
There exist at least four lines, no three of which are concurrent.

Proof
Let *A*, *B*, *C*, *D* be four points, no three collinear, as guaranteed by Axiom 4.3. Then by Axiom 4.1, there exist four lines *AB*, *AC*, *CD*, and *BD*. If any three of these were concurrent, the dual of Axiom 4.1 would be contradicted. ∎

As in the preceding proof, points of this geometry are denoted by uppercase letters, *A*, *B*, *C*, and so on, while lines are denoted by lowercase letters *a*, *b*, *c*, and so on. The pair of letters *AB* refers to the unique line determined by points *A* and *B*. Since a pair of lines *a* and *b* also determines a unique point, we denote this point by *a·b*. In addition, we use the notation *AIa* or *aIA* to indicate that point *A* and line *a* are incident.

Since Axiom 4.3 guarantees the existence of three noncollinear points, figures resembling Euclidean triangles exist. However, since there is no concept of betweenness in this geometry, the sides of a triangle are lines, *not* segments. This latter change makes the following definition self-dual so that the definition is unchanged when the terms "line" and "point" are interchanged.

Definition 4.1
A *triangle* is a set of three noncollinear points and the three lines determined by these points. The points are called *vertices* and the lines are called *sides* of the triangle (Fig. 4.1).

Figs. consisting of four points and the lines they determine also exist. Unlike triangles, these figures have no comparable analogues in Euclidean geometry.

Definition 4.2

A (*complete*) *quadrangle* is a set of four points, no three collinear, and the six lines determined by these four points. The points are called vertices and the lines are called sides of the quadrangle. If A, B, C, D are the four points of a quadrangle, then AB and CD, AC and BD, and AD and BC are said to be pairs of *opposite sides*. The points at which pairs of opposite sides intersect are called *diagonal points* of the quadrangle (Fig. 4.2).

As asserted in Axiom 4.4, the diagonal points of a complete quadrangle form a triangle known as the *diagonal* triangle of the quadrangle. The existence of this diagonal triangle can be used to show that each line in the projective plane contains at least four points (see Exercise 2).

To determine whether the dual of Axiom 4.4 is a theorem, it is necessary to consider the dual of Definition 4.2. Unlike the definition of a triangle, Definition 4.2 is not self-dual. Therefore the dual of a quadrangle is another figure of this geometry.

Definition 4.3

A (*complete*) *quadrilateral* is a set of four lines, no three concurrent, and the six points determined by these lines. The points are called *vertices* and the lines are called *sides* of the quadrilateral. If a, b, c, d are the four lines of the quadrilateral, $a \cdot b$ and $c \cdot d$, $a \cdot c$ and $b \cdot d$, and $a \cdot d$ and $b \cdot c$ are said to be pairs of *opposite vertices*. The lines joining

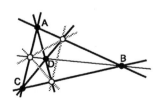

FIGURE 4.2   A complete quadrangle.

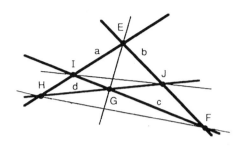

FIGURE 4.3 A complete quadrilateral.

pairs of opposite vertices are called *diagonal lines* of the quadrilateral (Fig. 4.3).

Theorem 4.2 (Dual of Axiom 4.4)
The three diagonal lines of a complete quadrilateral are never concurrent.

Proof
Let *abcd* be an arbitrary complete quadrilateral. Let $E = a \cdot b$, $F = b \cdot c$, $G = c \cdot d$, $H = a \cdot d$, $I = a \cdot c$, and $J = b \cdot d$. Then the diagonal lines are *EG*, *FH*, and *IJ*. Assume these three lines are concurrent; that is, *EG*, *FH*, and *IJ* intersect at a point. But *EFGH* forms a complete quadrangle with diagonal points $EF \cdot GH = b \cdot d = J$, $EG \cdot FH$, and $EH \cdot FG = a \cdot c = I$, but since *EG*, *FH*, and *IJ* are concurrent, this implies that the diagonal points of the complete quadrangle *EFGH* are collinear, contradicting Axiom 4.4. Thus, the diagonal lines of complete quadrilateral *abcd* are not concurrent. ∎

Hence, the diagonal lines of a complete quadrilateral also determine a triangle known as the *diagonal triangle* of the quadrilateral.

With the proof of Theorem 4.2 we have completed the process of showing that the axiomatic system consisting of Axioms 4.1 through 4.4 satisfies the *principle of duality* (see Section 1.3). Eventually we shall add two more axioms to this system and verify that this larger system also satisfies the principle of duality.

Even though our objective in this chapter is the study of the real projective plane, it is interesting to note that Axioms 4.1 through 4.3 are essentially the same as three of the four axioms for finite projective planes given in Section 1.3. The remaining axiom for finite projective planes (Axiom P.2) refers to the number of points on a line. As indicated previously in this section, Axiom 4.4 guarantees that there are at least four points on each line. Thus, any finite model of our current axiomatic system is of order $n \geq 3$ and so contains at least 13 points. In fact, the 13-point model (Model P.3) given in Section 1.3 is also a model for Axioms 4.1 through 4.4. The verification that this model actually satisfies Axiom 4.4 consists of a tedious case-by-case check of all possible quadrangles (see Exercise 6).

An infinite model of this axiomatic system can be obtained by slightly extending a Euclidean plane as follows.

An Infinite Model for the Projective Plane

Let π be a plane parallel to, but not equal to the x, y-plane in *Euclidean* 3-space, and let O denote the origin of the Cartesian coordinate system. Note that each point P in π, together with the point O, determines a unique line p, so P can be said to correspond to a unique line through O, namely, the line p. Similarly, each line l in π, together with the point O, determines a unique plane λ, so l can be said to correspond to a plane through O, namely, λ (Fig. 4.4). This correspondence is clearly a one-to-one mapping of the set of points and lines in π into the set of lines and planes through O. However, there

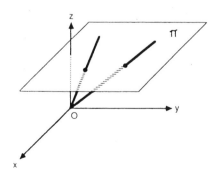

FIGURE 4.4 Creating a projective plane model.

is one plane, namely, the x, y-plane, and a subset of lines, namely, the set of all lines through O in the x, y-plane, that are "missed" by this mapping.

A model, π', of the projective plane is obtained by adding an *ideal line* and *ideal points* to π to make this correspondence not only one-to-one but also onto. The ideal line, which is added to π, corresponds to x, y-plane and the ideal points added to π correspond to those lines through O that lie in the x, y-plane. Once added, this ideal line and these ideal points are considered to be indistinguishable from the other lines and points in π'.

In addition to describing the points and lines of π' it is necessary to describe the interpretation of the term "incident." A point and line in π' are said to be incident if and only if the corresponding line through O lies in the corresponding plane through O. Thus, the ideal points are incident with the ideal line. Under this interpretation, π' can be shown to be a model of the projective plane (see Exercise 5).

Exercises

1. Write out the proof of the dual of Axiom 4.1.

2. (a) Prove that there exist at least three points on every line of a projective plane. (Note: You cannot assume the existence of *any* points on a line.) (b) Extend your proof in part (a) to show that there exist at least four points on every line of a projective plane.

3. Find a model for the axiom system consisting of Axioms 4.1–4.3 that has exactly three points on every line. What is the total number of points in this model? The total number of lines? Does your model satisfy Axiom 4.4?

4. Show that Axiom4.4 is independent of Axioms 4.1–4.3. (Note: Axiom 4.4 is known as *Fano's axiom*.)

5. Verify that π' satisfies Axioms 4.1–4.3. Which points in π' are points of intersection of lines that are parallel in the Euclidean plane π?

6. (a) List all possible quadrangles in Model P.3 of Section 1.3 that contain the points A and B as two of the four vertices, (b) Verify Axiom 4.4 for the four quadrangles in this model in which three of the vertices are A, B, and E.

4.3 Perspective Triangles*

Although Axioms 4.1 through 4.4 describe the basic properties of our projective plane, we will require two more important properties, which are formalized in Axioms 4.5 and 4.6. The first of these properties concerns two relations between pairs of triangles. As the following definition indicates, one of these relations requires a correspondence between vertices and the other requires a correspondence between sides. As in the familiar case of congruent triangles in Euclidean geometry, the order in which the vertices of the triangles are named is used to indicate the correspondence.

Definition 4.4

Triangles $\triangle ABC$ and $\triangle A'B'C'$ are said to be *perspective from a point* if the three lines joining corresponding vertices, AA', BB', and CC', are concurrent. The triangles are said to be *perspective from a line* if the three points of intersection of corresponding sides, $AB \cdot A'B'$, $AC \cdot A'C'$, and $BC \cdot B'C'$, are collinear (Fig. 4.5).

Axiom 4.5 (Desargues' Theorem)

If two triangles are perspective from a point, they are perspective from a line.

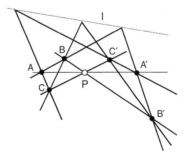

FIGURE 4.5 $\triangle ABC$ and $\triangle A'B'C'$ perspective from P and l.

---

* Dynamic geometry software can be used to carry out exercises in this and other sections marked with an asterisk. For an introduction to this software, see http://www.stolaf.edu/people/cederj/geotext/info.htm.

This statement can be easily proved in projective geometry of 3-space (see Coxeter, 1987, *Projective Geometry*), and hence is frequently referred to as Desargues' theorem, thus honoring the French mathematician who anticipated the development of projective geometry. However, in plane projective geometry, either this statement or an equivalent statement must be assumed as an axiom, since in some geometries that satisfy Axioms 4.1 through 4.4 this statement does not hold.

To ensure that our axiom system still satisfies the principle of duality, we must prove the dual of Axiom 4.5. In this case the dual is just the converse of the axiom.

Theorem 4.3 (Dual of Axiom 4.5)
If two triangles are perspective from a line, they are perspective from a point.

Proof
Assume $\triangle ABC$ and $\triangle A'B'C'$ are perspective from a line, that is, $AB \cdot A'B' = P$, $B'C' \cdot BC = Q$, and $AC \cdot A'C' = R$ are collinear (see Fig. 4.6). It is sufficient to show that AA', BB', and CC' are concurrent. Let $O = AA' \cdot BB'$, and consider $\triangle RAA'$ and $\triangle QBB'$. Then P is on RQ since P, Q, and R are collinear and P is on AB and on $A'B'$ by definition of P. Thus, $\triangle RAA'$ and $\triangle QBB'$ are perspective from P, so by Axiom 4.5 they are perspective from a line; that is, $RA \cdot QB = C$, $RA' \cdot QB' = C'$, and $AA' \cdot BB' = O$ are collinear. Thus AA', BB', and CC' are concurrent. ∎

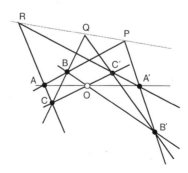

FIGURE 4.6 $\triangle ABC$ and $\triangle A'B'C'$ perspective from a line.

The importance of Axiom 4.5 and its implications cannot be over-stated. It provides a means of proving that three points are collinear and the preceding proof offers a typical example of this use. It will also be used to show that the fourth point of a set known as a harmonic set is unique.

Exercises

Dynamic geometry software can be used to carry out Exercises 1, 2, and 4. See http://www.stolaf.edu/people/cederj/geotext/info.htm.

1. Construct two triangles that are perspective from a point. From which line are they perspective?

2. Construct two triangles that are perspective from a line. From which point are they perspective?

3. (a) Will a Desargues' configuration (see Section 1.5) be a projective plane? Why? (b) Show that in the configuration illustrated in Fig. 1.8 that $\triangle BEH$ and $\triangle ADI$ are perspective from a point and from a line.

4. If the vertices of $\triangle PQR$ lie, respectively, on the sides of $\triangle ABC$ so that AP, BQ, and CR are concurrent, and if $AB \cdot PQ = U$, $AC \cdot PR = V$, and $BC \cdot QR = W$, show that U, V and W are collinear.

4.4 Harmonic Sets*

This section introduces special sets of four collinear points (and dual sets of four concurrent lines) that are defined entirely in terms of a construction involving points and lines. In Section 4.5, we shall see that point and line constructions can be used to define correspondences between two sets of collinear points, two sets of concurrent lines, and between a set of collinear points and a set of concurrent lines; in Section 4.6, point and line constructions are used to define conics.

Definition 4.5

Four collinear points, A, B, C, D are said to form *harmonic set* $H(AB, CD)$ if there is a complete quadrangle in which two opposite sides pass through A, two other opposite sides pass through B, while the remaining two sides pass through C and D, respectively. C is called the *harmonic conjugate* of D (or D is the harmonic conjugate of C) with respect to A and B.

Note that A and B are diagonal points of the quadrangle and are named first. Also note that the points of the first pair in the harmonic set are distinguished from the points of the second pair but there is no distinction made between points of the first pair or points of the second pair: that is,

$$H(AB, CD) \Leftrightarrow H(BA, CD) \Leftrightarrow H(AB, DC) \Leftrightarrow H(BA, DC).$$

Using this definition, given any three distinct collinear points, A, B, C, a fourth point D, the harmonic conjugate of C with respect to A and B, can be constructed as follows.

Construction of the Fourth Point of a Harmonic Set

Let E be an arbitrary point not on AB and m be a line through B that is distinct from AB and not incident with E (Fig. 4.7). Let $m \cdot AE = F$, $m \cdot CE = G$, and $AG \cdot EB = H$. As you can verify, the points E, F, G,

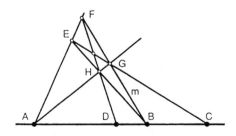

FIGURE 4.7 Harmonic set $H(AB, CD)$.

and H form a complete quadrangle with two opposite sides through A, two opposite sides through B, and one of the remaining sides through C. Therefore, $D = FH \cdot AB$.

Using Axiom 4.4, we can verify that D is distinct from A, B, and C (see Exercise 4), thus demonstrating again that each line of our projective plane contains at least four points.

Both the definition and the preceding construction for finding D, the harmonic conjugate of C with respect to the points A and B, may make the point D appear somewhat arbitrary. However, the following theorem shows that if we begin with three given points A, B, and C, any construction that satisfies Definition 4.5 will give the same point D; that is, D is uniquely determined.

Theorem 4.4

If A, B, and C are three distinct, collinear points, then D, the harmonic conjugate of C with respect to A and B, is unique.

Proof

Let $EFGH$ be a quadrangle used to find the point D. Assume a second quadrangle $E'F'G'H'$ is also constructed so that $E'H' \cdot F'G' = B$, $E'F' \cdot G'H' = A$, and $E'G' \cdot AB = C$, and let $D^* = F'H' \cdot AB$ (Fig. 4.8). It suffices to show that $D^* = D$. To do this, Axiom 4.5 and its dual are employed.

Note that $\triangle EFG$ and $\triangle E'F'G'$ are perspective from line AB. So by Theorem 4.3, they are perspective from a point; that is, EE', FF', and GG' are concurrent. Similarly $\triangle EGH$ and $\triangle E'G'H'$ are perspective from AB, and hence EE', GG', and HH' are concurrent. Thus, the

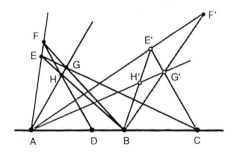

FIGURE 4.8 Uniqueness of D in $H(AB, CD)$.

four lines EE', FF', GG', and HH' are all concurrent. So $\triangle FHG$ and $\triangle F'H'G'$ are perspective from a point, and by Axiom 4.5 it follows that they are perspective from a line. So $FH \cdot F'H'$, $FG \cdot F'G' = B$, and $HG \cdot H'G' = A$ are collinear. But $FH \cdot AB = D$, $F'H' \cdot AB = D^*$. Thus, $D = D^*$. ∎

In addition to the possible order changes within the first and last pairs of points of a harmonic set, the following theorem indicates that the pairs themselves may be interchanged.

Theorem 4.5
$H(AB, CD) \Leftrightarrow H(CD, AB)$.

Proof
We assume $H(AB, CD)$ and show $H(CD, AB)$. A similar proof can be used to verify the second half of the equivalence.

Since $H(AB, CD)$, there is a quadrangle $EFGH$ such that $A = EF \cdot GH$, $B = EH \cdot FG$, $C = EG \cdot n$, and $D = FH \cdot n$ where $n = AB$. Now let $S = DG \cdot FC$ and $T = GE \cdot FH$, and consider quadrangle $TGSF$ (Fig. 4.9). Note the two lines $SF = FC$ and $TG = GE$ are both incident with C. Also $GS = DG$ and $TF = FH$ are both incident with D. Furthermore, line GF is incident with B. Thus, it suffices to show that TS is incident with A. Note that $A = EF \cdot GH$. So consider $\triangle THE$ and $\triangle SGF$. If these triangles can be shown to be perspective from a point, it immediately follows that A is incident with TS, and therefore that $H(CD, AB)$.

Since the intersections of corresponding sides of these triangles are $TE \cdot SF = GE \cdot FC = C$, $TH \cdot SG = FH \cdot DG = D$, and $HE \cdot GF = B$,

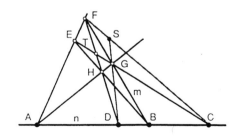

FIGURE 4.9 $H(AB, CD) \Rightarrow H(CD, AB)$.

these triangles are perspective from line n and therefore they are perspective from a point. ■

Corollary

$H(AB, CD) \Leftrightarrow H(AB, DC) \Leftrightarrow H(BA, CD) \Leftrightarrow H(BA, DC) \Leftrightarrow$
$H(CD, AB) \Leftrightarrow H(CD, BA) \Leftrightarrow H(DC, AB) \Leftrightarrow H(DC, BA)$.

As in previous sections, the dual of this definition of a harmonic set of points can be formulated.

Definition 4.6

Four concurrent lines, a, b, c, d, are said to form the *harmonic set* $H(ab, cd)$ if there is a complete quadrilateral in which two opposite vertices lie on a, two other opposite vertices lie on b, while the remaining two vertices lie on c and d, respectively (see Fig. 4.10 where lines e, f, g, and h form a quadrilateral yielding $H(ab, cd)$).

The construction of the fourth line of a harmonic set and the following theorems follow automatically by dualizing the previous results.

Theorem 4.6

If lines a, b, and c are concurrent, then d, the harmonic conjugate of c with respect to a and b, is unique.

Theorem 4.7

$H(ab, ad) \Leftrightarrow H(cd, ab)$.

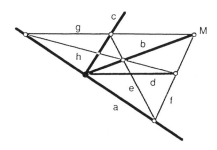

FIGURE 4.10 Harmonic set $H(ab, cd)$.

FIGURE 4.11 Exercise 1a.

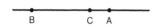

FIGURE 4.12 Exercise 1b.

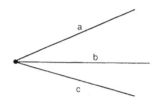

FIGURE 4.13 Exercise 2a.

Eventually, we shall see that the harmonic property is an invariant under the transformations of projective geometry. In addition, the harmonic property can be used to coordinatize the projective plane, that is, using constructions involving only lines and points and without any notion of distance, a coordinate system can be constructed that assigns to each point in the projective plane an ordered pair of numbers. (For a detailed presentation of this process see Tuller, 1967, *Modern Introduction to Geometries.*)

Exercises

Dynamic geometry software can be used to carry out Exercises 1, 2, 5, and 6. See http://www.stolaf.edu/people/cederj/geotext/info.htm.

1. Let points *A, B, C* be located as shown in Figures 4.11 and 4.12. Construct the harmonic conjugate of *C* with respect to *A* and *B*: (a) in Figure 4.11; and (b) in Figure 4.12.

2. Let lines *a, b, c* be located as shown in Figure 4.13 and 4.14. Construct the harmonic conjugate of *c* with respect to *a* and *b*: (a) in Figure 4.13; and (b) in Figure 4.14.

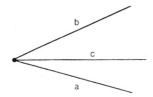

FIGURE 4.14 Exercise 2b.

3. In Figure 4.7, let $I = EG \cdot FH$. Show that I is an element of two nonequivalent harmonic sets in this figure. Be sure to specify the quadrangle involved in each.

4. Prove that the fourth point of a harmonic set is distinct from the three other points of the harmonic set; that is, if $H(AB, CD)$, prove that D is distinct from A, B, and C.

5. Suppose in the Euclidean plane that B is the midpoint of segment $\overline{AC}$. Try to construct the harmonic conjugate of B with respect to A and C. What happens?

The following exercise is reprinted with permission from Coxeter (1987, *Projective Geometry*, p. 23).

6. Working in the Euclidean plane, draw a line segment OC, take G two-thirds of the way along it, and E two-fifths of the way from G to C. (For instance, make the distances in centimeters $OG = 10$, $GE = 2$, $EC = 3$.) If the segment OC represents a stretched string tuned to the note C, the same string stopped at E or G will play the other notes of the major triad. By drawing a suitable quadrangle, verify experimentally that $H(OE, CG)$. (This phenomenon explains our use of the word *harmonic*.)

4.5 Perspectivities and Projectivities*

Transformations of the projective plane. known as *collineations*, are Introduced analytically in Section 4.10. In that section we will see that, as the name suggests, these transformations preserve *collinearity*; that is, the images of collinear points are also collinear. Thus, if we restrict our view to points on a particular line, we will be able to say that a collineation induces a mapping from this set of collinear points to another set of collinear points. As you may expect, we shall see that collineations preserve *concurrence* as well; that is, the images of concurrent lines will be concurrent lines. So collineations will also induce mappings from a set of concurrent lines to another set of concurrent lines. Other transformations, known as a *correlations*, will induce mappings from collinear points to concurrent lines and vice versa.

In this section, we learn how to use point and line constructions to synthetically obtain correspondences, which we later show are exactly the correspondences given analytically by the induced mappings described above. Many of the terms and properties involved in these constructions reflect the artistic origins of projective geometry.

In order to facilitate our description of these constructions we will begin by adopting the following dual definitions.

Definition 4.7
The set of all lines through a point P is called a *pencil of lines with center P* (Fig. 4.15); the set of all points on a line p is called a *pencil of points with axis p* (Fig. 4.16).

With these definitions, the mappings mentioned previously can be formally defined in terms of mappings between pencils. The most elementary of these mappings are known as *perspectivities*.

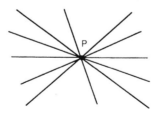

FIGURE 4.15   Pencil of lines with center P.

FIGURE 4.16   Pencil of points with axis p.

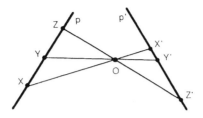

FIGURE 4.17   Perspectivity between pencils of points.

Definition 4.8a
A one-to-one mapping between two pencils of points with axes p and p' is called a *perspectivity* if each line joining the point X on p with the corresponding point X' on p' is incident with a fixed point O. O is called the *center of the perspectivity*. Such a perspectivity is denoted $X \underset{\wedge}{\overset{O}{=}} X'$ (Fig. 4.17).

Definition 4.8b
A one-to-one mapping between two pencils of lines with centers P and P' is called a *perspectivity*, if each point of intersection of the corresponding lines x on P and x' on P' lies on a fixed line o. o is called the *axis of the perspectivity*. Such a perspectivity is denoted $x \underset{\wedge}{\overset{o}{=}} x'$ (Fig. 4.18).

Definition 4.8c
A one-to-one mapping between a pencil of points with axis p and a pencil of lines with center P is called a *perspectivity* if each point X on p is incident with the corresponding line x on P. Such a perspectivity is denoted $X \overline{\wedge} x$ or $x \overline{\wedge} X$ (Fig. 4.19).

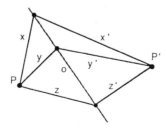

FIGURE 4.18   Perspectivity between pencils of lines.

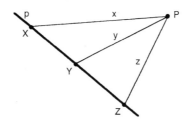

FIGURE 4.19 Perspectivity between a pencil of points and a pencil of lines.

Note that Definition 4.8c includes two types of perspectivities. In one the first pencil is a pencil of points, and the second is a pencil of lines; in the other the first pencil is a pencil of lines, and the second is a pencil of points. Furthermore, the representation of this perspectivity uses the symbol "$\overline{\wedge}$" without any letter above the symbol.

In each of the three definitions, the pencils are said to be *perspectively related*. If the perspectively related pencils are of the same kind, we can show (see Exercise 1) that the perspectivity is uniquely determined by two pairs of corresponding elements (provided no element of the two pairs is on both pencils). In other words, once two pairs of corresponding elements are specified, the image of any third element of the first pencil is uniquely determined.

Since perspectivities are one-to-one mappings, their inverses exist and are clearly again perspectivities. Also a finite product of perspectivities, that is, a finite number of perspectivities used in succession, produces another mapping known as a *projectivity*. It is to these mappings that our final axiom refers.

Definition 4.9
A one-to-one mapping between the elements of two pencils is called a *projectivity* if it consists of a finite product of perspectivities.

Figures 4.20 through 4.22 show projectivities between pencils of points, pencils of lines, and a pencil of lines and a pencil of points, respectively. Notice that the notation for projectivities uses the unadorned symbol "$\wedge$." When a projectivity exists between two pencils, the pencils are said to be *projectively related*. If a projectivity maps

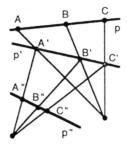

FIGURE 4.20 $ABC \wedge A''B''C''$.

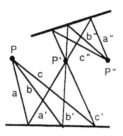

FIGURE 4.21 $abc \wedge a''b''c''$.

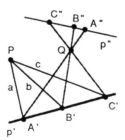

FIGURE 4.22 $abc \wedge A''B''C''$.

either a pencil of points or a pencil of lines onto itself, it is called a *projectivity on the pencil*. Axiom 4.6, which is self-dual, describes an important property of projectivities on pencils.

Axiom 4.6

If a projectivity on a pencil leaves three elements of the pencil invariant, it leaves every element of the pencil invariant.

Thus, a projectivity on a pencil that keeps three elements invariant is necessarily the identity mapping. Other observations that should be made at this point include: (1) a projectivity does not have a center or an axis unless it consists of just one perspectivity; and (2) the inverse of a projectivity and the product of two projectivities are again projectivities.

Whereas a perspectivity between two pencils is uniquely determined by two pairs of corresponding elements of the pencils, the existence of a projectivity between two pencils that maps any three elements of the first pencil to three corresponding elements of the second pencil can be demonstrated by construction. This construction is demonstrated for two distinct pencils of points.

Construction of a Projectivity Between Pencils of Points

Let A, B, C be elements of the pencil with axis p and A', B', C' corresponding elements of the pencil with axis p' ($p \neq p'$). Construct line AA' and choose a point $P \neq A'$ on this line. Let $m \neq p'$ be an arbitrary line through A'. Let $B_1 = BP \cdot m$, $C_1 = CP \cdot m$. Thus, $ABC \overset{P}{\wedge} A'B_1C_1$. Now let $Q = B_1B' \cdot C_1C'$. Then $A'B_1C_1 \overset{Q}{\wedge} A'B'C'$, and therefore $ABC \wedge A'B'C'$ (Fig. 4.23).

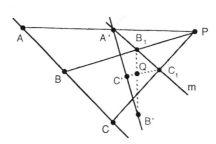

FIGURE 4.23 Constructing the projectivity $ABC \wedge A'B'C'$.

Note that the preceding construction requires only two perspectivities, but the construction of these perspectivities is not unique.

The existence of a projectivity between pencils of lines that maps any three lines of the first pencil to three corresponding lines of the second pencil follows by duality. The existence of a projectivity that maps three concurrent lines to three corresponding collinear points can also be easily demonstrated (see Exercise 4).

Thus, any three elements of one pencil can be projectively related to three arbitrary elements of a second pencil and the correspondence defined by the projectivity constructed from these three pairs can be extended to pair all the remaining elements of the two pencils. However, since the construction involved is not uniquely specified, it is not immediately apparent that the images of any fourth element of the first pencil determined by different constructions always turn out to be the same. The remarkable result that says this does indeed happen is known as the *fundamental theorem of projective geometry*.

Theorem 4.8 (Fundamental Theorem)
A projectivity between two pencils is uniquely determined by three pairs of corresponding elements.

Proof
The existence of a projectivity has been demonstrated. The uniqueness follows from Axiom 4.6 as shown.

Case 1: Two pencils of points. Assume that A, B, C are elements of a pencil of points with axis p and that A', B', C' are the corresponding elements of a second pencil with axis p'. By the preceding result, there exists a projectivity T such that

$$T : ABC \to A'B'C'.$$

If T is not unique, there exists another projectivity S such that

$$S : ABC \to A'B'C'.$$

Then, under the projectivity ST^{-1},

$$A'B'C' \wedge ABC \wedge A'B'C',$$

or in other words ST^{-1} is a projectivity on p' keeping the three points A', B', and C' invariant. Therefore, by Axiom 4.6, $ST^{-1} = I$, or $S = T$.

Case 2: Two pencils of lines. The proof follows automatically by duality of case 1.

Case 3: A pencil of points and a pencil of lines. This case follows from cases 1 and 2 and the use of a perspectivity between a pencil of points and a pencil of lines that is also uniquely determined. ∎

The construction used to demonstrate the existence of a projectivity mapping three elements of one pencil to three corresponding elements of a second pencil also provides direct proofs of two corollaries to the fundamental theorem (see Exercise 8).

Corollary 1
If in a projectivity between two distinct pencils an element corresponds to itself, then the projectivity is a perspectivity (i.e., the mapping requires only one perspectivity).

Corollary 2
A projectivity between two pencils can be expressed as the product of at most three perspectivities.

Since projectivities are mappings induced by the general transformations of the projective plane, it is important to note that the harmonic relation remains invariant under projectivities.

Theorem 4.9
The harmonic relation is invariant under a projectivity. So, for example, if $H(AB, CD)$ and $ABCD \wedge A'B'C'D'$, then $H(A'B', C'D')$.

Proof
Since the projective plane possesses duality, and any projectivity is a product of perspectivities, it is sufficient to show that $H(AB, CD)$ implies $H(ab, cd)$ where $ABC \overline{\wedge} abcd$. Let $O = a \cdot b$ thus $a = OA$, $b = OB$, and so on. Since $H(AB, CD)$, there exists a quadrangle with one vertex at O, namely $OEFG$, such that A and B are diagonal points of the quadrangle, etc. Let $A = EF \cdot OG$, $B = OE \cdot GF$, $C = OF \cdot AB$, and $D = GE \cdot AB$ (Fig. 4.24). Now consider quadrilateral GF, GE, AE, AB. Then $GF \cdot GE = G$, and $AE \cdot AB = A$ are on a; $GE \cdot AE = E$ and

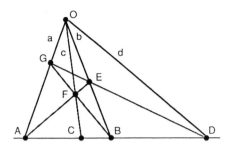

FIGURE 4.24 $H(AB, CD) \Rightarrow H(ab, cd)$.

$GF{\cdot}AB = B$ are on b; $GE{\cdot}AB = D$ is on d, and $GF{\cdot}AE = F$ is on c. Thus, $H(ab, cd)$. ∎

As we have seen, three elements of one pencil can always be mapped to three elements of a second pencil via a projectivity, but a set of four elements of one pencil cannot in general be mapped to a set of four elements of a second pencil. If, however, both the first and second sets are harmonic sets, the desired projectivity will exist. This is formalized in the following theorem, which holds for both pencils of points and pencils of lines, even though the notation used is suggestive of pencils of points.

Theorem 4.10
If four elements A, B, C, D of one pencil form a harmonic set, $H(AB, CD)$, and four elements A′, B′, C′, D′ of a second pencil form a second harmonic set, $H(A'B', C'D')$, then there exists a projectivity mapping A, B, C, D to A′, B′, C′, D′, respectively.

Proof
By Theorem 4.8, there is a projectivity such that $ABC \wedge A'B'C'$. Let D^* be the image of D under this projectivity. Then by Theorem 4.9, $H(A'B', C'D^*)$: but by Theorem 4.4, the harmonic conjugate of C' with respect to A' and B' is unique. Thus, $D^* = D'$. ∎

Before leaving the topic of projectivities, it is useful to note that there is a second, frequently more convenient method for constructing the images under a projectivity between pencils of points. This method makes use of the following definition and theorem.

Definition 4.10
If A and A', B and B' are pairs of corresponding points, the *cross joins* of these pairs of points are the lines AB' and BA'.

Theorem 4.11
A projectivity between two distinct pencils of points determines a unique line called the axis of homology, which contains the intersections of the cross joins of all pairs of corresponding points.

Proof
Consider two distinct pencils of points with axes p and p'. Assume $ABC \wedge A'B'C'$, where $P = p \cdot p'$ is none of the six points. Clearly $A'A$, $A'B$, $A'C \overline{\wedge} ABC$ and $A'B'C' \overline{\wedge} AA'$, AB', AC'. Thus, $A'A$, $A'B$, $A'C \wedge AA'$, AB', AC', so by Corollary 1, of the fundamental theorem $A'A$, $A'B$, $A'C \overset{h}{\wedge} AA'$, AB', AC' for some axis h. So $A'B \cdot AB'$ and $A'C \cdot AC'$, are both on h (Fig. 4.25).

To use h to find the image of another point D on p, proceed as follows. Construct $A'D$. Let $D_1 = A'D \cdot h$. Then $D' = AD_1 \cdot p'$.

To show that h is unique, it is necessary to show that h is independent of the choices for the centers of the pencils of lines (here A and A') and thus that the intersections of cross joins of all pairs of corresponding points are on h. To do this it is sufficient to find two points on h that are independent of these choices. Let $Q = h \cdot p'$ and $R = h \cdot p$. Using the technique described earlier to locate the image of R, let

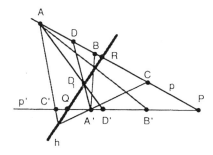

FIGURE 4.25   Axis of homology for $ABC \wedge A'B'C'$.

$R_1 = A'R \cdot h$. But $A'R \cdot h = R$. So $R_1 = R$. Then $R' = AR \cdot p' = p \cdot p' = P$; that is, the image of R is P. Likewise, the image of P can be shown to be Q. But the image and preimage of P are uniquely determined by Theorem 4.8. (Note that $Q \neq R$, since this projectivity is not a perspectivity.) Thus $h = QR$ is uniquely determined. ∎

The proof of Theorem 4.11 contains a description of the method used to construct h, the axis of homology, and to find the image of any arbitrary point. Clearly the cross joins of two pairs of lines can be defined by dualizing Definition 4.10 and the dual of Theorem 4.11 can be used to construct the images of lines under projectivities between pencils of lines using a *center of homology*.

Exercises

Dynamic geometry software can be used to carry out Exercises 3, 4, 6, 7, and 9. See `http://www.stolaf.edu/people/cederj/geotext/info.htm`.

1. Prove that a perspectivity between two pencils of the same kind is uniquely determined by two pairs of corresponding elements (provided no element of the two pairs is on both pencils).

2. Given a perspectivity between two distinct pencils of points with axes p and p', verify each of the following: (a) the center of the perspectivity is not incident with either p or p'; and (b) the point $P = p \cdot p'$ maps to itself under this perspectivity.

3. Demonstrate the existence of a projectivity mapping concurrent lines a, b, c in a pencil with center P to concurrent lines a', b', c' in a pencil with center P' (assume $P \neq P'$).

4. Demonstrate the existence of a projectivity mapping concurrent lines a, b, c to collinear points A, B, C.

5. Let a, b, c be three concurrent lines and P, Q two points not on any of them. Let $A_1, A_2, \ldots$ and $B_1, B_2, \ldots$ be points on a and b, respectively, such that $A_i P \cdot B_i Q = C_i$ where C_i is on line c. Show that $A_i \wedge B_i$.

6. Given four distinct collinear points A, B, C, D, construct the following projectivities: (a) $ABC \wedge ABD$; (b) $ABC \wedge ACD$; (c) $ABC \wedge BAD$; (d) $ABC \wedge ACB$. Find the image of D under part (d).

7. What is the minimum number of perspectivities required for each part in Exercise 5?

8. Prove the corollaries to Theorem 4.8.

9. Use the dual of Theorem 4.11 to find the center of homology determined by two projectively, but nonperspectively related pencils of lines. Demonstrate the construction of an image line.

4.6 Conics in the Projective Plane*

So far in Chapter 4, we have studied projective figures determined by sets of n points, where no three of these points are collinear. For $n = 3$ we considered figures known as triangles, and for $n = 4$ we considered figures known as quadrangles. We now consider figures that we shall eventually discover are uniquely determined by such sets when $n = 5$. These figures, known as *point conics*, are defined in terms of projectivities.

Definition 4.11
A *point conic* is the set of points of intersection of corresponding lines of two projectively, but not perspectively, related pencils of lines with distinct centers (Fig. 4.26).

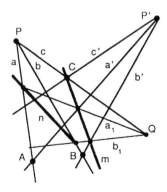

FIGURE 4.26 *A, B, C* on a point conic.

It is not obvious that the point conics just defined are in any way related to the familiar conics of Euclidean geometry. In this section, we demonstrate that point conics are determined uniquely by five points, no three collinear (Theorem 4.14), but the connection between the point conics of projective geometry and Euclidean conics does not become apparent until much later. However, the following definition of a *tangent* does resemble the familiar Euclidean definition.

Definition 4.12

A *tangent to a point conic* is a line that has exactly one point in common with the point conic.

Both the definition of a point conic and the definition of a tangent can be dualized to define other concepts in projective geometry. The figure described by the dual of Definition 4.11 is known as a *line conic* and the point described by the dual of Definition 4.12 is known as a *point of contact*. With these definitions, each of the theorems describing properties of point conics developed in this section can be dualized to describe corresponding properties of line conics.

Definition 4.13

A *line conic* is the set of lines joining corresponding points of two projectively, but not perspectively, related pencils of points with distinct axes.

Definition 4.14

A *point of contact of a line conic* is a point that lies on exactly one line of the line conic.

As Definition 4.11 indicates, a point conic is determined by a projectivity between two pencils of lines, and as stated by the fundamental theorem, these mappings are uniquely determined when three pairs of corresponding lines are specified. Thus, given pencils of lines with centers at P and P' ($P \neq P'$), we can arbitrarily pick three lines a, b, and c incident with P and three corresponding lines a', b', and c' incident with P'. Provided this correspondence does not yield a perspectivity, we can immediately locate three points of the point conic determined by this projectivity, namely, $a \cdot a'$, $b \cdot b'$, and $c \cdot c'$. (Note that different choices of lines and/or their corresponding lines may yield different point conics.) The following theorem shows that there are two more easily obtainable points of this point conic. However, other points in addition to these five must be located either by a construction of the projectivity or by other constructions described later in this section.

Theorem 4.12

The centers of the pencils of lines in the projectivity defining a point conic are points of the point conic.

Proof

Let P and P' be the centers of the pencils. Let $m = PP'$, and consider m as a line in the pencil with center P (Fig. 4.27). Then there is a corresponding line m' in the pencil with center P'. Note that $m \neq m'$ since the projectivity is not a perspectivity. So $m \cdot m = P'$ is a point of the point conic. Similarly, by considering m as a line in the pencil with center P', and finding its corresponding line, P can be shown to be a point of the point conic. ∎

As a result of this theorem, any five points P_1, P_2, P_3, P_4, P_5 (no three collinear) can be used to determine a conic as follows.

Choose two of the points, say P_1 and P_2, as centers of pencils and construct lines P_1P_3, P_1P_4, P_1P_5 and P_2P_3, P_2P_4, P_2P_5. Then the projectivity P_1P_3, P_1P_4, $P_1P_5 \wedge P_2P_3$, P_2P_4, P_2P_5 defines a point conic containing the five points.

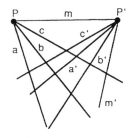

FIGURE 4.27 Proof 4.12.

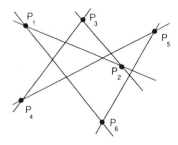

FIGURE 4.28 Hexagon $P_1P_2P_3P_4P_5P_6$.

The point conic obtained by this construction clearly contains the original set of five points. To show that such a set of five points *uniquely* determines a point conic, we will use a projective figure consisting of six points (here, however, we do *not* require the condition that no three of the points are collinear).

Definition 4.15
A *hexagon* is a set of six distinct points called *vertices*, say P_1, P_2, P_3, P_4, P_5, P_6, and the six lines P_1P_2, P_2P_3, P_3P_4, P_4P_5, P_5P_6, and P_6P_1 (Fig. 4.28). These lines are called the *sides* of the hexagon $P_1P_2P_3P_4P_5P_6$. Points P_1 and P_4, P_2 and P_5, P_3 and P_6 are pairs of *opposite vertices* and lines P_1P_2 and P_4P_5, P_2P_3 and P_5P_6, P_3P_4 and P_6P_1 are pairs of *opposite sides*. The three points of intersection of opposite sides are *diagonal points*.

It is important to observe that a given set of six points does not determine a unique hexagon, since a hexagon is determined by the order in which its vertices are named. In fact, a given set of six points can determine $6!/12 = 60$ different hexagons (see Exercise 3). Thus, in Theorem 4.13 it is important to notice that P and P', the centers of the pencils used to define the point conic, are used as the first and third vertices of the hexagon, respectively.

Theorem 4.13
If A, B, C, D are four points on a point conic defined by projectively related pencils with centers P and P', then the diagonal points of hexagon $PBP'ACD$ are collinear; and conversely, if the diagonal points of hexagon

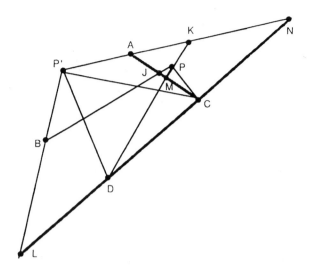

FIGURE 4.29 Proof 4.13.

*PBP'ACD are collinear, then A, B, C, D are points of the point conic
determined by the projectively related pencils with centers P and P'.*

Proof

(a) The diagonal points for hexagon *PBP'ACD* are *PB·AC* = *J*,
BP'·CD = *L*, and *P'A·DP* = *K*. Let *AC·PD* = *M* and *AP'·DC* = *N*
(Fig. 4.29). By using these and the definition of a point conic, we
obtain the following projectivities:

$$AJCM \wedge PA, PB, PC, PD \wedge P'A, P'B, P'C, P'D \wedge NLCD.$$

So *AJCM ∧ NLCD*. But since *C ∧ C*, this projectivity is a perspectivity.
And since *AN·MD* = *AP'·PD* = *K*, the center of the perspectivity is
K. Thus *J, L,* and *K* are collinear.

(b) The proof of the converse is merely a reverse argument of
the previous proof.　　　　　　　　　　　　　　　　　　■

Using this result, we can now show that a set of five points, no
three collinear, uniquely determines a point conic. This means that
the constructions determined by using different pairs of the five
points as centers of the projectively related pencils all yield the same
set of points.

Theorem 4.14

A point conic is uniquely determined by five distinct points, no three of which are collinear.

Proof

Let P_1, P_2, P_3, P_4, P_5 be five points, no three collinear. Then there exists a point conic determined by the pencils with centers P_1, and P_2 and the projectivity P_1P_3, P_1P_4, $P_1P_5 \wedge P_2P_3$, P_2P_4, P_2P_5 which contains these five points. Let D be any sixth point on this point on conic. To show that the conic is uniquely determined, that is, that the same set of points is determined when points other than P_1 and P_2 are used as the centers of the pencils, it is sufficient to show that D is on the point conic defined by pencils with centers at any two of the other points. Consider hexagon $P_1P_4P_2P_3P_5D$. By Theorem 4.13, the diagonal points $P_1P_4 \cdot P_3P_5$, $P_4P_2 \cdot P_5D$, $P_2P_3 \cdot DP_1$ are collinear. But this hexagon is the same as hexagon $P_4P_2P_3P_5DP_1$, and thus by the second part of Theorem 4.13, D is on the point conic determined by pencils with centers P_3 and P_4, By similarly renaming this hexagon or using other hexagons with P_1 and P_2 as the first and third vertices, it can be shown that D is on the point conic determined by pencils with centers at any two of the points P_1, P_2, P_3, P_4, P_5. ∎

This theorem has several interesting corollaries. The first of these is known by the intriguing title *Pascal's mystic hexagon theorem* and was proved by Pascal in 1640, when he was 17. The dual of this corollary was not proved until 1806 when Brianchon developed its proof.

Corollary 1 (Pascal's Theorem)
If a hexagon is inscribed in a point conic (i.e., the vertices of the hexagon are points of the point conic), its diagonal points are collinear (Fig. 4.30).

By considering hexagon $P_1'P_1P_2P_3P_4P_5$ and letting point P_1' approach P_1 so that line $P_1'P_1$, becomes the tangent at P_1, we can verify a second corollary that gives an efficient method for constructing tangents to a point conic. Applying a similar process to two hexagons, namely, $P_1P_2P_2'P_4P_3P_3'$ and $P_1P_1'P_2P_4P_4'P_3$, yields a third corollary (see Exercise 8).

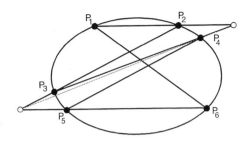

FIGURE 4.30   Corollary 1, Theorem 4.14.

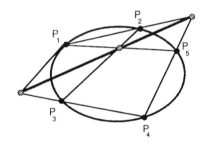

FIGURE 4.31   Corollary 2, Theorem 4.14.

Corollary 2

If the five points P_1, P_2, P_3, P_4, P_5 are points of a point conic, then the three points $P_1P_2 \cdot P_4P_5$, $P_2P_3 \cdot P_5P_1$, and $P_3P_4 \cdot$ tangent (at P_1) are collinear (Fig. 4.31).

Corollary 3

If P_1, P_2, P_3, P_4 are four points of a point conic, then the four points $P_1P_2 \cdot P_3P_4$, $P_1P_3 \cdot P_2P_4$, tan $P_2 \cdot$ tan P_3, and tan $P_1 \cdot$ tan P_4 are collinear (Fig. 4.32).

The construction of additional points of a point conic by setting up a construction for the projectivity involved is a fairly tedious procedure. However, the process can be simplified somewhat by using a center of homology as described by the dual of Theorem 4.11. A third method of constructing additional points uses Pascal's theorem as follows.

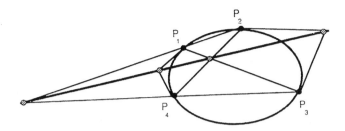

FIGURE 4.32 Corollary 3, Theorem 4.14.

Construction of Points of a Point Conic Using Pascal's Theorem

Let A, B, C, D, E be five points of a point conic. Then any additional point F, on the point conic can be considered as the sixth point of inscribed hexagon $ABCDEF$. Since the diagonal points $P = AB{\cdot}DE$, $Q = BC{\cdot}EF$, and $CD{\cdot}FA$ will be collinear, choose a line m through E (this will be the line EF). Construct points P and Q. Then $R = CD{\cdot}PQ$ and $F = RA{\cdot}m$ (Fig. 4.33). To locate other points on the point conic, merely choose other lines through E.

Even though the second corollary of Theorem 4.14 describes an easy method for constructing a tangent at a specific point, it does not give any insight into how tangent lines to a point conic are related to the projectivity defining the point conic. The proof of the following theorem not only demonstrates this relation, but also leads to a

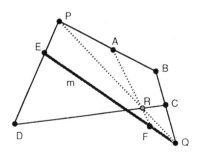

FIGURE 4.33 Constructing F on the point conic $ABCDE$.

corollary we will use in Section 4.11 to find an equation for a point conic.

Theorem 4.15

For any point A of a point conic, there is exactly one line tangent to the conic at A. (This tangent is the line corresponding to line AB considered as a line of the pencil through B when the conic is defined by projectively related pencils with centers A and B).

Proof

Let B, C, D, E be four more points of the point conic. Then the point conic can be defined by projectively related pencils with centers A and B. Let h be the line in the pencil with center A that corresponds to line AB considered as a line in the pencil with center B. Clearly h contains the point A of the point conic, and $h \cdot AB = A$. Assume h contains a second distinct point of the point conic, say X.

Case 1: X is on AB. Then $h = AB$ and h corresponds to itself under the projectivity, and hence by Corollary 1 of Theorem 4.8, the projectivity is a perspectivity contradicting the definition of a point conic.

Case 2: X is not on AB. Then $h = AX$ corresponds to line AB and to line BX, which is distinct from AB. But this contradicts the one-to-one property of projectivities. Thus, h contains exactly one point of the point conic and is, therefore, a tangent.

To show that there is no other tangent to the point conic at A, assume that a second line h' is also a tangent at A. Since $h'IA$, there is a line m in the pencil with center B that corresponds to h'. Then $m \cdot h'$ is a point of the point conic. But since h' is a tangent at A, it contains only one point of the conic, namely A. Thus, $m \cdot h' = A$, so $m = AB$, and hence $h' = h$. ■

Corollary

A point conic is uniquely determined by three distinct noncollinear points and the tangents at two of them.

By definition, tangents are the lines that intersect a conic exactly once. Other lines may or may not intersect the conic, but as the next theorem shows, a line can never intersect a conic *more* than twice.

This result will be used in Section 4.11 when we use an analytic approach to study further properties of point conics.

Theorem 4.16
A line intersects a point conic in at most two points.

Proof
Assume line n intersects a point conic in three distinct points Q, R, and S. Let P and P' be two other points of the conic and consider the pencils with centers P and P'. Then, as shown previously, the conic can be defined in terms of a projectivity between these pencils where Q, R, and S are points of intersection of the corresponding pairs of lines PQ and $P'Q$, PR and $P'R$, PS and $P'S$. Under this projectivity, PQ, PR, $PS \wedge P'Q$, $P'R$, $P'S$. However, the three points Q, R, and S all lie on n, so in fact PQ, PR, $PS \overset{n}{\wedge} P'Q$, $P'R$, $P'S$. It follows by the fundamental theorem that the projectivity is a perspectivity, contradicting the definition of a point conic. ∎

Exercises

For dynamic geometry software instructions duplicating Exercises 1, 2, 5, and 6. See http://www.stolaf.edu/people/cederj/geotext/info.htm.

1. Given five points, no three collinear, construct two more points of the point conic they determine and a tangent at one of the original five points using each of the following methods: (a) construction of the projectivity as a product of two perspectivities; and (b) using the center of homology.

2. Dualize Exercise 1 and perform the construction.

3. Explain why 6 points determine 60 different hexagons.

4. Prove: If alternate vertices of a hexagon lie on two lines (i.e., in hexagon $P_1P_2P_3P_4P_5P_6$, P_1, P_3, and P_5 are collinear, as are P_2, P_4, and P_6) then the diagonal points are collinear. (This is known as *Pappus' theorem* and dates from the 3rd century) [*Hint*: Find a projectivity between the two lines for which the points of intersection of the cross joins are the diagonal points of the hexagon.]

5. Given five points, no three collinear, construct two more points of the point conic they determine using Pascal's theorem.

6. Dualize Exercise 5, and perform the construction.

7. Prove that the tangent to a point conic at A is the line joining A to the center of homology determined by a projectivity between two pencils defining the conic where A is the center of one of the pencils.

8. Prove Corollary 3 of Theorem 4.14.

9. Show that omitting the phrase "but not perspectively" from Definition 4.11 would allow inclusion of sets of two lines (i.e., the points on these lines) as point conics. Which two lines would they be?

4.7   An Analytic Model for the Projective Plane

Until now we have considered plane projective geometry from a strictly synthetic point of view. We now change our point of view and adopt the approach suggested by Klein's definition of geometry; that is, we begin exploring the invariants of the projective plane under a group of transformations. To obtain matrix representations of these projective transformations, we need an analytic model of the projective plane. Since our goal is to look at the real projective plane, we consider an analytic model of the projective plane similar to the model of the Euclidean plane. Our matrix representations then resemble the matrices that we used for isometries, similarities, and affinities, so we are able to use techniques similar to those used in Chapter 3. Thus, this approach enables us to both explore additional properties of the real projective plane and view projective geometry as the next logical step in the progression from Euclidean to similarity to affine geometry.

Our analytic model for the projective plane uses the nonzero equivalence classes determined by the relation on R^3 defined in Section 3.5 not only as lines but also as points. (Recall that $(a_1, a_2, a_3) \sim (b_1, b_2, b_3)$ if there is a nonzero real number k such that $(a_1, a_2, a_3) = k(b_1, b_2, b_3)$.) As in Chapter 3, ordered triples used to represent

TABLE 4.1 Analytic Model of the Projective Plane.

Undefined Term	Interpretation
Point	A nonzero equivalence class of ordered triples of real numbers; any element (x_1, x_2, x_3) of the equivalence class will be called *homogeneous coordinates* of the point
Line	A nonzero equivalence class of ordered triples of real numbers; any element $[u_1, u_2, u_3]$ of the equivalence class will be called *homogeneous coordinates* of the line
Incident	The line u is said to be incident with the point X if the dot product $u \cdot X = 0$, or in matrix notation, $$[u_1, u_2, u_3] \begin{bmatrix} x_1 \\ x_2 \\ x_3 \end{bmatrix} = 0$$

points are denoted with parentheses as (x_1, x_2, x_3), while ordered triples used to represent lines are denoted with square brackets as $[u_1, u_2, u_3]$. It is important to observe that the additional restrictions required for the interpretations of point and line in the Euclidean model are no longer required.

To show that is set of interpretations is a model of our projective plane, it is necessary to verify that it satisfies Axioms 4.1 through 4.6. The verification of Axioms 4.1 through 4.3 is left as an exercise (see Exercise 2). We verify Axiom 4.5 at the end of this section, but postpone the verification of Axioms 4.4 and 4.6 to Sections 4.10 and 4.8, respectively.

We can visualize this analytic model in terms of the extended Euclidean plane π' introduced in Section 4.2. There we saw how to obtain π' from π (a Euclidean plane parallel to, but distinct from, the plane $x_3 = 0$) by extending the following correspondence between the set of points and lines in π and the set of lines and planes through the origin in E^3 (Euclidean 3-space):

1. A point P in π corresponds to the line through the origin that intersects π at P.

2. A line l in π corresponds to the plane through the origin that intersects π along l.

To show that this correspondence yields homogeneous coordinates for the points and lines of π' we need to recall several analytic geometry facts about E^3. In particular the following observations are useful:

1. Any line through the origin can be represented in vector notation as $\mathbf{x} = t\mathbf{s}$ where $\mathbf{x} = (x_1, x_2, x_3)$ is a vector from the origin to an arbitrary point X on the line, and $\mathbf{s} = (s_1, s_2, s_3)$ is a direction vector for the line. (Note that any nonzero scalar multiple of a direction vector $\mathbf{s}$ is also a direction vector for the same line.)
2. Any plane through the origin can be represented by an equation of the form $\mathbf{n} \cdot \mathbf{x} = n_1 x_1 + n_2 x_2 + n_3 x_3 = 0$, where $\mathbf{x} = (x_1, x_2, x_3)$ is a vector from the origin to an arbitrary point X on the plane and $\mathbf{n} = (n_1, n_2, n_3)$ is a vector normal (i.e., perpendicular) to the plane. (Note that any nonzero scalar multiple of a normal vector $\mathbf{n}$ is also a normal vector for the same plane.)
3. Thus, a line through the origin with direction vector $\mathbf{s}$ will lie in a plane through the origin with normal vector $\mathbf{n}$ if and only if $\mathbf{n} \cdot \mathbf{s} = 0$.

We can then identify each point P in π with a nonzero equivalence class of R^3, namely, the set of all possible direction vectors for the line through the origin that intersects π at P. Likewise, we can identify each line l in π with a nonzero equivalence class of R^3, namely, the set of all possible normal vectors for the plane through the origin that intersects π at l. In this way, elements of the equivalence classes become the homogeneous coordinates of the points and lines in π.

To complete the process, we need to find homogeneous coordinates for the ideal points and line added to π to obtain π'. We can do this by identifying the ideal points with the nonzero equivalence classes that give direction vectors for lines through the origin that do not intersect π, and by identifying the ideal line added to π with the equivalence class of normal vectors for the plane $x_3 = 0$. It is interesting to note the form of the homogeneous coordinates for these ideal points and the ideal line (see Exercise 3).

Using this identification, it should become apparent that points in π' are collinear if and only if the corresponding lines through the origin in E^3 are coplanar, but a result from linear algebra says these lines in E^3 are coplanar if and only if their direction vectors are linearly dependent. Likewise, lines in π' are concurrent if and only if the corresponding planes through the origin in E^3 intersect along a common line, but this happens if and only if their normal vectors are linearly dependent. These observations anticipate the following results, which give algebraic conditions for the collinearity of points and concurrence of lines. (The proofs of these results are nearly identical to those used in Chapter 3.)

Theorem 4.17
Three points X, Y, Z are collinear if and only if the determinant

$$\begin{vmatrix} x_1 & y_1 & z_1 \\ x_2 & y_2 & z_2 \\ x_3 & y_3 & z_3 \end{vmatrix} = 0$$

Corollary
The equation of the line PQ can be written

$$\begin{vmatrix} x_1 & p_1 & q_1 \\ x_2 & p_2 & q_2 \\ x_3 & p_3 & q_3 \end{vmatrix} = 0$$

The dual statements give algebraic methods for determining when three lines are concurrent and for finding the equation of a point determined by two lines. Here, however, the coordinates of the lines are used as rows rather than columns.

Theorem 4.18
Three lines u, v, w are concurrent if and only if the determinant

$$\begin{vmatrix} u_1 & u_2 & u_3 \\ v_1 & v_2 & v_3 \\ w_1 & w_2 & w_3 \end{vmatrix} = 0$$

Corollary

The equation of the point p·q can be written

$$
\begin{vmatrix}
u_1 & u_2 & u_3 \\
p_1 & p_2 & p_3 \\
q_1 & q_2 & q_3
\end{vmatrix} = 0
$$

Example 4.1

Find the equation of the point of intersection of lines $p[-2, 5, 7]$ and $q[3, 1, 2]$.

Solution

Using the corollary to Theorem 4.18, we can find the equation of the point by setting the following determinant equal to 0:

$$
\begin{vmatrix}
u_1 & u_2 & u_3 \\
-2 & 5 & 7 \\
3 & 1 & 2
\end{vmatrix} = 0
$$

Expanding this determinant results in the equation $3u_1 + 25u_2 - 17u_3 = 0$, which is the equation of a point. Note that the coordinates of this point are $(3, 25, -17)$. $\qquad\square$

In this model we can now show that projectivities between pencils can be represented via 2×2 matrices. (The analytic form of the transformations of the entire projective plane, transformations which induce projectivities, will require 3×3 matrices and be developed later. This matrix representation of projectivities requires that points and lines be assigned ordered pairs of real numbers rather than ordered triples. This is done by picking *base elements* for a pencil and making use of the following theorem.

Theorem 4.19

If $P(p_1, p_2, p_3)$ and $Q(q_1, q_2, q_3)$ are two distinct points, any point R of the line PQ has homogeneous coordinates (r_1, r_2, r_3) where $r_i = \lambda_1 p_i + \lambda_2 q_i$, $i = 1, 2, 3$, and λ_1, λ_2 are real but not both 0; and conversely any point R with homogeneous coordinates of this form is on line PQ.

Proof

(a) Assume R has homogeneous coordinates $(\lambda_1 p_1 + \lambda_2 q_1, \lambda_1 p_2 + \lambda_2 q_2, \lambda_1 p_3 + \lambda_2 q_3)$; then

$$
\begin{vmatrix} r_1 & p_1 & q_1 \\ r_2 & p_2 & q_2 \\ r_3 & p_3 & q_3 \end{vmatrix} = \begin{vmatrix} \lambda_1 p_1 + \lambda_2 q_1 & p_1 & q_1 \\ \lambda_1 p_2 + \lambda_2 q_2 & p_2 & q_2 \\ \lambda_1 p_3 + \lambda_2 q_3 & p_3 & q_3 \end{vmatrix} = 0
$$

So by Theorem 4.17, the points P, Q, and R are collinear.

(b) If R is on PQ then $|PQR| = 0$, or in other words, the vectors corresponding to these three points are linearly dependent. Thus, there exist real numbers $\lambda_1, \lambda_2, \lambda_3$, not all zero, such that $\lambda_1 P + \lambda_2 Q + \lambda_3 R = 0$. Note that $\lambda_3 \neq 0$, since P and Q are distinct points, therefore, assume $\lambda_3 = -1$; thus, $\lambda_1 P + \lambda_2 Q = R$. ∎

Definition 4.16

The points P and Q used in Theorem 4.19 are called *base points*, while λ_1 and λ_2 are called *homogeneous parameters* of R with respect to P and Q.

Clearly the homogeneous parameters of the base points P and Q are $(1, 0)$ and $(0, 1)$, respectively. In general, the homogeneous parameters of a point depend on the base points chosen and on their homogeneous coordinates. So specific homogeneous coordinates for the base points must be used (see Exercise 9). Even so, there is not a unique set of homogeneous parameters for each point, since (λ_1, λ_2) and $(k\lambda_1, k\lambda_2)$ represent the same point $(k \neq 0)$; but the ratio $\lambda = \lambda_1 / \lambda_2$, is unique. This ratio is called the *parameter* of the point. Note that the parameter of Q is 0, while the parameter of P is said to be ∞. Thus, the real numbers can be put into one-to-one correspondence with all points on a line except one, namely, the first base point.

Using homogeneous parameters and Theorem 4.19, we can now show that our analytic model satisfies Axiom 4.5. (If two triangles are perspective from a point, then they are perspective from a line.)

Verification of Axiom 4.5

Let the two triangles have vertices $A(a_1, a_2, a_3)$, $B(b_1, b_2, b_3)$, $C(c_1, c_2, c_3)$ and $A'(a'_1, a'_2, a'_3)$, $B'(b'_1, b'_2, b'_3)$, $C'(c'_1, c'_2, c'_3)$. Assume these triangles are perspective from $P(p_1, p_2, p_3)$. Let $Q = AB \cdot A'B$, $R = BC \cdot B'C'$, and $S = AC \cdot A'C'$. We need to show that Q, R, and S are collinear (Fig. 4.34).

To do this we make use of homogeneous parameters. Since P is on line AA', BB', and CC', it has homogeneous parameters (α_1, α_2), (β_1, β_2), and (γ_1, γ_2) with respect to base points A and A', B and B', C and C', respectively. Thus, the homogeneous coordinates of P are given by $p_i = \alpha_1 a_i + \alpha_2 a'_i = \beta_1 b_i + \beta_2 b'_i = \gamma_1 c_i + \gamma_2 c'_i, i = 1, 2, 3$. The first two of these yield $\alpha_1 a_i - \beta_1 b_i = \beta_2 b'_i - \alpha_2 a'_i$, so $(\alpha_1 a_1 - \beta_1 b_1, \alpha_1 a_2 - \beta_1 b_2, \alpha_1 a_3 - \beta_1 b_3) = (\beta_2 b'_1 - \alpha_2 a'_1, \beta_2 b'_2 - \alpha_2 a'_2, \beta_2 b'_3 - \alpha_2 a'_3)$, but the first of these ordered triples gives homogeneous coordinates for a point on line AB, whereas the second gives homogeneous coordinates for a point on line $A'B'$. Since the two triples are equal, both must be coordinates for the point Q. We will use the first set. Likewise we can show that $R(\beta_1 b_1 - \gamma_1 c_1, \beta_1 b_2 - \gamma_1 c_2, \beta_1 b_3 - \gamma_1 c_3)$ and finally that $S(\alpha_1 a_1 - \gamma_1 c_1, \alpha_1 a_2 - \gamma_1 c_2, \alpha_1 a_3 - \gamma_1 c_3)$. Using these homogeneous coordinates, we can show that $|QRS| = 0$ so that the three points are indeed collinear.

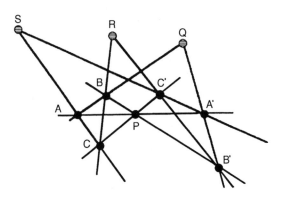

FIGURE 4.34   Verification of Axiom 4.5.

Exercises

1. Show that the interpretation of incident used in our analytic model is independent of the particular homogeneous coordinates used for the point X and the line u.

2. Verify that the set of interpretations of the undefined terms given in this section satisfies Axioms 4.1–4.3.

3. (a) Describe the homogeneous coordinates of the ideal points. (b) Find homogeneous coordinates of the ideal line. (c) Show analytically that the ideal points lie on the ideal line.

4. Let $l[a, b, c]$ be a line. Find homogeneous coordinates of the ideal point(s) on l. How many ideal points are there on l?

5. (a) Find the equation of the line joining the points $(0, 2, 1)$ and $(1, 1, 0)$. (b) Find a set of coordinates for this line. (c) Find the point of intersection of the lines $2x_2 + x_3 = 0$ and $x_1 + x_2 = 0$. (d) Find the line joining the points $2u_2 + u_3 = 0$ and $u_1 + u_2 = 0$.

6. Let $l[a, b, c]$ and $m[a, b, d]$ be two distinct lines in the projective plane (i.e., $c \neq d$). (a) Find the point of intersection of l and m (b) Do l and m intersect in the Euclidean plane? Why?

7. Let X, Y, Z be the points with homogeneous coordinates $(1, 0, 0)$, $(0, 1, 0)$, and $(0, 0, 1)$, respectively. (a) Show that X, Y, Z are non-collinear. (b) Show that if $P(p_1, p_2, p_3)$ is any point distinct from Z then the point $P' = ZP \cdot XY$ has homogeneous coordinates $(p_1, p_2, 0)$.

8. Show that the points $P(2, 3, -2)$, $Q(1, 2, -4)$, and $R(0, 1, -6)$ are collinear and find homogeneous parameters of R with respect to P and Q. What is the corresponding parameter of R?

9. Find an example showing that the homogeneous parameters of a point with respect to a given pair of base points depend on the homogeneous coordinates used for the base points.

10. Use ordered triples consisting of 0's, and 1's and arithmetic modulo 2 to coordinatize the finite projective plane with three points on a line (see Section 1.3).

4.8 The Analytic Form of Projectivities

Using our analytic model of the projective plane, it is now possible to find 2×2 matrix representations of the one-to-one correspondences between the elements of two pencils known as projectivities.

Theorem 4.20

A projectivity between the elements of two pencils can be represented by a real matrix equation of the form

$$s\begin{bmatrix} \lambda_1' \\ \lambda_2' \end{bmatrix} = \begin{bmatrix} a_{11} & a_{12} \\ a_{21} & a_{22} \end{bmatrix}\begin{bmatrix} \lambda_1 \\ \lambda_2 \end{bmatrix}$$

where $a_{11}a_{22} - a_{21}a_{12} = |A| \neq 0$, $s \neq 0$, and where (λ_1, λ_2) and (λ_1', λ_2') are homogeneous parameters of the original and image elements with respect to predetermined base elements.

Proof

We first show that a perspectivity from a pencil of points to a pencil of lines has this algebraic form.

Let P and Q be base points of the pencil of points and let the lines m and n be base lines of the pencil of lines. Let $X(\lambda_1, \lambda_2)$ be any other point on line PQ; assume it corresponds to line $x'(\lambda_1', \lambda_2')$. By the definition of the perspectivity, $x' \cdot X = 0$. Writing this out in terms of components, gives the following equation:

$$[\lambda_1' m_1 + \lambda_2' n_1, \lambda_1' m_2 + \lambda_2' n_2, \lambda_1' m_3 + \lambda_2' n_3] \cdot$$
$$(\lambda_1 p_1 + \lambda_2 q_1, \lambda_1 p_2 + \lambda_2 q_2, \lambda_1 p_3 + \lambda_2 q_3) = 0$$

or

$$\lambda_1' \lambda_1(p_1 m_1 + p_2 m_2 + p_3 m_3) + \lambda_1' \lambda_2(q_1 m_1 + q_2 m_2 + q_3 m_3)$$
$$+ \lambda_2' \lambda_1(p_1 n_1 + p_2 n_2 + p_3 n_3) + \lambda_2' \lambda_2(q_1 n_1 + q_2 n_2 + q_3 n_3) = 0 \quad (4.1)$$

To simplify Equation (4.1), we use a substitution for each of the sums in parentheses:

$$a_{21} = \sum p_i m_i, \quad a_{22} = \sum q_i m_i, \quad a_{11} = -\sum p_i n_i, \quad a_{12} = -\sum q_i n_i$$

so

$$a_{21}\lambda_1' \lambda_1 + a_{22}\lambda_1' \lambda_2 - a_{11}\lambda_2' \lambda_1 - a_{12}\lambda_2' \lambda_2 = 0 \quad (4.2)$$

or

$$\lambda_1'(a_{21}\lambda_1 + a_{22}\lambda_2) = \lambda_2'(a_{11}\lambda_1 + a_{12}\lambda_2)$$

This gives

$$\frac{\lambda_1'}{\lambda_2'} = \frac{a_{11}\lambda_1 + a_{12}\lambda_2}{a_{21}\lambda_1 + a_{22}\lambda_2}$$

which can be written in matrix notation as

$$s\begin{bmatrix} \lambda_1' \\ \lambda_2' \end{bmatrix} = \begin{bmatrix} a_{11} & a_{12} \\ a_{21} & a_{22} \end{bmatrix}\begin{bmatrix} \lambda_1 \\ \lambda_2 \end{bmatrix}$$

where $s \neq 0$. Note that $a_{11}a_{22} - a_{21}a_{12} = |A| \neq 0$ since the projectivity is a one-to-one mapping.

If we solve Equation (4.2) for λ_1/λ_2 we obtain a similar representation for a perspectivity from a pencil of lines to a pencil of points. Since any projectivity is a finite product of perspectivities and any perspectivity either maps from a pencil of points to a pencil of lines, or from a pencil of lines to a pencil of points, or is a product of these two, it is sufficient to note that the product of two matrices of this form will also be a matrix of this form. ∎

Using the matrix representation given in Theorem 4.20, it is now relatively easy to verify Axiom 4.6 (see Exercise 3). However, the verification of this axiom, as well as any other use of the matrix equation for a projectivity, requires careful attention to s, the scalar involved. Since the homogeneous parameters of elements of pencils are not unique, it is essential to allow s to take on different values even within the context of a given projectivity. The following example illustrates the way in which this indeterminate nature of the scalar must be handled in finding the matrix of a particular projectivity.

Example 4.2
Find a matrix of the projectivity that maps points on p with homogeneous parameters $(1, 3)$, $(1, 2)$, and $(2, 3)$ to points on p' with homogeneous parameters $(1, -4)$, $(0, 1)$, and $(-1, 1)$, respectively.

Solution

By Theorem 4.20, the projectivity can be represented by a 2×2 matrix A where

$$s_1 \begin{bmatrix} \lambda_1' \\ \lambda_2' \end{bmatrix} = \begin{bmatrix} a & b \\ c & d \end{bmatrix} \begin{bmatrix} \lambda_1 \\ \lambda_2 \end{bmatrix}$$

The algebra involved in finding such a matrix can be simplified somewhat by first considering any cases where the homogeneous parameters of either a point or its image include the value 0. In this case we will first impose the condition that the ordered pair $(1, 2)$ map to $(0, 1)$. It is also helpful to find and use all convenient substitutions as soon as possible. We will make use of both techniques in the following calculations.

In order to map $(1, 2)$ to $(0, 1)$ we must have

$$s_2 \begin{bmatrix} 0 \\ 1 \end{bmatrix} = \begin{bmatrix} a & b \\ c & d \end{bmatrix} \begin{bmatrix} 1 \\ 2 \end{bmatrix} \quad \text{or} \quad \begin{aligned} 0 &= a + 2b \qquad (4.3) \\ s_1 &= c + 2d \qquad (4.4) \end{aligned}$$

Equation (4.3) yields $a = -2b$, so we can use this substitution when requiring that the matrix map $(1, 3)$ to $(1, -4)$.

$$s_2 \begin{bmatrix} 1 \\ -4 \end{bmatrix} = \begin{bmatrix} -2b & b \\ c & d \end{bmatrix} \begin{bmatrix} 1 \\ 3 \end{bmatrix} \quad \text{or} \quad \begin{aligned} s_2 &= b \qquad (4.5) \\ -4s_2 &= c + 3d \qquad (4.6) \end{aligned}$$

Equation (4.5) allows us to replace s_2 with b in equation (4.6), giving $c = -3d - 4b$. Using this substitution, the third point and its image give the following equations:

$$s_3 \begin{bmatrix} -1 \\ 1 \end{bmatrix} = \begin{bmatrix} -2b & b \\ -3d - 4b & d \end{bmatrix} \begin{bmatrix} 2 \\ 3 \end{bmatrix} \quad \text{or} \quad \begin{aligned} -s_3 &= -b \qquad (4.7) \\ s_3 &= -3d - 8b \qquad (4.8) \end{aligned}$$

Since Equations (4.7) and (4.8) involve the three unknowns b, d, and s_3; we can choose a value for one of the unknowns. Let $s_3 = 1$. Then Equation (4.7) gives $b = 1$ and Equation (4.8) gives $d = -3$. Using these values in Equations (4.5) and (4.6) yields $c = 5$, and finally Equation (4.3) gives $a = -2$. So the matrix A is

$$\begin{bmatrix} -2 & 1 \\ 5 & -3 \end{bmatrix}$$

Note that the scalar s did assume different values, namely, $s_1 = -1$ while $s_2 = s_3 = 1$. □

The following proof of Theorem 4.21 (the converse of Theorem 4.20) also illustrates the way in which the matrix of a projectivity is determined.

Theorem 4.21

A mapping given by an equation of the following form is a projectivity

$$s\begin{bmatrix} \lambda_1' \\ \lambda_2' \end{bmatrix} = \begin{bmatrix} a & b \\ c & d \end{bmatrix}\begin{bmatrix} \lambda_1 \\ \lambda_2 \end{bmatrix}, \quad ad - bc \neq 0, \quad s \neq 0 \qquad (4.9)$$

Proof

The proof assumes that both pencils are pencils of points; however, identical arguments can be made for the other cases. Let $P(1, 0)$ and $Q(0, 1)$ be the base points for the first pencil of points. Let R be the point with parameters $(1, 1)$ with respect to P and Q. Then under the mapping given by this matrix equation, $P'(a, c)$, $Q'(b, d)$, and $R'(a + b, c + d)$ are the corresponding elements of the second pencil with respect to a predetermined basis. By the fundamental theorem, there is a unique projectivity T such that $T : PQR \rightarrow P'Q'R'$, but by Theorem 4.20 the projectivity T has a matrix equation

$$s\begin{bmatrix} \lambda_1' \\ \lambda_2' \end{bmatrix} = \begin{bmatrix} a_{11} & a_{12} \\ a_{21} & a_{22} \end{bmatrix}\begin{bmatrix} \lambda_1 \\ \lambda_2 \end{bmatrix}$$

It is then sufficient to show that this matrix is a scalar multiple of the matrix in Equation (4.9). To evaluate a, b, c, d, we will determine the algebraic conditions necessary for mapping P to P', Q to Q', and R to R'. Since the scalar s may differ from point to point, we need to allow s to assume different values in each of these cases leading to the following three equations:

$$s_1\begin{bmatrix} a \\ c \end{bmatrix} = \begin{bmatrix} a_{11} & a_{12} \\ a_{21} & a_{22} \end{bmatrix}\begin{bmatrix} 1 \\ 0 \end{bmatrix} \quad s_2\begin{bmatrix} b \\ d \end{bmatrix} = \begin{bmatrix} a_{11} & a_{12} \\ a_{21} & a_{22} \end{bmatrix}\begin{bmatrix} 0 \\ 1 \end{bmatrix}$$

$$s_3\begin{bmatrix} a + b \\ c + d \end{bmatrix} = \begin{bmatrix} a_{11} & a_{12} \\ a_{21} & a_{22} \end{bmatrix}\begin{bmatrix} 1 \\ 1 \end{bmatrix}$$

These matrix equations yield the following:

$$\begin{array}{lll} s_1 a = a_{11} & s_2 b = a_{12} & s_3(a + b) = a_{11} + a_{12} \\ s_1 c = a_{21} & s_2 d = a_{22} & s_3(c + d) = a_{21} + a_{22} \end{array}$$

Since there are six equations in seven unknowns, one unknown can be chosen. Chose $s_3 = 1$. Then

$$a + b = a_{11} + a_{12} = s_1 a + s_2 b$$
$$c + d = a_{21} + a_{22} = s_1 c + s_2 d$$

so

$$a(1 - s_1) + b(1 - s_2) = 0$$
$$c(1 - s_1) + d(1 - s_2) = 0$$

and since $ad - bc \neq 0$, the solution $s_1 = 1$, $s_2 = 1$ is unique. Thus, $a = a_{11}$ and so on, and the matrix equation

$$s \begin{bmatrix} \lambda_1' \\ \lambda_2' \end{bmatrix} = \begin{bmatrix} a_{11} & a_{12} \\ a_{21} & a_{22} \end{bmatrix} \begin{bmatrix} \lambda_1 \\ \lambda_2 \end{bmatrix}$$

is the representation of a projectivity. ∎

Together, Theorems 4.20 and 4.21 tell us that there is a one-to-one correspondence between the set of projectivities between two pencils relative to predetermined base elements and the set of equivalence classes of 2×2 matrices with nonzero determinants where $A \sim B$ if and only if $A = sB$ for some nonzero constant s.

According to Axiom 4.6, projectivities on a pencil other than the identity have two or fewer invariant elements. The next theorem characterizes the matrix representations of projectivities with two, one, and zero invariant elements, respectively. The proof of this theorem makes use of an important result about eigenvectors from linear algebra.

Theorem 4.22
A projectivity on a pencil other than the identity, with matrix

$$\begin{bmatrix} a_{11} & a_{12} \\ a_{21} & a_{22} \end{bmatrix},$$

has two distinct invariant elements, one invariant element, or no invariant elements according as

$$(a_{22} - a_{11})^2 + 4a_{12}a_{21} > 0, \ = 0, \ or \ < 0.$$

Proof

Note (λ_1, λ_2) is an invariant element if and only if

$$s \begin{bmatrix} \lambda_1 \\ \lambda_2 \end{bmatrix} = \begin{bmatrix} a_{11} & a_{12} \\ a_{21} & a_{22} \end{bmatrix} \begin{bmatrix} \lambda_1 \\ \lambda_2 \end{bmatrix}$$

that is, if and only if (λ_1, λ_2) is a characteristic vector or eigenvector of the matrix. But eigenvectors exist if and only if there is a nonzero solution of the characteristic equation $|A - sI| = 0$. Evaluating $|A - sI|$ gives $(a_{11} - s)(a_{22} - s) - a_{12}a_{21} = 0$. Expanding and solving for s yields the following:

$$s = \frac{(a_{22} + a_{11}) \pm \sqrt{(a_{22} + a_{11})^2 - 4(a_{11}a_{22} - a_{12}a_{21})}}{2}.$$

If the expression under the radical is positive, there are two distinct solutions for s and therefore two linearly independent eigenvectors and hence two distinct invariant points of the projectivity. If this expression is zero, there is exactly one solution for s and therefore exactly one invariant point of the projectivity (see Exercise 5). Finally, if the expression is negative, there are no real-valued solutions for s and so no invariant points of the projectivity. Since this expression is algebraically equivalent to the expression in the statement of the theorem, the result follows. ∎

Definition 4.17

A projectivity on a pencil is called *hyperbolic, parabolic,* or *elliptic* if the number of invariant elements is 2, 1, or 0, respectively.

These definitions are suggestive of a connection between projectivities on pencils and similarly named conics, which will be formalized in Section 4.12.

Exercises

1. If under a projectivity between pencils, the base elements P and Q of the first pencil correspond to the base elements P' and Q' of the

second pencil, respectively, show that the matrix of the projectivity is a diagonal matrix.

2. Find the matrix of the projectivity that maps points on p with homogeneous parameters $(0, 1)$, $(1, 0)$, and $(1, 1)$ to points on p' with homogeneous parameters $(1, 2)$, $(2, 3)$, and $(-1, 0)$, respectively.

3. Use Theorem 4.20 to verify that our analytic model satisfies Axiom 4.6. [*Hint*: You may want to choose two of the invariant elements as base elements.]

4. Find the homogeneous parameters of the invariant elements under the projectivity on a pencil that has the following matrix representation:

$$\begin{bmatrix} 6 & -4 \\ 1 & 1 \end{bmatrix}$$

5. A result from linear algebra says that there is at least one eigenvector corresponding to each solution s of the equation $|A - sI| = 0$. Show that there cannot be two linearly independent eigenvectors corresponding to the same solution s when A is a 2×2 nonscalar matrix, i.e., when $A \neq sI$ for a scalar s.

The following exercises refer to a special type of projectivity known as an *involution*. An involution is a transformation $T \neq I$ such that $T^2 = I$.

6. Prove that a projectivity on a pencil that interchanges one pair of distinct elements is an *involution*. [*Hint*: Use the two points that are interchanged as base points and find the matrix representation.]

7. Show that in general the matrix of an involution is of the form

$$\begin{bmatrix} a & b \\ c & -a \end{bmatrix} \quad \text{where} \quad a^2 + bc \neq 0.$$

8. Show that an involution with a matrix of the form given in Exercise 7 is elliptic if and only if $a^2 + bc < 0$.

9. By using two points that are interchanged as base points, show that the matrix of an elliptic involution is of the form given in Exercise 7 with $a = 0$, and $bc < 0$.

4.9 Cross Ratios

Within the context of the analytic model of the projective plane, it is natural to ask if the Euclidean concept of distance is relevant. However, as previously indicated, projective geometry studies invariants under transformations—transformations that can be considered as generalized affinities and affinities in turn are generalizations of similarities. In Chapter 3, we discovered that similarities do not preserve distances but only ratios of distances, and affinities only preserve segment division ratios. This suggests that the concept of distance may not be relevant in projective geometry, so it is surprising that we are able to show that projective transformations do preserve a numerical value called the *cross ratio*, which can actually be interpreted as a ratio of ratios of distances.

Definition 4.18

If A, B, C, D are four distinct elements of a pencil with homogeneous parameters (α_1, α_2), (β_1, β_2), (γ_1, γ_2), and (δ_1, δ_2) with respect to given base points, then the *cross ratio* $R(A, B, C, D)$ of the four elements, in the given order, is the number given by the following equation involving determinants:

$$R(A, B, C, D) = \frac{\begin{vmatrix} \gamma_1 & \alpha_1 \\ \gamma_2 & \alpha_2 \end{vmatrix}}{\begin{vmatrix} \gamma_1 & \beta_1 \\ \gamma_2 & \beta_2 \end{vmatrix}} \div \frac{\begin{vmatrix} \delta_1 & \alpha_1 \\ \delta_2 & \alpha_2 \end{vmatrix}}{\begin{vmatrix} \delta_1 & \beta_1 \\ \delta_2 & \beta_2 \end{vmatrix}}.$$

In this definition, if none of the four elements A, B, C, D is the first base element, each will also have homogeneous parameters $(\alpha, 1)$, $(\beta, 1)$, $(\gamma, 1)$, $(\delta, 1)$, respectively, where α, β, γ, δ are the corresponding (nonhomogeneous) parameters. Note in this case the cross ratio becomes

$$R(A, B, C, D) = \frac{\gamma - \alpha}{\gamma - \beta} \div \frac{\delta - \alpha}{\delta - \beta}.$$

It is this restatement of the definition that makes the interpretation of "a ratio of ratios of distances" more apparent (see Exercise 3). Even though the notation used in the previous definition is suggestive of a pencil of points, the definition applies to both pencils of points and pencils of lines. We will make use of similar notation in the following theorems, which indicate how changes in the order of the elements affect the cross ratio. The proofs of these theorems follow from the definition by algebraic computation.

Theorem 4.23

If A, B, C, D are four distinct elements of a pencil. then the cross ratio $R(A, B, C, D)$ remains unchanged when any two pairs of the elements are interchanged; that is, $R(A, B, C, D) = R(B, A, D, C) = R(C, D, A, B) = R(D, C, B, A)$.

Theorem 4.24

If the cross ratio of four distinct elements of a pencil named in a given order is r, interchanging either the first or second pair of elements changes the cross ratio to its reciprocal $1/r$, interchanging either the inner pair or the outer pair changes the cross ratio r to $1 - r$.

Corollary

The 24 possible permutations of four distinct elements of a pencil can be categorized into six sets of four, corresponding to cross ratios of

$$r, \quad 1/r, \quad 1 - r, \quad (r - 1)/r, \quad r/(r - 1), \quad \text{and} \quad 1/(1 - r).$$

Theorem 4.25

The cross ratio of four distinct elements of a pencil cannot be 0, 1, or ∞.

Since projective transformations will induce projectivities mapping one pencil to another, demonstrating the invariance of the cross ratio under projectivities will verify its invariance under projective transformations.

Theorem 4.26

The cross ratio of four distinct elements of a pencil is invariant under a projectivity (so, e.g., if $ABCD \wedge A'B'C'D'$, then $R(A, B, C, D) = R(A', B', C', D')$).

Proof

Assume that distinct elements A, B, C, D of one pencil map to corresponding elements A', B', C', D' of a second pencil under a projectivity with matrix $A = [a_{ij}]$. Then

$$\begin{vmatrix} \gamma_1' & \alpha_1' \\ \gamma_2' & \alpha_2' \end{vmatrix} = \begin{vmatrix} a_{11} & a_{12} \\ a_{21} & a_{22} \end{vmatrix} \begin{vmatrix} \gamma_1 & \alpha_1 \\ \gamma_2 & \alpha_2 \end{vmatrix}$$

where A has homogeneous parameters (α_1, α_2), A' has homogeneous parameters (α_1', α_2') and so on, with respect to predetermined base elements. So

$$R(A', B', C', D') = \frac{\begin{vmatrix} \gamma_1' & \alpha_1' \\ \gamma_2' & \alpha_2' \end{vmatrix}}{\begin{vmatrix} \gamma_1' & \beta_1' \\ \gamma_2' & \beta_2' \end{vmatrix}} \div \frac{\begin{vmatrix} \delta_1' & \alpha_1' \\ \delta_2' & \alpha_2' \end{vmatrix}}{\begin{vmatrix} \delta_1' & \beta_1' \\ \delta_2' & \beta_2' \end{vmatrix}}$$

$$= \frac{\begin{vmatrix} a_{11} & a_{12} \\ a_{21} & a_{22} \end{vmatrix} \begin{vmatrix} \gamma_1 & \alpha_1 \\ \gamma_2 & \alpha_2 \end{vmatrix}}{\begin{vmatrix} a_{11} & a_{12} \\ a_{21} & a_{22} \end{vmatrix} \begin{vmatrix} \gamma_1 & \beta_1 \\ \gamma_2 & \beta_2 \end{vmatrix}} \div \frac{\begin{vmatrix} a_{11} & a_{12} \\ a_{21} & a_{22} \end{vmatrix} \begin{vmatrix} \delta_1 & \alpha_1 \\ \delta_2 & \alpha_2 \end{vmatrix}}{\begin{vmatrix} a_{11} & a_{12} \\ a_{21} & a_{22} \end{vmatrix} \begin{vmatrix} \delta_1 & \beta_1 \\ \delta_2 & \beta_2 \end{vmatrix}}$$

$$= \frac{\begin{vmatrix} \gamma_1 & \alpha_1 \\ \gamma_2 & \alpha_2 \end{vmatrix}}{\begin{vmatrix} \gamma_1 & \beta_1 \\ \gamma_2 & \beta_2 \end{vmatrix}} \div \frac{\begin{vmatrix} \delta_1 & \alpha_1 \\ \delta_2 & \alpha_2 \end{vmatrix}}{\begin{vmatrix} \delta_1 & \beta_1 \\ \delta_2 & \beta_2 \end{vmatrix}}$$

$$= R(A, B, C, D).$$

∎

This theorem leads to a useful corollary, which enables the computation of the cross ratio of four elements directly from the homogeneous coordinates of the elements rather than from homogeneous parameters, which in turn must be first computed relative to given base points.

Corollary

If A, B, C, D, with homogeneous coordinates (a_1, a_2, a_3) and so on, are four distinct elements of a pencil not containing $Z(0, 0, 1)$ then

$$\frac{\begin{vmatrix} c_1 & a_1 \\ c_2 & a_2 \end{vmatrix}}{\begin{vmatrix} c_1 & b_1 \\ c_2 & b_2 \end{vmatrix}} \div \frac{\begin{vmatrix} d_1 & a_1 \\ d_2 & a_2 \end{vmatrix}}{\begin{vmatrix} d_1 & b_1 \\ d_2 & b_2 \end{vmatrix}} = R(A, B, C, D).$$

Thus, if $Z(0, 0, 1)$ is not an element of the pencil, the first two homogeneous coordinates of each element can be used in the role of homogeneous parameters in the cross ratio. But if the pencil, *does* contain $Z(0, 0, 1)$ (so this corollary fails to hold), then it cannot also contain both $X(1, 0, 0)$ and $Y(0, 1, 0)$, and comparable corollaries can be proved for pencils not containing X and for pencils not containing

Y (see Exercise 8), The use of one of these comparable statements is demonstrated in Example 4.3.

Example 4.3
Find $R(A, B, C, D)$ where $A(1, 2, 1)$, $B(3, 6, 1)$, $C(2, 4, 1)$, and $D(1, 2, 0)$ are points on $l[2, -1, 0]$. (Note that if these points are identified as points in the Euclidean plane, C would be called the midpoint of segment $\overline{AB}$.)

Solution
Since $Z(0, 0, 1)$ is clearly a point on l, we cannot use the corollary to Theorem 4.26 directly. However, since $X(1, 0, 0)$ is not incident with l, we can use a comparable result; that is, we can use the last two homogeneous coordinates of each point in the role of homogeneous parameters in order to compute the cross ratio. This gives

$$R(A, B, C, D) = \frac{\begin{vmatrix} 4 & 2 \\ 1 & 1 \end{vmatrix}}{\begin{vmatrix} 4 & 6 \\ 1 & 1 \end{vmatrix}} \div \frac{\begin{vmatrix} 2 & 2 \\ 0 & 1 \end{vmatrix}}{\begin{vmatrix} 2 & 6 \\ 0 & 1 \end{vmatrix}} = \frac{2}{-2} \div \frac{2}{2} = -1$$

Recall that the fundamental theorem of projective geometry indicates that in general there exists a projectivity mapping any three elements of one pencil to any three corresponding elements of a second pencil. However, as will be shown in Theorem 4.28, if any four elements of the first pencil are named and any four corresponding elements of the second pencil *with the same cross ratio* are given, there is a projectivity mapping the first set of four elements to the second set of four elements. The proof of this result requires one additional property of cross ratios that can also be verified by algebraic computation.

Theorem 4.27
If three distinct elements A, B, C of a pencil and a real number $r(r \neq 0, 1)$ are given, then there exists a unique point D such that $R(A, B, C, D) = r$.

Theorem 4.28
If A, B, C, D are four distinct elements of one pencil and A', B', C', D' are four distinct elements of a second pencil with $R(A', B', C', D') =$

$R(A, B, C, D)$, then there exists a projectivity mapping A, B, C, D to A', B', C', D', respectively.

Proof
By the fundamental theorem, there exists a projectivity such that $ABC \wedge A'B'C'$. Let D^* be the unique image of D under this projectivity. By Theorem 4.26, $R(A, B, C, D) = R(A', B', C', D^*)$; but $R(A, B, C, D) = R(A', B', C', D')$. So $D^* = D'$. ∎

The proof of Theorem 4.28, together with the previous theorems indicating the changes in the cross ratio resulting from various possible changes in the ordering of the four elements, is reminiscent of similar theorems about harmonic sets and suggests a possible relation between the two concepts. This relation is formalized in the final theorem of this section.

Theorem 4.29
If A, B, C, D are four distinct elements of a pencil, then

$$R(A, B, C, D) = -1$$

if and only if $H(AB, CD)$.

Proof
(a) Since $H(AB, CD)$, it follows that $H(AB, DC)$ and, by Theorem 4.10, there is a projectivity such that $ABCD \wedge ABDC$. Thus, by Theorem 4.26 $R(A, B, C, D) = R(A, B, D, C)$; but by Theorem 4.24, if $R(A, B, C, D) = r$, then $R(A, B, D, C) = 1/r$. Thus, $r = 1/r$, or $r^2 = 1$. Since $r \neq 1$, this implies that $r = -1$.
(b) Assume $R(A, B, C, D) = -1$. Let D' be a fourth element of a pencil such that $H(AB, CD')$. Thus, by the previous part of the proof, $R(A, B, C, D') = -1$, and it follows by Theorem 4.27 that $D = D'$. ∎

Exercises

1. Given collinear points with their homogeneous parameters $A(1, 1)$, $B(3, 2)$, $C(1, 0)$, $D(-1, 2)$, find $R(A, B, C, D)$ and $R(C, A, B, D)$.

2. Find the coordinates of a point D that is collinear with $A(3, 1, 2)$, $B(1, 0 - 1)$, $C(1, 1, 4)$, and $R(A, B, C, D) = -\frac{2}{3}$.

3. In the Euclidean plane, let A, B, C, D be distinct points on a number line with coordinates α, β, γ, δ respectively. Show that the (nonhomogeneous) parameters form of the cross ratio $R(A, B, C, D)$ is the ratio of two segment division ratios of these four points (see Section 3.13).

4. Show that if C has homogeneous parameters $(1, 1)$ and D has homogeneous parameters $(r, 1)$ with respect to A and B, then

$$R(A, B, C, D) = r.$$

5. Prove Theorem 4.24.

6. Prove Theorem 4.25.

7. Prove the corollary to Theorem 4.26. [*Hint*: See Exercise 7 in Section 4.7]

8. What is the comparable statement to the corollary to Theorem 4.26 for pencils not containing $X(1, 0, 0)$? For pencils not containing $Y(0, 1, 0)$?

9. Prove Theorem 4.27.

10. Prove: If A, B, C, D, E are five distinct collinear points, then $R(A, B, C, D) \cdot R(A, B, D, E) = R(A, B, C, E)$.

4.10   Collineations

There are two distinct types of transformations of the projective plane. The transformations considered in this section map collinear points to collinear points (and thus lines to lines). These transformations, called *collineations*, form a group; it is the invariants of this group that are studied in projective geometry. In the next section, we consider transformations that map collinear points to concurrent lines (and thus lines to points). These transformations, called *correlations*, allow mappings between dual figures and provide an analytic equation for conics.

If we let V be the set of points of the analytic model of the projective plane together with $\{(0, 0, 0)\}$ (i.e., V is the set of *all* equivalence classes of R^3), we can show that V is a vector space under the usual addition and scalar multiplication in R^3 (see Exercise 1). Collineations are defined as linear transformations of this vector space.

Definition 4.19
A one-to-one linear transformation of V onto itself is a *collineation*.

With this definition, a slight modification of Theorem 3.3 leads to the following result giving the analytic form for collineations (see Exercise 2).

Theorem 4.30
A collineation can be represented by a 3×3 real-valued matrix A where $|A| \neq 0$. The matrix equation for the collineation is $sX' = AX$ where $X \in R^3$ and $s \neq 0$.

There are two important observations about this theorem we should make. First, equations of collineations, like equations of projectivities, contain nonzero scalars, and it is essential to allow this scalar to take on different values even within the context of the same collineation. Second, the matrix of a collineation is not unique (since if A is the matrix of a given collineation, kA will also be a matrix of the collineation for any nonzero scalar k), but there is a unique equivalence class of matrices corresponding to each collineation (see Exercise 4).

To show that the term "collineation" is appropriate, we need to verify that these mappings do indeed preserve collinearity as previously claimed. We can then conclude that collineations induce mappings from lines to lines, so it is appropriate to look for an equation that gives the image of a line directly.

Theorem 4.31
A collineation maps collinear points to collinear points. The image of a line $u[u_1, u_2, u_3]$ under a collineation with matrix A is given by the equation $ku' = uA^{-1}$, $k \neq 0$.

Proof
Assume that P is a point on line QR. Then it suffices to show that P', the image of P under the collineation, is collinear with the images of Q and R, namely, Q' and R'. Since P is on QR, Theorem 4.19 implies that there are two real numbers λ_1 and λ_2 such that $P = \lambda_1 Q + \lambda_2 R$. Then $sP' = AP = A(\lambda_1 Q + \lambda_2 R)$ for some nonzero scalar s, or $P' =$

$(\lambda_1/s)AQ + (\lambda_2/s)AR = \lambda_1 Q' + \lambda_2 R'$ so, again by Theorem 4.19, P' is on line $Q'R'$.

To find the equation of the image line, assume the collineation with matrix A maps the line with coordinates u and equation $uX = 0$ to the line with coordinates u' and equation $u'X' = 0$ where $sX' = AX$ for some nonzero scalar s. Replacing X' in the equation of the image line with $(1/s)AX$ yields $u'X' = (1/s)u'AX = 0$. Thus, the point X' is on the line $u'X' = 0$ if and only if X is on the line $(u'A)X = 0$, but X' is on $u'X' = 0$ if and only if X is on $uX = 0$. Since collineations are one-to-one mappings, $u'AX = 0$ and $uX = 0$ must be the same line. Thus, $u = ku'A$ or $ku' = uA^{-1}$. ■

This means that the *same* collineation that maps points according to the equation $sX' = AX$ maps lines according to the equation $ku' = uA^{-1}$. Thus, there are two equations that describe the mapping of any particular collineation: a *point equation*, that gives the images of points; and a *line equation*, that gives the images of lines. The matrix A used in the point equation is called the *matrix of the collineation*.

Since a collineation maps collinear points to collinear points, duality suggests that it will also map concurrent lines to concurrent lines. The proof of this corollary begins with the line equation of the collineation and is an exact parallel of the first part of the proof of Theorem 4.31.

Corollary
Under a collineation, concurrent lines are mapped to concurrent lines.

The set of collineations under the operation of composition form a group as can be verified by using the definition of group (see Exercise 5).

Theorem 4.32
The set of collineations forms a group under composition.

As noted several times previously, Klein defined projective geometry as the study of properties of V that are invariant under the group of collineations. The following theorem shows that the properties of cross ratio and harmonic relation, which we have previously shown invariant under projectivities, are also invariant under collineations.

Theorem 4.33

A collineation of the projective plane induces a projectivity between the elements of corresponding pencils.

Proof

Let P, Q, R be three collinear points, so $R = \lambda_1 P + \lambda_2 Q$. Let P', Q', and R' be their images under a collineation with matrix A. Then P', Q', and R' are also collinear so $R' = \mu_1 P' + \mu_2 Q'$. Applying the collineation to P, Q, and R yields $s_1 P' = AP$, $s_2 Q' = AQ$, $s_3 R' = AR$, where each $s_i \neq 0$. Since $R = \lambda_1 P + \lambda_2 Q$, this last equation gives $s_3 R' = A(\lambda_1 P + \lambda_2 Q) = \lambda_1 AP + \lambda_2 AQ = s_1 \lambda_1 P' + s_2 \lambda_2 Q'$. So when P and Q are base elements of the first pencil and P' and Q' are base elements of the second pencil, the element R of the first pencil has homogeneous parameters (λ_1, λ_2), whereas its image R' has homogeneous parameters (μ_1, μ_2), where

$$s_3 \begin{bmatrix} \mu_1 \\ \mu_2 \end{bmatrix} = \begin{bmatrix} s_1 & 0 \\ 0 & s_2 \end{bmatrix} \begin{bmatrix} \lambda_1 \\ \lambda_2 \end{bmatrix} \quad \text{and} \quad \begin{vmatrix} s_1 & 0 \\ 0 & s_2 \end{vmatrix} \neq 0.$$

Therefore, by Theorem 4.21 the induced mapping between pencils of points is a projectivity. The proof for pencils of lines follows by duality. ∎

Corollary

Cross ratios and harmonic sets are invariant under collineations.

Having established the connection between collineations of the projective plane and projectivities of pencils, we will now study the general properties of collineations. Whereas projectivities are uniquely determined by three pairs of corresponding elements, the next theorem shows that collineations are uniquely determined by four pairs of corresponding elements. The proof of this theorem illustrates a useful technique for finding the matrix of a collineation.

Theorem 4.34

There exists a unique collineation that maps any four points, no three collinear, to any four points, no three collinear.

Proof

The verification of this theorem consists of algebraically finding a matrix A of the collineation that maps any four points P, Q, R, S (no three collinear) to any four points P', Q', R', S' (no three collinear) and noting that this matrix is uniquely determined modulo the equivalence relation. This procedure can be simplified somewhat by first finding a matrix B such that $s_1 P' = BX$, $s_2 Q' = BY$, $s_3 R' = BZ$ and $s_4 S' = BU$ where $X(1, 0, 0)$, $Y(0, 1, 0)$, $Z(0, 0, 1)$, and $U(1, 1, 1)$ and then finding a matrix C such that $s_5 P = CX$, $s_6 Q = CY$, $s_7 R = CZ$, $s_8 S = CU$. The matrix A is then given by $A = BC^{-1}$. ∎

Corollary

A collineation of the plane with four invariant points, no three collinear, is the identity transformation.

Clearly a collineation is also uniquely determined by four lines (no three concurrent) and four image lines (no three concurrent) and the matrix A^{-1} used in the line equation of the collineation can be found by a procedure similar to that outlined in the proof of Theorem 4.34. This "simplified" procedure for finding the matrix of a collineation that maps a given set of four points (no three collinear) to a given set of four image points (no three collinear) is demonstrated in Example 4.4.

Example 4.4

Find a matrix of the collineation that maps $P(1, -3, 2)$, $Q(2, -1, 3)$, $R(0, 3, -2)$, and $S(-1, 3, 0)$ to $P'(3, 7, 7)$, $Q'(0, 0, 1)$, $R'(5, 7, 6)$, and $S'(1, 9, 7)$, respectively,

Solution

The verification that no three of the points P, Q, R, and S are collinear requires the verification that none of the four determinants $|PQR|$, $|PQS|$, $|PRS|$, and $|QRS|$ are zero. Similar computations are required to show that no three of the points P', Q', R', and S' are collinear.

Following the procedure outlined in the proof of Theorem 4.34, we first find the matrix B by writing out the matrix equations for each of the equations: $s_1 P' = BX$, $s_2 Q' = BY$, $s_3 R' = BZ$, and $s_4 S' = BU$.

The first of these equations becomes

$$\begin{bmatrix} b_{11} & b_{12} & b_{13} \\ b_{21} & b_{22} & b_{23} \\ b_{31} & b_{32} & b_{33} \end{bmatrix} \begin{bmatrix} 1 \\ 0 \\ 0 \end{bmatrix} = s_1 \begin{bmatrix} 3 \\ 7 \\ 7 \end{bmatrix} \quad \text{or} \quad \begin{aligned} b_{11} &= 3s_1 \\ b_{21} &= 7s_1 \\ b_{31} &= 7s_1 \end{aligned} \qquad (4.10)$$

Before writing out the matrix version of the second equation, we replace the first column by these values.

$$\begin{bmatrix} 3s_1 & b_{12} & b_{13} \\ 7s_1 & b_{22} & b_{23} \\ 7s_1 & b_{32} & b_{33} \end{bmatrix} \begin{bmatrix} 0 \\ 1 \\ 0 \end{bmatrix} = s_2 \begin{bmatrix} 0 \\ 0 \\ 1 \end{bmatrix} \quad \text{or} \quad \begin{aligned} b_{12} &= 0 \\ b_{22} &= 0 \\ b_{32} &= s_2 \end{aligned} \qquad (4.11)$$

By replacing the second column, the third equation becomes

$$\begin{bmatrix} 3s_1 & 0 & b_{13} \\ 7s_1 & 0 & b_{23} \\ 7s_1 & s_2 & b_{33} \end{bmatrix} \begin{bmatrix} 0 \\ 0 \\ 1 \end{bmatrix} = s_3 \begin{bmatrix} 5 \\ 7 \\ 6 \end{bmatrix} \quad \text{or} \quad \begin{aligned} b_{13} &= 5s_3 \\ b_{23} &= 7s_3 \\ b_{33} &= 6s_3 \end{aligned} \qquad (4.12)$$

Finally the fourth equation becomes

$$\begin{bmatrix} 3s_1 & 0 & 5s_3 \\ 7s_1 & 0 & 7s_3 \\ 7s_1 & s_2 & 6s_3 \end{bmatrix} \begin{bmatrix} 1 \\ 1 \\ 1 \end{bmatrix} = s_4 \begin{bmatrix} 1 \\ 9 \\ 7 \end{bmatrix} \quad \text{or} \quad \begin{aligned} 3s_1 & + 5s_3 = s_4 \\ 7s_1 & + 7s_3 = 9s_4 \\ 7s_1 &+ s_2 + 6s_3 = 7s_4 \end{aligned} \ (4.13)$$

Applying straightforward row reduction to the coefficient matrix for these equations yields $s_1 = -19$, $s_2 = 24$, $s_3 = 10$, and $s_4 = -7$; so the matrix B can be obtained by substituting these values in the matrix in (4.13):

$$B = \begin{bmatrix} -57 & 0 & 50 \\ -133 & 0 & 70 \\ -133 & 24 & 60 \end{bmatrix}$$

Having found the matrix B, we now need to find the matrix C, which is determined by the four equations $s_5 P = CX$, $s_6 Q = CY$, $s_7 R = CZ$, and $s_8 S = CU$. We can simplify these calculations considerably by merely noting that we are again mapping the points X, Y, and Z with the matrix C so that the matrix equation comparable to (4.13) can be obtained by merely replacing the first, second, and third columns with s_5P, s_6Q, and s_7R giving

$$\begin{bmatrix} 1s_5 & 2s_6 & 0 \\ -3s_5 & -1s_6 & 3s_7 \\ 2s_5 & 3s_6 & -2s_7 \end{bmatrix} \begin{bmatrix} 1 \\ 1 \\ 1 \end{bmatrix} = s_8 \begin{bmatrix} -1 \\ 3 \\ 0 \end{bmatrix}$$

or

$$\begin{aligned} 1s_5 + 2s_6 &= -s_8 \\ -3s_5 - s_6 + 3s_7 &= 3s_8 \\ 2s_5 + 3s_6 - 2s_7 &= 0 \end{aligned} \tag{4.14}$$

These equations yield $s_5 = 19$, $s_6 = -6$, $s_7 = 10$, and $s_8 = -7$; so the matrix C is given by

$$C = \begin{bmatrix} 19 & -12 & 0 \\ -57 & 6 & 30 \\ 38 & -18 & -20 \end{bmatrix}$$

Finally, computing the matrix product BC^{-1} gives the matrix of the collineation:

$$A = \begin{bmatrix} 2 & 1 & -1 \\ 0 & 3 & 1 \\ -1 & 2 & 0 \end{bmatrix}$$

$\square$

Since collineations preserve collinearity, concurrence, and cross ratios, Theorem 4.34 allows us to simplify analytic proofs involving these properties by choosing any four points, no three collinear, as the points X, Y, Z, and U; as before, we will assume these points have the following coordinates: $X(1, 0, 0)$, $Y(0, 1, 0)$, $Z(0, 0, 1)$, and $U(1, 1, 1)$. This technique is illustrated in the following proof, which shows that our analytic model satisfies Axiom 4.4.

Verification of Axiom 4.4

Let $X(1, 0, 0)$, $Y(0, 1, 0)$, $Z(0, 0, 1)$, and $U(1, 1, 1)$ be the four points of a quadrangle. Using straightforward calculations, we can show that the diagonal points of this quadrangle are $XY \cdot UZ = A(1, 1, 0)$, $XZ \cdot UY = B(1, 0, 1)$. and $UX \cdot ZY = C(0, 1, 1)$. A quick computation shows that $|ABC| \neq 0$, so the diagonal points of the quadrangle are not collinear (see Exercise 7).

As indicated by Theorem 4.22, projectivities need not have any invariant elements. Collineations, on the other hand, always have at least one invariant point and one invariant line. The proof of this statement is a direct application of the theory of eigenvectors from linear algebra.

Theorem 4.35
A collineation has at least one invariant point and one invariant line.

Proof
To show that a collineation with matrix A has at least one invariant point, note that there will be an invariant point X if and only if there is a nonzero scalar s such that $sX = AX$. But $sX = AX$ if and only if $sIX - AX = (sI - A)X = 0$ where I is the identity matrix. This last equation has a nontrivial solution X if and only if $|sI - A| = 0$; but since A is a 3×3 matrix with real entries $|sI - A|$ is a third degree polynomial in s and so has at least one real solution for s. (Note this solution cannot be 0.) To show that the collineation with matrix A has at least one invariant line, the same procedure is used, beginning with the equation $ku' = uA^{-1}$. ∎

The invariant line of a collineation need not be *pointwise* invariant; that is, even though points on the invariant line must remain on the line under the collineation, the points themselves may not remain fixed.

Definition 4.20
A collineation that has one pointwise invariant line is called a *perspective collineation*. The pointwise invariant line is called the *axis*.

By Theorem 4.34 a perspective collineation other than the identity can have at most one invariant point not on the axis. The following theorem demonstrates that there is always one *linewise* invariant point under a perspective collineation.

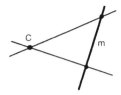

FIGURE 4.35 Proof 4.36, case 1.

Theorem 4.36

Every perspective collineation has a linewise invariant point. (This point is called the center).

Proof

Let m be the axis of the perspective collineation.

Case 1: There is an invariant point not on m. Let this invariant point be called C. Then any line through C intersects m in a second invariant point (Fig. 4.35). Thus, each line through C has two invariant points, and hence is invariant. It follows that C is linewise invariant.

Case 2: The only invariant points are those on m. Let P be any point not on m. Consider the line $n = PP'$ where P' is the image of P under the perspective collineation. Let $C = n \cdot m$. Then $n = CP = CP'$ is invariant. If R is another point not on m or n, there similarly exists an invariant line $o = RR'$. Let $X = o \cdot n$ (Fig. 4.36). Then since o and n are both invariant, it follows that X is invariant so X is on m. But $n \cdot m = C$, thus $X = C$. Therefore, every point not on m lies on an invariant line through C, or in other words, every line through C is invariant. ∎

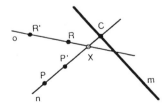

FIGURE 4.36 Proof 4.36, case 2.

The proof of Theorem 4.36 shows that a perspective collineation with center C and axis m maps a given point P ($P \neq C$) not on m to a point P' on PC. Subject to this condition, however, the image of P can be arbitrary, However, once the image of P is named, the image of any other point under a perspective collineation with a given axis and center is completely determined.

Theorem 4.37

There exists a unique perspective collineation with axis m and center C that maps a given point P ($P \neq C$ and P not on m) to a given point P' on PC.

Proof

Case 1: C is not on m. Let $PC \cdot m = D$ and let E and F be two additional points on m (Fig. 4.37). Then by Theorem 4.34 there exists a unique collineation that maps P to P', C to C, E to E, and F to F. Clearly, this collineation keeps m invariant since it keeps E and F invariant. Note that $PC = P'C$ is a second invariant line. Thus, $D = PC \cdot m$ is a third invariant point on m, and it follows that the projectivity induced on m by this collineation is the identity (Theorem 4.8), and so m is pointwise invariant. Thus, the collineation is a perspective collineation with axis m, and as in the proof of Theorem 4.36, the center can be shown to be C.

Case 2: C is on m. Let $PX \cdot m = D$ where X is a point not on either PC or m (Fig. 4.38). Then if a perspective collineation exists as desired, it must map X to $X' = CX \cdot P'D$ (see Exercise 10). But by Theorem 4.34, there exists a unique collineation mapping P to P', X to X', C to C, and D to D. As before, m is invariant under the collineation because C and D are invariant. However, m must be

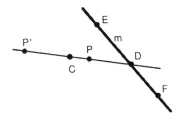

FIGURE 4.37 Proof 4.37, case 1.

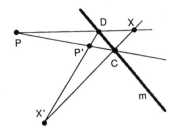

FIGURE 4.38   Proof 4.37, case 2.

shown pointwise invariant and C linewise invariant. As shown in Problem 9, it is sufficient to show that C is linewise invariant and then note that since m has at least two invariant points, it must be the axis.

To show that C is linewise invariant, note that $CP = CP'$, m, and $CX = CX'$ are three invariant lines through C. Thus, by the dual of the argument in case 1, C is linewise invariant and the result follows. ∎

These collineations are called *perspective collineations* since they map triangles to perspective triangles. The proof of this result follows directly from the definitions of the center and axis of a perspective collineation and from the definition of perspective triangles.

Theorem 4.38
$\triangle P'Q'R'$ is the image of $\triangle PQR$ under a perspective collineation with center C and axis m if and only if the triangles are perspective from the point C and perspective from the line m.

Proof
(a) For the first half of the proof, see Exercise 11.
(b) Now assume that $\triangle PQR$ and $\triangle P'Q'R'$ are perspective from C and m. Since $\triangle PQR$ is a triangle, the three points P, Q, R are not collinear. Thus, at least one of the points, say P, is not on m. Furthermore, since $\triangle PQR$ and $\triangle P'Q'R'$ are perspective from C, P' is on PC. So by Theorem 4.37, there is a perspective collineation T with center C and axis m that maps P to P'. It must now be shown that $T(Q) = Q'$ and $T(R) = R'$.

By the proof of Theorem 4.37, $T(Q) = P'D \cdot QC$ where $D = PQ \cdot m$. But $PQ \cdot m = P'Q' \cdot m$, since the triangles are perspective from m, so $P'D = P'Q'$.

Thus, $T(Q) = P'Q' \cdot QC$. But Q' is on QC since the triangles are perspective from C, so $T(Q) = Q$. Likewise, $T(R) = R'$. ∎

As the proof of Theorem 4.37 indicates, there is a distinction between the perspective collineations that have their centers on their axes and those that do not.

Definition 4.21
A perspective collineation other than the identity is called an *elation* if its center lies on its axis and a *homology* if its center does not lie on its axis.

Homologies have another property worthy of note.

Theorem 4.39
Under a homology, with center C and axis m, any point P not on m ($P \neq C$) has an image P' such that C, P, and P' are collinear, and, if $m \cdot CP = Q$, then $R(C, Q, P, P')$ is constant for all P.

Proof
The fact that C, P, and P' are collinear for all perspective collineations has been noted previously.

Case 1: X is a point not on CP or on m. Let X' be its image under the homology, and let $D = CX \cdot m$, $E = PX \cdot m$. So $X' = XC \cdot EP'$ (Fig. 4.39). Then $CQPP' \overset{E}{\wedge} CDXX'$, and thus by Theorem 4.26, $R(C, Q, P, P') = R(C, D, X, X')$.

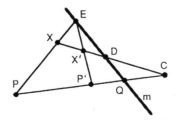

FIGURE 4.39 Proof 4.39, case 1.

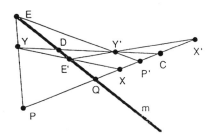

FIGURE 4.40 Proof 4.39, case 2.

Case 2: X *is a point on* CP. Then let Y be a point not on CP (Fig. 4.40). By case 1, $R(C, Q, P, P') = R(C, D, Y, Y')$ and Y can then be used in place of P in case 1 to yield a similar result for X. ∎

If this constant cross ratio is −1, the homology is called a *harmonic homology*.

Exercises

1. Prove that the set of points of the analytic model (i.e., nonzero equivalence classes of ordered triples from R^3) together with the equivalence class $\{(0, 0, 0)\}$ form a vector space under the usual addition and scalar multiplication in R^3.

2. Prove Theorem 4.30.

3. Given the collineation with matrix

$$\begin{bmatrix} 2 & 0 & 1 \\ 0 & 2 & 3 \\ 0 & 0 & 1 \end{bmatrix}$$

   (a) Write out the point equation for this collineation and find P' and Q', the images of P(1, 2, 3) and Q(−1, 0, 1), respectively. (b) Find the coordinates of the line P'Q'. (c) Write out the line equation for this collineation and find the image of l[1, −2, 1]. (d) Do your answers for parts *b* and *c* agree?

4. Show that the relation "∼" defined below is an equivalence relation on the set of 3 × 3 matrices:
   $A \sim B$ if and only if $A = kB$ for some nonzero scalar k.

5. Prove Theorem 4.32.

6. Find the matrix of the collineation that maps $P(1, 0, 1)$, $Q(2, 0, 1)$, $R(0, 1, 1)$, and $S(0, 2, 1)$ to $X(1, 0, 0)$, $Y(0, 1, 0)$, $Z(0, 0, 1)$, and $U(1, 1, 1)$, respectively.

7. Complete the details in the verification of Axiom 4.4.

8. Find the invariant points and lines of the collineations with the following matrices:

(a) $\begin{bmatrix} 1 & 1 & 0 \\ 0 & 1 & 0 \\ 0 & 0 & a \end{bmatrix}$ (b) $\begin{bmatrix} 1 & 0 & 0 \\ 0 & 1 & 0 \\ 0 & 1 & 1 \end{bmatrix}$ (c) $\begin{bmatrix} a & 1 & 0 \\ 0 & a & 1 \\ 0 & 0 & a \end{bmatrix}$

where $a \neq 0, 1$.   where $a \neq 0$.

9. Prove: Every collineation with a linewise invariant point is a perspective collineation.

10. Show that in the proof of case 2 of Theorem 4.37, $X' = CX \cdot P'D$.

11. Prove the first part of Theorem 4.38.

12. Show that the collineation with the following matrix is a homology. Is it a harmonic homology?

$$\begin{bmatrix} 1 & 0 & 0 \\ 0 & 1 & 0 \\ 2 & 0 & -1 \end{bmatrix}$$

13. Find the matrix of an elation with axis $[0, 0, 1]$ and center $(1, 0, 0)$.

4.11   Correlations and Polarities

The second type of transformations of the projective plane, known as *correlations*, are also one-to-one linear transformations. Here, however, the images of points are lines.

Definition 4.22
A *correlation* is a one-to-one linear transformation of the set of points of the projective plane onto the set of lines of the projective plane.

Correlations, too, can be represented by 3×3 matrices with matrix equations much like those used for collineations; except in this case, the ordered triples resulting from these mappings are interpreted as homogeneous coordinates of lines. Just as for collineations, there is an entire equivalence class of matrices corresponding to each correlation. These and several other results characterizing properties of correlations can be proved using arguments nearly identical to those used to prove similar results about collineations.

Theorem 4.40
A correlation can be represented by a 3×3 real-valued matrix A where $|A| \neq 0$. The matrix equation for the correlation is $su^t = AX$ where $X \in R^3$ and $s \neq 0$.

Theorem 4.41
A correlation maps collinear points to concurrent lines. The image of a line u under a correlation with matrix A is given by the equation $kX^t = uA^{-1}$, $k \neq 0$.

Corollary
Under a correlation, concurrent lines are mapped to collinear points.

Theorem 4.42
A correlation of the projective plane induces a projectivity between the elements of the corresponding pencils.

Corollary
Cross ratios and harmonic sets are invariant under correlations.

Theorem 4.43
There exists a unique correlation that maps any four points, no three collinear, to any four lines, no three concurrent.

Thus, a given correlation that maps points to lines according to the equation $su^t = AX$ also maps lines to points according to the equation $kX^t = uA^{-1}$. (The transpose is used in both equations, since points are represented by column matrices and lines are represented by row matrices.) In general, correlations map any given set to the dual set. For example, the image of a quadrangle under a correlation is a quadrilateral, and vice versa. It follows that correlations give us an analytic method for studying duality.

Since correlations map points to lines and lines to points, it seems reasonable to expect that a correlation that maps a point P to a line p will automatically map the line p to the point P. However, this does not necessarily happen, since a correlation that maps a point X to a line u according to $su^t = AX$ will map the line u to a point Y according to $kY^t = uA^{-1}$. Solving the first equation for u gives $u = (1/s)(AX)^t = (1/s)X^tA^t$. If each point X mapped to line u, which in turn is mapped back to X, so that $X = Y$ for each point X, then $kX^t = k'Y^t = uA^{-1} = ((1/s)X^tA^t)A^{-1}$ or $sk\,X^t = X^t(A^tA^{-1})$. This will hold for all possible points X if and only if $A^tA^{-1} = I$, that is, if and only if $A^t = A$. So a correlation maps every point X to a line u and the line u back to X if and only if its matrix is symmetric. Correlations of this type are called *polarities*. Since we shall soon show that the set of polarities give analytic expression to conics, we begin using the letter C to denote matrices of polarities.

Definition 4.23
A correlation whose matrix is symmetric is called a *polarity*. If a polarity maps a point P to a line p (and thus p to P), then p is called the *polar* of P and P is called the *pole* of p with respect to the given polarity.

Since polarities are correlations, they are one-to-one mappings; hence polars of distinct points are distinct lines, and vice versa. This polarity relation also has the characteristic property first described in Section 1.5 in that it pairs points that lie on one another's polar. Such points are called *conjugate* points with respect to the polarity.

Theorem 4.44
A point P is on the polar of a point Q under a given polarity if and only if Q is on the polar of P under this same polarity.

Proof
Let C be the matrix of the polarity and let q and p be the polars of Q and P, that is, $s_1q^t = CQ$ and $s_2p^t = CP$. Since P is on the polar of Q, $qP = 0$; but $s_1q = Q^tC$, so $Q^tCP = 0$. Transposing gives $P^tCQ = 0$ or $pQ = 0$, that is, Q is on the polar of P. ∎

Corollary

P is on the polar of Q with respect to a polarity with matrix C if and only if $Q^t C P = 0$. And p contains the pole of q with respect to this same polarity if and only if $p C^{-1} q^t = 0$.

Definition 4.24

Two points are called *conjugate points* with respect to a given polarity if each point is on the polar of the other. A point that lies on its own polar is called a *self-conjugate point* with respect to the given polarity.

Two lines are called *conjugate lines* with respect to a given polarity if each line is incident with the pole of the other. A line that is incident with its own pole is called a *self-conjugate* line with respect to the given polarity.

The corollary to the previous theorem leads directly to a matrix equation for sets of self-conjugate points (see Exercise 2). Multiplying out the matrix product in this equation yields a quadratic form whose similarity to the quadratic forms encountered in Section 3.13 should be suggestive of a connection between sets of self-conjugate points and point conics.

Theorem 4.45

The set of self-conjugate points of a polarity with matrix C is the set of points X satisfying the equation $X^t C X = 0$. The set of self-conjugate lines of this same polarity is the set of lines satisfying the equation $u C^{-1} u^t = 0$.

Corollary

The set of self-conjugate points of a polarity with matrix C is the set of points X satisfying the equation:

$$c_{11}x_1^2 + c_{22}x_2^2 + c_{33}x_3^2 + 2c_{12}x_1x_2 + 2c_{13}x_1x_3 + 2c_{23}x_2x_3 = 0$$

Using the matrix equation for a set of self-conjugate points, we can now show that such sets are preserved under collineations. A similar procedure can be used to show that the pole–polar relation is also preserved under these mappings, that is, if P and p are pole and polar with respect to a polarity with matrix C; then P' and p', their images under a collineation, will be pole and polar with respect to the polarity with matrix C' (see Exercise 3).

Theorem 4.46

A collineation with matrix A maps a set of self-conjugate points with matrix C to a set of self-conjugate points with matrix $C' = (A^{-1})^t C (A^{-1})$.

Proof

Let S be a set of self-conjugate points with equation $X^t CX = 0$ where C is a 3×3 nonsingular, symmetric matrix. Let A be the matrix of an arbitrary collineation. Then A is also a 3×3 nonsingular matrix, and the corresponding point equation is $sX' = AX$. Solving for X and X^t gives $X = sA^{-1}X'$ and $X^t = s(X')^t(A^{-1})^t$. Substituting into the equation $X^t CX = 0$ yields $(X')^t(A^{-1})^t C(A^{-1})X' = 0$ or $(X')^t((A^{-1})^t CA^{-1})X' = 0$. But $(A^{-1})^t CA^{-1}$ is a 3×3 nonsingular, symmetric matrix and hence the matrix of a polarity. Thus, X is in the set S of self-conjugate points with matrix C if and only if X' is in the set S' of self-conjugate points with matrix $C' = (A^{-1})^t CA^{-1}$. ∎

The previous theorem will allow us to simplify our work with self-conjugate sets of points by "assigning" special coordinates to some of the points involved, much as we did when we verified Axiom 4.4 in Section 4.10. In particular, we use this technique to demonstrate that sets of self-conjugate points (which are defined analytically in terms of polarities) are point conics—figures that can be constructed entirely with points and lines. Even with this simplifying technique, the proof of this result is somewhat long and involved, but it nicely illustrates the use of analytic methods in projective geometry. The significance of the theorem and corollaries make the effort worthwhile.

Theorem 4.47

A nonempty set of self-conjugate points with respect to a given polarity is a point conic and a nonempty set of self-conjugate lines with respect to a given polarity is a line conic. Conversely, any point conic is a set of self-conjugate points with respect to some polarity and any line conic is a set of self-conjugate lines with respect to some polarity.

Proof

By the principle of duality, it is sufficient to verify the result for point conics.

Let C be a nonempty set of self-conjugate points. Since C is nonempty, we can show that C contains at least three distinct, non-collinear points (see Exercise 6). We will assume these points are $X(1,0,0)$, $Z(0,0,1)$, and $U(1,1,1)$ and that the polars at X and Z intersect at $Y(0,1,0)$. Since X and Z are self-conjugate points, their polars relative to C are $XY[0,0,1]$ and $ZY[1,0,0]$. Algebraically, this means we need a symmetric matrix C that satisfies the following:

$$C[1,0,0]^t = s_1[0,0,1]^t \quad \text{and} \quad C[0,0,1]^t = s_2[1,0,0]^t$$

These equations yield $c_{11} = c_{12} = c_{23} = c_{33} = 0$ and $c_{13} \neq 0$. Finally, requiring that the point U also be self-conjugate gives $c_{22} = 1$ and $c_{13} = -\frac{1}{2}$ so the equation of C becomes $(x_2)^2 - x_1 x_3 = 0$. It is then sufficient to show that the set of points satisfying this equation is a point conic, that is, a set of points of intersection of corresponding lines of two projectively related pencils of lines.

We will use the two pencils centered at X and Z. The projectivity we will use is uniquely determined by the correspondence: $XY\,XZ\,XU \wedge ZX\,ZY\,ZU$. Note that under this projectivity, X, Z, and U are all points of intersection of corresponding lines; and since XY corresponds to ZX, the line between the centers of the two pencils, it will be a tangent at X. Similarly, ZY will be a tangent at Z. Letting XY and XZ be base lines of the first pencil and ZX and ZY base lines of the second pencil will give us a projectivity with a diagonal matrix (see Section 4.8, Exercise 1). Finally, requiring that $XU[0,1,-1]$ with homogeneous parameters $(-1,1)$ maps to $ZU[1,-1,0]$, also with homogeneous parameters $(-1,1)$, gives the 2×2 identity matrix as the matrix of the projectivity.

To show that C is exactly the set of points of intersection of corresponding lines under this projectivity, let $P(p_1,p_2,p_3)$ be an arbitrary point of C. Then the projectivity will map the line $XP = l[0,-p_3,p_2]$ with homogeneous parameters $(p_2,-p_3)$ to line l' through Z with the same homogeneous parameters. So l' has coordinates $[-p_3,p_2,0]$. Using the determinant condition to find the point $l \cdot l'$ gives $(-(p_2)^2, -p_3 p_2, -(p_3)^2)$ as the coordinates of this point of intersection, but since P is a point in C, $(p_2)^2 = p_1 p_3$, so the point $l \cdot l'$ has coordinates (p_1,p_2,p_3). In other words, the point P is the point of intersection of the projectively related lines l and l' if and only if P is in C.

To complete the first half of the proof, we need to verify that this projectivity is not a perspectivity. To do this, it is sufficient to note that the line XZ, which joins the two centers of the pencils, does not correspond to itself.

Conversely, to show that any point conic C is the set of self-conjugate points with respect to a polarity we can use a similar procedure. Let P, Q, R be three distinct points of C and let S be the point of intersection of the tangents to C at P and Q. Then P, Q, R, and S are four distinct points, no three collinear (see Exercise 7). Since collineations preserve incidence and therefore conics, we can assume that P, Q, R, and S are the points $X(1, 0, 0)$, $Z(0, 0, 1)$, $U(1, 1, 1)$, and $Y(0, 1, 0)$, respectively.

By the corollary to Theorem 4.15, the tangents at X and Z, together with the three points X, Z, and U, uniquely determine the conic, so it is sufficient to show that these tangents and points determine a polarity with matrix C relative to which C is a set of self-conjugate points. Since in the first part of the proof, the two self-conjugate lines became tangents to the conic, here we will find a polarity under which the two tangent lines are self-conjugate. This, together with the condition that U be a self-conjugate point, leads to the same equation as before, namely, $(x_2)^2 - x_1 x_3 = 0$. So there is indeed a polarity under which C is a set of self-conjugate points. ∎

Corollary 1

A point conic has an equation of the form $X^t\, CX = 0$ and a line conic has an equation of the form $uC^{-1}u^t = 0$ where C is a symmetric, nonsingular 3×3 matrix.

Therefore, any point conic corresponds to a symmetric matrix that is the matrix of a polarity. This polarity matrix is called the *matrix of the point conic*. Furthermore, if line p corresponds to point P under the polarity determined by the conic, P and p are said to be pole and polar *with respect to the conic*. This terminology is used in the statement of two more corollaries to Theorem 4.47, which formalize the relationship between self-conjugate lines and tangents.

Corollary 2

Let P be a point of a point conic C. The polar of P with respect to C is the tangent at P; conversely, the tangent to C at P is the polar of P with respect to C.

Corollary 3

If X is a point of a point conic C, with matrix C, then u, the tangent to C at X, is given by the equation $su^t = CX$.

Using this last corollary, we can show that the line conic determined by a given polarity consists of the tangents to the point conic determined by the same polarity.

Theorem 4.48

The tangents to a point conic are the lines of the line conic determined by the same polarity.

Proof

Let X be a point on a point conic with matrix C. By Corollary 3 to Theorem 4.47, u, the tangent at X, is given by $su^t = CX$. Solving this equation for X gives $X = sC^{-1}u^t$.

Since X is on the point conic, $X^tCX = 0$ by Corollary 1 of the same theorem. Substituting the previous expression for X into this equation gives $(sC^{-1}u^t)^tC(sC^{-1}u^t) = 0$, or $uC^{-1}CC^{-1}u^t = uC^{-1}u^t = 0$. So u satisfies the equation of the line conic determined by the same polarity. ∎

A polarity also determines polars of points not on the corresponding conic. The following theorems and definitions yield a method of constructing polars of other points (and, by duality, poles of lines other than tangents). These constructions will assume added importance in Section 4.12 when we describe non-Euclidean geometries as subgeometries of projective geometry.

Theorem 4.49

The point of intersection of two tangents to a point conic is the pole of the line joining the points of tangency.

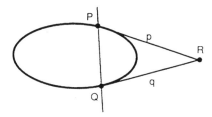

FIGURE 4.41 Proof 4.49.

Proof

Let p and q be tangents to a point conic at points P and Q, respectively; that is, p and q are the polars of P and Q, respectively. Let $R = p \cdot q$ (Fig. 4.41). Then R is on both the polar of P and the polar of Q so by Theorem 4.44, P and Q are both on the polar of R, so PQ is the polar of R, and therefore R is the pole of line PQ by definition. ∎

Corollary

Any point lies on at most two tangents to a given point conic.

The proof of Theorem 4.49 demonstrates the existence of triangles where one vertex is the pole of the opposite side. Triangles in which each vertex is the pole of the opposite side are particularly significant. The existence of triangles like this is demonstrated by the next theorem.

Definition 4.25

If each vertex of a triangle is the pole of the opposite side of the triangle with respect to a conic, then the triangle is said to be *self-polar* relative to the conic.

Theorem 4.50

If A, B, C, and D are four distinct points of a point conic then the diagonal triangle of quadrangle ABCD is self-polar.

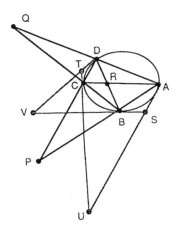

FIGURE 4.42 Proof 4.50.

Proof
Let $P = CD \cdot AB$, $Q = CB \cdot AD$, and $R = AC \cdot BD$ be the diagonal points of the quadrangle, and let

$$S = \tan B \cdot \tan A \quad \text{and} \quad T = \tan C \cdot \tan D,$$
$$U = \tan C \cdot \tan A \quad \text{and} \quad V = \tan D \cdot \tan B.$$

Then by a corollary to Theorem 4.14, Q, R, S, and T are collinear, as are P, Q, U, and V (Fig. 4.42). By Theorem 4.49, P is on the polars of both S and T, so $TS = QR$ is the polar of P. Similarly, R is on the polars of both U and V, so $UV = PQ$ is the polar of R. And finally, since Q is on the polars of P and R, then PR is the polar of Q. ∎

Corollary
If a line m through a point P not on a point conic intersects the conic, the points of intersection are harmonic conjugates with respect to P and the point of intersection of m with the polar of P.

Theorem 4.49 indicates how to construct poles of lines that intersect a conic twice. Lines that intersect a conic exactly once are just the tangents and hence the polars of the point of intersection, but there are lines that do not intersect the conic at any point. This distinction provides the basis for the next definition.

Definition 4.26

If the polar of P with respect to a given conic does not intersect a given point conic, P is said to be an *interior point* of the conic. If the polar of P with respect to a given point conic intersects the conic in two distinct points, P is said to be an *exterior point* of the conic.

In order to demonstrate the construction of polars of interior and exterior points and the construction of poles of lines that do and do not contain any interior points, we will make use of the following lemma (see Exercise 11).

Lemma

A line contains interior points of a point conic if and only if it intersects the conic at two distinct points.

Construction of Poles and Polars

Case 1 : Construction of the polar of a point P not on the conic. Let l and m be two lines through P, both of which intersect the conic C at two points. Let A and B be the points of intersection of l with C and let C an D be the points of intersection of m with C. Then A, B, C, and D form a quadrangle so by Theorem 4.50, its diagonal triangle is self-polar. In other words, the line joining $Q = AC \cdot BD$ and $R = AD \cdot BC$ is the polar of P (see Fig. 4.43).

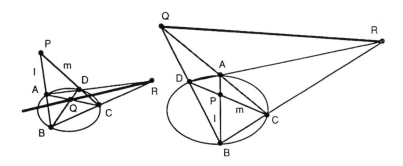

FIGURE 4.43 Constructing polar of P.

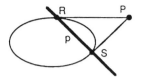

FIGURE 4.44 Constructing pole of p, case 1.

Case 2 : Construction of the pole of a line p not tangent to a conic. If p intersects the conic at distinct points R and S, then $P = \tan R \cdot \tan S = $ pole of p by Theorem 4.49 (Fig. 4.44). If p does not intersect the conic, let R and S be two distinct points on p. Then since p does not intersect the conic, it follows from the preceding lemma that all points on p and in particular R and S, are exterior points of the conic. Hence, their respective polars r and s each intersect the conic twice. Let $P = r \cdot s$ (Fig. 4.45). Then, since P is on the polar of R and the polar of S, it follows that P is the pole of p. (Note that P is an interior point.)

Self-polar triangles are also used in mapping a particular point conic to another point conic in *standard form*. (A conic in standard form will play an important role in the next section.) The proof of the first of the theorems necessary to achieve this mapping involves a special self-polar triangle and makes use of techniques similar to those used in part of the proof of Theorem 4.47 (see Exercise 13).

Theorem 4.51
The triangle $\triangle XYZ$ (where $X(1, 0, 0)$, $Y(0, 1, 0)$, and $Z(0, 0, 1)$) is a self-polar triangle with respect to a conic if and only if the matrix of the conic is diagonal.

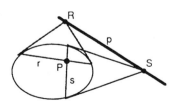

FIGURE 4.45 Constructing pole of p, case 2.

Thus, any point conic is *equivalent*, that is, can be mapped via a collineation, to a conic with an equation of the form $a(x_1)^2 + b(x_2)^2 + c(x_3)^2 = 0$. However, the next theorem shows that conics with equations of this form can, in turn, be mapped to conics with yet a simpler equation. This theorem will even include the case where the original point conic contains no points in the real projective plane.

Theorem 4.52
Any point conic is projectively equivalent to a conic with an equation of the form $(x_1)^2 + (x_2)^2 \pm (x_3)^2 = 0$ (i.e., any conic can be mapped via a collineation to a conic with this equation).

Proof
Let $\triangle PQR$ be a self-polar triangle with respect to a given point conic $\mathcal{C}$, and let T be a collineation that maps P, Q, R to X, Y, Z, respectively. Then $\triangle XYZ$ will be self-polar with respect to the conic $T(\mathcal{C})$, so this latter conic will have a diagonal matrix by Theorem 4.51. Now either all of the diagonal entries are of the same sign or one of the entries differs in sign from the other two. In the first case, we will use a matrix representation in which the diagonal entries are all positive. In the second case we can, if necessary, make use of a collineation that switches an appropriate pair of the points X, Y, and Z to obtain a conic with a diagonal matrix representation with a negative third entry (see Exercise 15). So we can assume that the matrix representation of the image conic $T(\mathcal{C})$ is of the following form where a and b are positive and c is nonzero:

$$C = \begin{bmatrix} a & 0 & 0 \\ 0 & b & 0 \\ 0 & 0 & c \end{bmatrix}$$

Finally, let S be the collineation with matrix

$$A = \begin{bmatrix} \sqrt{a} & 0 & 0 \\ 0 & \sqrt{b} & 0 \\ 0 & 0 & \sqrt{|c|} \end{bmatrix}$$

Then by Theorem 4.46 the conic $ST(\mathcal{C})$ will have matrix $C' = (A^{-1})C(A^{-1})$. Computing this matrix product gives

$$C' = \begin{bmatrix} 1 & 0 & 0 \\ 0 & 1 & 0 \\ 0 & 0 & \pm 1 \end{bmatrix}$$

So conic $ST(\mathcal{C})$ has an equation of the form $(x_1)^2 + (x_2)^2 \pm (x_3)^2 = 0.$ ■

A point conic whose equation is of this form is said to be in *standard form*. The two possible standard forms determine two types of polarities. The names assigned to these two types are meant to be suggestive of two non-Euclidean geometries. In the next section, we explore the connection between these polarities and the corresponding geometries.

Definition 4.27
A polarity whose associated conic is equivalent to the conic with equation $(x_1)^2 + (x_2)^2 - (x_3)^2 = 0$ is called *hyperbolic*. A polarity whose associated conic is equivalent to the conic with equation $(x_1)^2 + (x_2)^2 + (x_3)^2 = 0$ is called *elliptic*.

Exercises

1. Given the polarity with matrix

$$\begin{bmatrix} 2 & 0 & -1 \\ 0 & 1 & 0 \\ -1 & 1 & 0 \end{bmatrix}$$

(a) Find the equations of the sets of self-conjugate points and self-conjugate lines determined by this polarity. (b) Find the pole of the line $[1, 1, 1]$. (c) Find a point conjugate to the point $(1, 1, 1)$.

2. Prove Theorem 4.45 and its corollary.

3. Show that the pole–polar relation is preserved under a collineation.

In Exercises 4–6, $\mathcal{C}$ is a nonempty self-conjugate set of points determined by a given polarity.

4. Using Theorem 4.44, prove: if P is a point of $\mathcal{C}$, then the polar of P contains exactly one point of $\mathcal{C}$.

5. Prove: If A is a point of C and $B \neq A$ is a second point on the polar of A, then the polar of B contains exactly two points of C. [*Hint:* Assume A and B are the points $Z(0, 0, 1)$ and $Y(0, 1, 0)$, respectively.]

6. Use the result of Exercise 5 to show that C contains at least three noncollinear points.

7. Show that the four points P, Q, R, and S chosen in the proof of the second half of Theorem 4.47 are distinct with no three collinear.

8. Given the conic $(x_1)^2 + 2(x_2)^2 + 5(x_3)^2 - 2x_2x_3 - 2x_1x_3 - 4x_1x_2 = 0$ find (a) the tangent at point $(1, 1, 1)$, (b) the polar of $(3, 1, 5)$, and (c) the tangents from the point $(1, -2, 0)$.

9. Prove the corollary to Theorem 4.49.

10. Prove the corollary to Theorem 4.50. [*Hint:* Let n be a second line through P intersecting the conic at two points. Find a harmonic set formed by these four points and then use a perspectivity.]

11. Let C be the conic with equation $(x_2)^2 - x_1x_3 = 0$. (a) Show that the point $P(p_1, p_2, p_3)$ is an interior point of C if and only if $(p_2)^2 - p_1p_3 < 0$. (In general, P is an interior point of the conic $X^tCX = 0$ if and only if $P^tCP < 0$) (b) Show that every line contains exterior points of C. (c) Use parts (a) and (b) to show that any line contains interior points of C if and only if it intersects C at two distinct points.

12. In the construction of the polar of a point P not on a conic, l and m were chosen as two lines through P, both of which intersect the conic twice. Describe how the polar of P can be obtained if l and/or m intersect the conic exactly once. Will this happen if P is an interior point?

13. Prove Theorem 4.51.

14. Show that a harmonic homology whose center and axis are pole and polar with respect to a point conic C keeps C invariant (i.e., it maps points on C back to points on C).

15. If C is the point conic with equation $a(x_1)^2 + b(x_2)^2 + c(x_3)^2 = 0$ where $a < 0$, $b > 0$, $c > 0$, find the matrix of a collineation T such that the point conic $T(C)$ has an equation $a'(x_1)^2 + b'(x_2)^2 + c'(x_3)^2 = 0$ where $a' > 0$, $b' > 0$, and $c' < 0$. [*Hint:* Use a collineation that interchanges the points X and Z and keeps Y invariant.]

16. Show that the point conic determined by an elliptic polarity contains no points in the real projective plane.

17. Show that any collineation with an orthogonal matrix A will keep the conic determined by an elliptic polarity invariant. [*Hint*: Use the standard form of the conic and note that the matrix A is *orthogonal* if and only if $A^t = A^{-1}$.]

18. Prove: If T is a correlation then T^2 is a collineation. If A is the matrix of T, what is the matrix of T^2?

4.12 Subgeometries of Projective Geometry

In this final section, we see that Klein's definition of geometry allows us to view projective geometry as an *umbrella* geometry under which affine, similarity, Euclidean, hyperbolic, and single elliptic geometries all reside. Our approach is to demonstrate that the respective plane geometries can all be obtained as subgeometries of plane projective geometry. Although we do not do so, this approach can be extended to demonstrate a similar relation among the corresponding three-dimensional geometries.

To obtain the appropriate viewpoint, we begin by selecting an *absolute polarity* (its corresponding conic is known as the *absolute conic C*) for each of the three geometries and then demonstrate that fundamental concepts of each geometry can be defined in terms of properties left invariant under a group of transformations that preserve C. Since we have already explored these geometries in some depth in Chapters 2 and 3, we do not dwell on the details of each geometry here. Rather, we concentrate on identifying concepts in terms of their projective counterparts and indicate ways in which theorems of projective geometry can be used to verify standard results in each geometry. The ease with which we are able to make these identifications and prove these results should increase your appreciation for both the significance and beauty of projective geometry.

As indicated earlier, we begin by considering a particular polarity of the projective plane. We refer to this polarity and its associated point conic as the *absolute polarity* and *absolute conic*.

As we discovered in Section 4.11, this absolute conic can be represented in standard form as $(x_1)^2 + (x_2)^2 \pm (x_3)^2 = 0$. In order to obtain both non-Euclidean and affine geometries, and eventually Euclidean geometry as subgeometries, we rewrite this equation as $c[(x_1)^2 + (x_2)^2] + (x_3)^2 = 0$, where $c = \pm 1$ or 0. The first two values of c yield the standard form given earlier, whereas $c = 0$ yields the degenerate conic $x_3 = 0$, that is, the line with coordinates $[0, 0, 1]$. So in this last case, the absolute conic consists of the ideal points, which were added to the affine plane to obtain an analytic model of the projective plane (see Section 4.7). It should then come as no surprise that the geometry obtained using this absolute conic is affine geometry. In the cases where $c = \pm 1$, we will also refer to points of the absolute conic as *ideal points*. The polarities determining the absolute conic when $c = 1$ and $c = -1$ are called *elliptic* and *hyperbolic* (Definition 4.27), since we shall see that these polarities determine elliptic and hyperbolic geometries, respectively.

We use the following procedure to demonstrate the relationship of each of these geometries to projective geometry. For each value of c, we select an absolute polarity and corresponding absolute conic $\mathcal{C}$. Using $\mathcal{C}$, we describe a special subset of points of the real projective plane. This subset of (*ordinary*) *points* will be the points remaining after the ideal (and in the case of hyperbolic geometry, *ultraideal*) points are deleted. In the case where $c = 1$, there are no real points on the absolute conic, so no points are deleted; that is, the set of points of the elliptic plane is identical to the set of points of the projective plane. (However, the absolute polarity that determines this *empty* conic is still useful.) It is important to observe that for each subgeometry, the only points of the geometry will be the (ordinary) points; that is, the ideal and ultraideal points are not points of the geometry. However, in order to make use of concepts in projective geometry, we will consider the point set of each geometry as a subset of the point set of the projective plane. We refer to this process as *embedding* the geometry into the projective plane. This embedding allows us to use the ideal and ultraideal points in addition to the (ordinary) points.

Following the identification of the appropriate set of points, we will list several definitions indicating how basic concepts of each geometry can be defined via properties of the projective plane. As you should note, these definitions are all stated in terms of projective properties that remain invariant under collineations that preserve the absolute conic. After we describe the definitions used in the non-Euclidean geometries, our presentation will focus on affine geometry, since this geometry includes the most familiar geometry, Euclidean. This approach will allow us to see that, with a slight stretch of the definition of a line conic, the cross ratio can be used to give a common definition of angle measure in all three geometries. Even though a similar definition can be used to define distance in the two non-Euclidean geometries, it is not possible to extend this definition to affine geometry.

Stating the definitions in terms of projective properties enables us to use theorems of projective geometry to verify that the concepts so defined do indeed have other expected properties. However, since the purpose of this section is to merely illustrate the relationships between the geometries, we will only indicate how a few such properties can be verified. You will be asked to verify a number of other properties. These exercises should increase your appreciation for the interrelatedness of the geometries we have studied, as well as provide an opportunity to review ideas from this chapter.

Hyperbolic Geometry

Interpretations of undefined terms

Ideal Points: Points of the absolute conic $C : (x_1)^2 + (x_2)^2 - (x_3)^2 = 0$.
Ultraideal Points: Points exterior to C.
(Ordinary) Points: Points of the real projective plane interior to C.
Lines: Open chords of C (i.e., parts of projective lines containing points interior to C).

Defined terms

1h. Two hyperbolic lines are *sensed parallel* if the corresponding projective lines intersect in ideal points.

2h. Two hyperbolic lines are *ultraparallel* if the corresponding projective lines intersect in ultraideal points.

3h. Two hyperbolic lines are *perpendicular* if the corresponding projective lines are conjugate with respect to the absolute conic.

4h. If A and B are two hyperbolic points, the *hyperbolic distance,* $d_h(A, B) = k\,|\ln(R(A, B, P, Q))|$ for some $k > 0$ where P and Q are ideal points of line AB, and "ln" represents the natural logarithm.

5h. If a and b are intersecting hyperbolic lines, then the *hyperbolic angle measure* $m_h(\angle(a, b)) = k'\ln(R(a, b, p, q))$ where p and q are tangents to C from the point $a \cdot b$.

Using these definitions, we can *embed* the hyperbolic plane into the projective plane and use theorems of projective geometry to construct proofs of hyperbolic theorems. We will illustrate this process by verifying an extension of Theorem 53h (see Section 2.8). Note that hyperbolic and projective lines are not identical, since hyperbolic lines contain only those points of the corresponding projective line that are interior to the absolute conic C. To keep track of this distinction, we will denote by l' the projective line that corresponds to the hyperbolic line l. We will also find it helpful to make use of a diagram within the projective plane. This diagram should took familiar, since it is merely a depiction within the Klein model described in Section 2.3.

Property 1h
Two hyperbolic lines are ultraparallel if and only if they have a unique common perpendicular.

Proof
(a) Let l and m be two ultraparallel lines. Then the corresponding projective lines l' and m' intersect in a point P' where P' is exterior

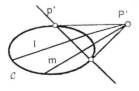

FIGURE 4.46 Ultraparallel lines l and m.

to $\mathcal{C}$ (Fig. 4.46). Let p' be the polar of P'. Since P' is exterior to $\mathcal{C}$, p' intersects $\mathcal{C}$ at two distinct points and therefore determines a hyperbolic line p (see the lemma in Section 4.11). Furthermore, p' is conjugate to both l' and m', so p is perpendicular to both l and m by Definition 3h. Since the polar of P' is unique, it follows that p' is the unique common perpendicular to l and m.

(b) Assume that l and m are two hyperbolic lines with a unique common perpendicular p. Then the corresponding projective lines l' and m' are both conjugate to p', the projective line corresponding to p, so they must intersect at the pole of p'. Denote this pole by P'. Since p' contains interior point of $\mathcal{C}$, p' must intersect $\mathcal{C}$ at two distinct points, so P' is an ultraideal point. It follows that l and m are ultraparallel lines (Definition 2h). ∎

The definitions used for sensed-parallel and ultraparallel lines in hyperbolic geometry do not apply to single elliptic geometry (why?). However, the definitions of *perpendicular*, *distance*, and *angle measure* do apply. Here, however, the points of intersection with $\mathcal{C}$ and the lines tangent to $\mathcal{C}$ referred to in Definitions 2e and 3e will necessarily have coordinates that involve complex numbers.

Single Elliptic Geometry

Interpretations of undefined terms

Ideal Points: Points of the absolute conic $\mathcal{C} : (x_1)^2 + (x_2)^2 + (x_3)^2 = 0$.
(Ordinary) Points: Points of the real projective plane.
Lines: Lines of the real projective plane.

Defined terms

1e. Two elliptic lines are *perpendicular* if the corresponding projective lines are conjugate with respect to $\mathcal{C}$.
2e. If A and B are two elliptic points, the *elliptic distance*, $d_e(A, B) = k \,|\ln(R(A, B, P, Q))|$ for some $k > 0$ where P and Q are points

of intersection of line AB with C, and "ln" represents the natural logarithm.

3e: If a and b are elliptic lines, then the *elliptic angle measure* $m_e(\angle(a, b)) = k' \ln(R(a, b, p, q))$ where p and q are tangents to C from $a \cdot b$.

Again these definitions and theorems of projective geometry can be used to verify properties of the single elliptic plane. Since the absolute conic used to define the point set of the elliptic plane is empty, it is often not possible to depict properties of the single elliptic plane within the context of the projective plane. However, these properties can be illustrated within the model described in Section 2.9.

It is fairly easy to see that parallel lines can be defined in affine geometry using a definition analogous to that used for sensed-parallel lines in hyperbolic geometry. Since perpendicularity and angle measure are properties of similarity geometry, but not of affine geometry, it is appropriate to postpone their definitions until later. We can, however, include definitions of midpoint and types of conics in affine geometry.

Affine Geometry

Interpretations of undefined terms

Ideal Points: Points of the absolute conic $C : x_3 = 0$.
(Ordinary) Points: Points of the real projective plane not on C.
Lines: All lines of the real projective plane except the line $x_3 = 0$.

Defined terms

1a: Two affine lines are *parallel* if the corresponding projective lines intersect in an ideal point.
2a: M is the *midpoint* of AB if $H(AB, PM)$ where P is the ideal point of line AB.
3a: A point conic is a *hyperbola*, *parabola*, or *ellipse* according to whether it contains two, one, or no real ideal points, respectively

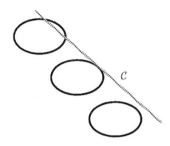

FIGURE 4.47 Hyperbola, parabola, and ellipse.

(Fig. 4.47). The *center* of a conic is the pole of the ideal line with respect to the conic. The polar of any ideal point with respect to the conic is a *diameter* of the conic. A tangent to a conic at an ideal point is called an *asymptote*.

These definitions and theorems of projective geometry can be used to verify a number of affine properties, including the following.

Property 1a

A line joining the midpoints of two sides of a triangle is parallel to the third side.

Proof

Let M be the midpoint of AB in $\triangle ABC$ and let l be the unique parallel to BC through M (see Exercise 16). We shall show that $N = l \cdot AC$ is the midpoint of AC (Fig. 4.48). Let $P = AB \cdot C$. Then we have the harmonic set $H(AB, PM)$ by Definition 2a. Let $V = BC \cdot C$; then $l = MV$. Finally, let $Q = AC \cdot C$. We need to show that $H(AC, QN)$. This

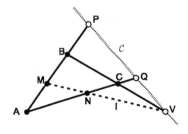

FIGURE 4.48 Proof 1a.

follows once we note that $ABPM \underset{\wedge}{\overset{V}{=}} ACQN$, since harmonic sets are preserved under perspectivities. So N is the midpoint of AC. ∎

In order to obtain similarity geometry, it is essential that we be able to give a definition for perpendicular lines. This was done in hyperbolic and single elliptic geometry using the absolute polarity. Since the absolute conic determining the affine and similarity planes is degenerate, there is no associated absolute polarity. However, we can introduce an absolute elliptic involution (i.e., a projectivity T such that $T^2 = I$) on $x_3 = 0$ to use in place of an absolute polarity. This absolute projectivity will have no invariant points since it is elliptic, but it will interchange pairs of points (i.e., if $T(P) = Q$, then $T(Q) = P$) since it is an involution. The projectivity we will choose will be the one that interchanges $X(1, 0, 0)$ and $Y(0, 1, 0)$.

In order to show that it is possible to use a definition of angle measure in similarity geometry like that used in the non-Euclidean geometries, it is necessary to determine what we mean by the line conic corresponding to our degenerate point conic $x_3 = 0$.

Recall that if a point conic has equation $X^t C X = 0$, then the corresponding line conic has equation $u C^{-1} u^t = 0$. In general, the absolute conic has matrix

$$C = \begin{bmatrix} c & 0 & 0 \\ 0 & c & 0 \\ 0 & 0 & 1 \end{bmatrix} \quad \text{with} \quad C^{-1} = \begin{bmatrix} 1 & 0 & 0 \\ 0 & 1 & 0 \\ 0 & 0 & c \end{bmatrix}$$

Hence, the line conic associated with the point conic $c[(x_1)^2 + (x_2)^2] + (x_3)^2 = 0$ is $(u_1)^2 + (u_2)^2 + c(u_3)^2 = 0$. In the case under consideration, $c = 0$, so the corresponding degenerate line conic is $(u_1)^2 + (u_2)^2 = 0$. We can factor this as $(u_1 + iu_2)(u_1 - iu_2) = 0$ where $i^2 = -1$. The lines of this *line conic* are all lines through the *points* $I(i, 1, 0)$ and $J(i, -1, 0)$; any point P will be on two tangents to the absolute conic, namely, PI and PJ. Using these two lines, it is then possible to give a definition for angle measure comparable to that used in hyperbolic and single elliptic geometries. This definition, together with the definition of perpendicular lines, is stated later. The affine definitions given previously also apply in similarity geometry, since this geometry is defined in terms of the same absolute conic and has the same point set as affine geometry.

Similarity Geometry

Interpretation of undefined terms

Absolute Conic: $C : x_3 = 0$.

Absolute Projectivity: The elliptic involution on C that interchanges $X(1, 0, 0)$ and $Y(0, 1, 0)$ and keeps $I(i, 1, 0)$ and $J(i, -1, 0)$ invariant.

Ideal Points: Points of the absolute conic C.

(Ordinary) Points: Points of the real projective plane not on C.

Lines: All lines of the real projective plane except the line $x_3 = 0$.

Defined terms

1s: Two lines of similarity geometry are *perpendicular* if their ideal points correspond under the absolute projectivity.

2s: If a and b are lines of similarity geometry, then the *angle measure* $m_a(\angle(a, b)) = k \ln(R(a, b, p, q))$ where p and q are the tangents to C from $a \cdot b$, and "ln" represents the natural logarithm.

Using these definitions it is also possible to verify a familiar property of similarity geometry.

Property 1s

Two lines $u[u_1, u_2, u_3]$ and $v[v_1, v_2, v_3]$ are perpendicular if and only if $u_1 v_1 + u_2 v_2 = 0$.

Proof

The line $u[u_1, u_2, u_3]$ has the ideal point $U(-u_2, u_1, 0)$, which has homogeneous parameters $(-u_2, u_1)$ with respect to X and Y. Using a matrix representation relative to these base points, we can obtain U', the image of U under the absolute projectivity as follows (see Exercise 5):

$$sU' = \begin{bmatrix} 0 & 1 \\ -1 & 0 \end{bmatrix} U$$

So U' has homogeneous parameters (u_1, u_2) and therefore homogeneous coordinates $(u_1, u_2, 0)$. The lines perpendicular to u are those lines with U' as ideal point, but these lines are the lines $v[v_1, v_2, v_3]$ where $v_1 u_1 + v_2 u_2 = 0$. ∎

It should be obvious after noticing the extra effort required to obtain the definitions for perpendicularity and angle measure for similarity and hence Euclidean geometry that it is more difficult to view Euclidean geometry as a subgeometry of projective geometry than it is to view the less familiar hyperbolic and single elliptic geometries this way. This added difficulty results since the absolute conic used to determine the point set for affine, similarity, and Euclidean geometry is a line rather than a conic determined by a polarity. In order to obtain similarity geometry, we had to introduce an elliptic involution on the ideal line. To obtain Euclidean geometry as a subgeometry of similarity geometry we could introduce a metric (i.e., a distance function). So Euclidean geometry can be described as a metric geometry based on an elliptic involution on the ideal line.

In closing, we will see that we can summarize the discussion in this section by applying one further adjective in the description of Euclidean geometry. This adjective describes a characterization based on the following comparison: (1) Each line in the Euclidean plane has one real ideal point; (2) each line in the hyperbolic plane has two distinct real ideal points; and (3) each line in the single elliptic plane has no real ideal points. This should be reminiscent of the definition of types of point conics in the affine plane. There a conic is labeled a parabola, a hyperbola, or an ellipse depending on whether it contains one, two, or zero real ideal points, respectively. The two non-Euclidean geometries are thus appropriately called "hyperbolic" and "elliptic." Likewise, Euclidean geometry can be classified as a *parabolic* geometry. The relations among these geometries are summarized in Table 4.2.

Exercises

1. Verify that the set of collineations that keep a given conic C invariant forms a group.

2. Explain why ultraparallel lines cannot be defined in either affine or single elliptic geometry.

3. Verify that the collineations that keep $x_3 = 0$ invariant are the affinities described in Section 3.13.

TABLE 4.2   The Subgeometries of Plane Projective Geometry

	Projective Geometry		
Points	Nonzero equivalence classes from $\{(x_1, x_2, x_3): x_i \in \mathbb{R}\}$		
Transformations	Collineations		
	Hyperbolic Geometry	**Affine Geometry**	**S. Elliptic Geometry**
Absolute Conic C:	$x_1^2 + x_2^2 - x_3^2 = 0$	$x_3 = 0$	$x_1^2 + x_2^2 + x_3^2 = 0$
Points	Points of real projective plane interior to C	Points of real projective plane not on C	All points of real projective plane.
Transformations:		Affinities	
		Similarity Geometry	
Points		Points of affine plane	
Transformations		Similarities	
		Euclidean Geometry	
Points		Points of affine plane	
Transformations		Isometries	

4. If $A(0, 0, 1)$ and $B(1, 0, 1)$ are points of the affine plane, use Definition 2a to find the coordinates of the midpoint of AB.

5. Show that the matrix of the absolute projectivity used to define similarity geometry is

$$\begin{bmatrix} 0 & 1 \\ -1 & 0 \end{bmatrix}$$

[*Hint*: See Exercise 9 in Section 4.8.]

6. Show that the affinities which preserve the absolute projectivity used to define similarity geometry are the similarities described in Section 3.12. [*Hint*: If $S(P) = P'$ where S is the absolute projectivity with the matrix given in Exercise 5 and T is an affinity, find the conditions under which $S(T(P)) = T(P')$ for all points P on the ideal line.]

7. Show that similarities that are also equiareal transformations are the isometries of Euclidean geometry. (See Exercise 13 in Section 3.13.)

8. Using Definition 2s with $k = -i/2$ (where $i^2 = -1$), show that the angle measure in similarity geometry for $\angle(a, b)$ where $a \cdot b = Z(0, 0, 1)$ is the same as that obtained using Definition 3.14 in Section 3.5.

Use the definitions of the appropriate properties listed in this section, together with theorems from projective geometry, to verify each of the following results in hyperbolic, single elliptic, affine, and similarity geometries.

Hyperbolic Geometry

9. Any two points determine a unique line.

10. Any two distinct lines determine at most one point.

11. Through a given point P, not on a given line l, there are exactly two lines sensed parallel to l.

12. Through a given point there is exactly one line perpendicular to a given line.

Single Elliptic Geometry

13. Two points determine a unique line.

14. Two lines determine a unique point.

15. All the lines perpendicular to a given line are concurrent at a point, namely, the pole of the line.

Affine Geometry

16. Through a given point P not on a given line m there exists exactly one line parallel to m.

17. Two distinct lines parallel to the same line are parallel to each other.

18. If a line intersects one of two parallel lines, it intersects the other.

19. The medians of a triangle are concurrent. [*Hint*: Use perspective triangles.]

20. A hyperbola has a center that is an exterior point, an ellipse has a center that is an interior point, a parabola has a center on the absolute conic, and thus has no center in the affine plane.

21. Hyperbolas are the only conics with asymptotes in the affine plane. Parabolas have only a single asymptote, namely, the ideal line; and as a result, have no asymptotes in the affine plane.

22. The diameters of a conic go through the center.

23. A conic $X'CX = 0$ is a hyperbola, parabola, or ellipse according to whether $(c_{12})^2 - c_{11}c_{12} >, =, < 0$.

Similarity Geometry

24. There is a unique line perpendicular to any given line through a given point.

25. A line perpendicular to one of two parallel lines is perpendicular to the other also.

26. Lines perpendicular to the same line are parallel to each other.

27. The altitudes of a triangle are concurrent. [*Hints*: First, recall that an altitude of $\triangle ABC$ is a line through vertex A and perpendicular to BC. Second, assume your triangle is $\triangle ABC$ where $A(0, 0, 1)$, $B(1, 0, 1)$, and $C(a, b, 1)$.]

4.13   Suggestions for Further Reading

Coxeter, H.S.M. (1957). *Non-Euclidean Geometry*, 3rd ed. Toronto: University of Toronto Press (Includes a detailed presentation of Euclidean and non-Euclidean geometries as subgeometries of projective geometry.)

Coxeter, H.S.M. (1961) *The Real Projective Plane*, 2nd ed. Cambridge: The University Press. (A primarily synthetic presentation restricted to the real plane, it includes the development of affine geometry.)

Coxeter, H.S.M. (1987). *Projective Geometry*, 2nd ed. New York: Springer-Verlag. (A classic text containing a detailed development of this geometry.)

Dorwart, H. (1966). *The Geometry of Incidence*. Englewood Cliffs, NJ: Prentice-Hall. (An expository overview of projective geometry.)

Meserve, B.E. (1983). *Fundamental Concepts of Geometry*. New York: Dover. (Chapters 5 and 8 give a more detailed presentation of the material in Section 4.12.)

Mihalek, R.J. (1972). *Projective Geometry and Algebraic Structures*. New York: Academic Press. (A detailed presentation emphasizing the interrelation between geometry and algebra.)

Pedoe, D. (1963). *An Introduction to Projective Geometry*. Oxford: Pergamon Press. (Contains an extensive treatment of the theorems of Desargues and Pappus.)

Penna, M.A., and Patterson, R.R. (1986). *Projective Geometry and Its Applications to Computer Graphics*. Englewood Cliffs, NJ: Prentice-Hall.

Seidenberg, A. (1962). *Lectures in Projective Geometry*. New York: Van Nostrand Reinhold. (The initial chapter introduces the major concepts in a fairly naive form: the remaining chapters develop the subject from axioms.)

Stevenson, F.W. (1972). *Projective Planes*. San Francisco: W.H. Freeman.

Tuller, A. (1967). *Modern Introduction to Geometries*. New York: Van Nostrand Reinhold. (Uses matrix representations of the projective transformations.)

Wylie, C.R. Jr. (1970). *Introduction to Projective Geometry*. New York: McGraw-Hill. (Contains both analytic and axiomatic developments.)

Young, J.W. (1930). *Projective Geometry*. The Carus Mathematical Monographs, No. 4. Chicago: Open Court Publishing Co. (for the MAA) (Develops concepts intuitively first, then incorporates metric properties and group concepts.)

Readings on the History of Projective Geometry

Bronowski, J. (1974). The music of the spheres. In *The Ascent of Man*, pp. 155–187 Boston: Little, Brown. This chapter is the companion to the 52-minute episode of the same name in *The Ascent of Man* television series.

Edgerton, S.Y. (1975). *The Renaissance Rediscovery of Linear Perspective.* New York: Basic Books.

Ivins, W.M. (1964). *Art and Geometry: A Study in Space Intuitions.* New York: Dover.

Kline, M. (1963). *Mathematics: A Cultural Approach.* Reading, MA: Addison-Wesley.

Kline, M. (1968). Projective geometry. In *Mathematics in the Modern World: Readings from Scientific American*, pp. 120–127. San Francisco: W.H. Freeman.

Kline, M. (1972). *Mathematical Thought from Ancient to Modern Times.* New York: Oxford University Press.

Pedoe, D. (1983). *Geometry and the Visual Arts.* New York: Dover.

Suggestions for Viewing

The Art of Renaissance Science (1991, 45 min). Part IV relates the discovery and implementation of perspective in drawing and painting. Available from Science TV, P.O. Box 2498, Times Square Station, New York, NY 10108.

Central Perspectivities (1971, 13.5 min). Demonstrates perspectivities and projectivities with flashing dots and lines. Produced by the College Geometry Project at the University of Minnesota. Available from International Film Bureau, 332 South Michigan Avenue, Chicago, IL 60604.

Masters of Illusion (1991, 30 min). Another illustration of the discovery and implementation of perspective in works of art. Produced and directed by Rick Harper, National Gallery of Art, Washington, DC.

Projective Generation of Conics (1971, 16 min). Illustrates four methods of constructing point conics and demonstrates their logical equivalence. Available from International Film Bureau, 332 South Michigan Avenue, Chicago, IL 60604.

Projective Geometry, Zeeman Masterclass Series with BBC (1986). Available from The Open University Production Centre, Walton Hall, Milton Keynes MK7 6BH, UK.

5

CHAPTER

Chaos to Symmetry: An Introduction to Fractal Geometry

Although the term "modern geometries" traditionally refers to post-Euclid geometries, namely the non-Euclidean and projective geometries presented in Chapters 2 and 4, it seems ironic to describe topics formalized hundreds of years ago as "modern." The topics presented in this chapter, on the other hand, are among those in a newly emerging area of mathematics and are honestly modern. In fact, the area known as *fractal geometry* is so new that its exact content has yet to be determined, let alone given a formal axiomatic structure. Thus, this chapter contains an informal presentation of concepts and themes basic to the topics currently regarded as part of fractal geometry. This presentation also attempts to convey the excitement experienced by professional mathematicians and scientists and large numbers of interested non-professionals as they discover and comprehend these new ideas and contemplate their far-reaching applications. In this vein, the presentation interweaves a number of exercises that will involve you in discovering and exploring concepts. Hopefully, in so doing, you will experience the excitement of mathematical discovery in a truly modern geometry as well as gain a deeper understanding of the affine transformations that are essential tools of fractal geometry. If you have access to appropriate computers and software, you can use these tools to conduct additional fractal explorations. Check the website `http://www.stolaf.edu/people/cederj/geotext/info.htm` for suggested computer-based explorations that complement sections marked with an asterisk.

5.1 A Chaotic Background*

"A mathematical definition of chaos would say something like 'deterministic behavior that appears to be random.'" [Davis, p. 325]

To understand the significance of fractals and their role in modern mathematics, it is necessary to know something about the area of scientific and mathematical inquiry known as *chaos theory*. The importance of this new area, together with the excitement and frustrations experienced by scientists and mathematicians as they made their initial discoveries, often without knowledge of other related work, is wonderfully portrayed in James Gleick's *Chaos: Making a New Science.*[1]

Gleick suggests [p. 5] that chaos is "a science of the global nature of systems" and notes that some consider chaos to be the third great revolution in twentieth century science, placing it on the same level as relativity and quantum mechanics. Gleick continues [p. 6]: "As one physicist put it: 'Relativity eliminated the Newtonian illusion of absolute space and time; quantum theory eliminated the Newtonian dream of a controllable measurement process; and chaos eliminates the Laplacian fantasy of deterministic probability.' Of the three, the revolution in chaos applies to the universe we see and touch, to objects at human scale."

The attitudes of science at the time initial discoveries in chaos were being made is summarized by Gleick as follows [p. 15]: "As one theoretician liked to tell his students: 'The basic idea of Western science is that you don't have to take into account the falling of a leaf on some planet in another galaxy when you're trying to

---

[1] Published in 1987, this bestseller achieved widespread critical acclaim and played a major role in bringing this new discipline to popular awareness.

account for the motion of a billiard ball on a pool table on earth. Very small influences can be neglected. There's a convergence in the way things work, and arbitrarily small influences don't blow up to have arbitrarily large effects.' Classically, the belief in approximation and convergence was well justified. It worked." However, as Gleick indicates, and as the quotation below confirms, chaos created a revolution in scientific thought.

> The magnificent successes in the fields of the natural sciences and technology had, for many, fed the illusion that the world on the whole functioned like a huge clockwork mechanism, whose laws were only waiting to be deciphered step by step. Once the laws were known, it was believed, the evolution or development of things could—at least in principle—be ever more accurately predicted. Captivated by the breathtaking advances in the development of computer technology and its promises of a greater command of information, many have put increasing hope in these machines.
>
> But today it is exactly those at the active core of modern science who are proclaiming that this hope is unjustified; the ability to see ever more accurately into future developments is unattainable. One conclusion that can be drawn from the new theories is that stricter determinism and apparently accidental development are *not* mutually exclusive, but rather that their coexistence is more the rule in nature. Chaos theory and fractal geometry address this issue. [Peitgen et al., (1992) pp. vii–viii].

5.1.1   A "Chaotic" Experiment

In the early 1960s Edward Lorenz, a meteorologist at the Massachusetts Institute of Technology, was working in the context of this classical scientific framework when he used a computer to investigate a simple mathematical model of a weather system. Since this was very early in the era of computer development, his computer (a Royal McBee LGP-300) used vacuum tubes and wires. It was downright sluggish compared to current models and Lorenz's calculations often lasted for days. One day in 1961, Lorenz decided to examine one particular output sequence more carefully. Rather than start the run from the beginning, Lorenz decided to start midway through by typing in the numbers from the earlier output as initial conditions. When he returned to look at the new output, he discovered that the new output diverged rapidly from the old. Lorenz realized that although he intended to put in the same numbers used in the previous run, he had entered numbers with only three decimal places, since these were the numbers on the printout. However, on the first run, the computer had used the six decimal place versions that it had stored. Lorenz later summarized this incident by saying, "I realized that any physical system that behaved nonperiodically [like the weather] would be unpredictable." [Gleick, p. 18]

Lorenz's continued examination of this phenomenon included the analysis of a model of convection developed by B. Saltzman. Further simplifying Saltzman's model, Lorenz used the following three differential equations where t represents time, x the rate of convective overturning, y the horizontal temperature variation, and z the vertical temperature variation.

$$\frac{dx}{dt} = -10x + 10y \qquad \frac{dy}{dt} = 28x - y - xz \qquad \frac{dz}{dt} = -\frac{8}{3}z + xy$$

He chose the value 28 in the second equation so that the model would represent a system just after the onset of unsteady convection. Lorenz summarized his results as follows in the abstract of a 1963 paper "Deterministic Nonperiodic Flow."[2]

> Finite systems of deterministic ordinary nonlinear differential equations may be designed to represent forced dissipative hydrodynamic flow. Solutions of these equations can be identified with trajectories in phase space. For those systems with bounded solutions, it is found that nonperiodic solutions are ordinarily unstable with respect to small modifications, so that slightly differing initial states can evolve into considerably different states. Systems with bounded solutions are shown to possess bounded numerical solutions.

---

[2]The term *phase space* in this summary refers to a "hypothetical" space with a dimension for each variable in the dynamical system. Coordinates of points in phase space thus represent a set of simultaneous values of the variables [Lorenz, p. 211].

A simple system representing cellular convection is solved numerically. All of the solutions are found to be unstable and almost all of them are nonperiodic.

The feasibility of very long-range weather prediction is examined in the light of these results. [Stewart, (1989) p. 133]

This paper was published in the *Journal of Atmospheric Sciences*, a journal not widely read by mathematicians and scientists who were concurrently exploring similar phenomena. However, with the advantage of hindsight, we note that Lorenz's abstract specifically identifies a phenomenon that has become a major concept in chaos theory, namely "sensitive dependence on initial conditions." As Gleick notes, "The modern study of chaos began with the creeping realization in the 1960s that quite simple mathematical equations could model systems every bit as violent as a waterfall. Tiny differences in input could quickly become overwhelming differences in output . . . " [Gleick, p. 8].

Even though the work of Lorenz and others in the 1960s is considered the beginning of chaos theory, some of its fundamental ideas were noted much earlier. Credited with creating the theory of dynamical systems, Henri Poincaré discussed unpredictability in *Science et Méthode* (1908), claiming that *chance* and *determinism* are reconciled by long term unpredictability and concluded: "[A] very small cause, which escapes us, determines a considerable effect which we cannot ignore, and we then say that this effect is due to chance." [Poincaré as quoted in Ruelle, p. 48] Poincaré's statement appears to be an even earlier description of *sensitive dependence on initial conditions.* In fact, he even gave two illustrative examples: (1) motion of a gas made up of many molecules, and (2) weather forecasting.

However, the ideas of Poincaré were apparently unknown by those exploring chaos in the 1960s. Ruelle gives two possible reasons for what he calls "this puzzling historical gap" in which the ideas of Poincaré fell into "oblivion instead of being followed by the modern theory of chaos: . . . The new [quantum] mechanics changed the scientific landscape of physicists and occupied all their energies for many years. . . . These ideas came too early: the tools to exploit them did not exist." [Ruelle, p. 49]

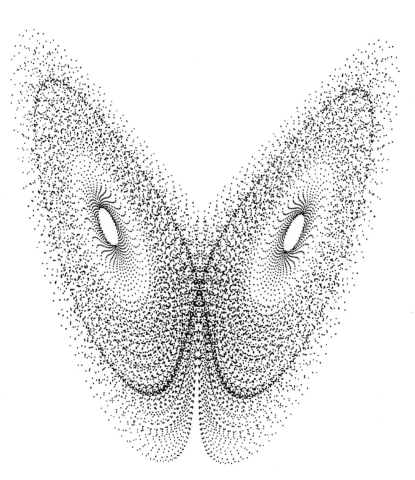

FIGURE 5.1   The Lorenz attractor, a.k.a. butterfly.

Thus it was left to Lorenz and his colleagues to rediscover and amplify Poincaré's ideas. In doing so, they made use of geometric representations of trajectories in phase space. The particular one that Lorenz referred to in his 1963 abstract is now known as the *Lorenz attractor* or the *Lorenz butterfly*. The latter name is suggestive of the attractor's shape (Fig. 5.1) and reminiscent of the term *butterfly effect*. This term apparently first arose in 1972 when Lorenz presented a paper entitled "Does the Flap of a Butterfly's Wings in Brazil Set Off a Tornado in Texas?" and the term became widely known after Gleick used it as a title for the first chapter in his book.

Interestingly, Lorenz indicates that the paper title was not his creation but that of the convener of the session where Lorenz was to present the paper.[3] Unable to contact Lorenz, the convener created this title for the paper [Lorenz, p. 15]. So, in a strange twist of fate, the sensitive dependence on initial conditions, a defining characteristic of chaotic systems such as Lorenz's weather models, has become known as the *butterfly effect*.

Although Lorenz is a meteorologist, his research is typical of that used to understand the long term behavior of a "dynamical system." The use of the term dynamical system to refer to a system of differential equations (or their discrete analogues, *difference* equations) apparently originated with an American topologist, Stephen Smale in the 1960s [Stewart, p.106]. The term now also refers to the branch of mathematics that studies the behavior of systems for which there is a deterministic rule for how the system evolves with time. Mathematical research in this area makes extensive use of computers, and as a result the research has taken on the nature of an experimental science. And following Smale's lead, this research often views the systems in terms of their geometry, not just in terms of their defining formulas.

The term "chaos" was introduced into the dynamical systems area in 1975 when researchers Li and Yorke published a paper titled "Period Three Implies Chaos." Lorenz notes, "Whatever they may have intended to do, they succeeded in establishing a new scientific term, although one with a somewhat different meaning from what they had in mind." [Lorenz, p. 120] Although chaos theory can be intuitively described as the theory of "complicated dynamical systems," so-called *chaotic behavior* can occur even when functions as simple as quadratics are iterated, thus making basic concepts of chaos accessible at a reasonably elementary level. Indeed, Devaney notes "This is a fundamental breakthrough made by mathematicians in recent years, the realization that chaotic systems need not depend on huge numbers of variables but may in fact depend on only one, as in the case of [the family of logistic functions]." [Devaney, (1990) p. 151]

---

[3]This paper is Appendix 1 in Lorenz's book, *The Essence of Chaos*.

5.1.2　Chaotic Behavior of Logistic Functions

As previously indicated, chaotic behavior can arise from iterating logistic functions, that is, functions of the form:

$$L_c(x) = cx(1 - x), \qquad c > 0$$

Since each value of the parameter c gives a distinct function, this is really a family of functions. Functions from this family are widely used to model population growth where the growth is restricted by an upper limit. In these functions, the variable x represents the current population and the function value $L_c(x)$ represents the population after one time period, for example, a year. Using subscripts to indicate time periods, we can write $x_{i+1} = L_c(x_i)$, allowing us to rewrite the equation as $x_{i+1} = cx_i(1 - x_i)$. We will use the latter form, with the usual convention that all values x_i represent fractions of the population limit, that is, they can only take on real number values in the interval $[0, 1]$.

Understanding the long term behavior of iterated functions like the logistic functions is one of the major goals of dynamic systems theory and is the major subject of entire texts.[4] As a brief example of the analysis of logistic functions, consider the logistic function in which $c = 4$, $L_4(x) = 4x(1 - x)$. The process of iterating this function consists of computing a sequence beginning as follows:

$$x_1 = L_4(x_0), \qquad x_2 = L_4(x_1) = L_4(L_4(x_0)),$$
$$x_3 = L_4(x_2) = L_4(L_4(x_1)) = L_4(L_4(L_4(x_0))), \ldots$$

The ordered set beginning with x_0 and followed by these successive images of x_0 is known as the *orbit of x_0 under (iteration by) L_4*. Applying L_4 to the endpoints of its domain gives $L_4(0) = L_4(1) = 0$, so all successive iterates x_i for both $x_0 = 0$ and $x_0 = 1$ yield the value 0. Thus, 0 is said to be an *invariant point* or a *fixed point*[5] of the logistic function L_4. Also, it is worth noting that 0 is an *attracting*

---

[4]See, for example, Richard Holmgren's *A First Course in Discrete Dynamical Systems*, 2nd ed..

[5]Here the term *point* is used as it is commonly used in the study of dynamical systems; namely, to represent a value of the dependent x-variable, as in the expression *p is a fixed point of the function f*. In this usage, *points* are represented by lowercase rather than uppercase letters. Frequently, the value represented by a

TABLE 5.1   Various Orbits of $L_4(x) = 4x(1 - x)$.

x_0	.1	.25	.3	.4	.49	.5	.74	.75	.8
x_1	.360	.75	.84	.96	1.00	1	.77	.75	.640
x_2	.922	.75	.538	.154	.002	0	.709	.75	.922
x_3	.289	.75	.994	.520	.006	0	.825	.75	.289
x_4	.822	.75	.022	.998	.025	0	.578	.75	.822
x_5	.585	.75	.088	.006	.099	0	.976	.75	.585
x_6	.971	.75	.321	.025	.357	0	.095	.75	.971
x_7	.113	.75	.872	.099	.918	0	.343	.75	.113
x_8	.402	.75	.448	.358	.302	0	.902	.75	.402
x_9	.962	.75	.989	.919	.843	0	.354	.75	.962
x_{10}	.148	.75	.043	.298	.530	0	.915	.75	.148
x_{11}	.504	.75	.166	.837	.996	0	.310	.75	.504
x_{12}	1.000	.75	.554	.547	.015	0	.856	.75	1.00
x_{13}	.000	.75	.988	.991	.058	0	.493	.75	.000
x_{14}	.001	.75	.046	.035	.220	0	1.00	.75	.001
x_{15}	.004	.75	.177	.135	.686	0	.001	.75	.004
x_{16}	.016	.75	.583	.466	.861	0	.003	.75	.016
x_{17}	.062	.75	.973	.995	.478	0	.013	.75	.062
x_{18}	.232	.75	.106	.018	.998	0	.051	.75	.232
x_{19}	.712	.75	.379	.071	.008	0	.193	.75	.712
x_{20}	.820	.75	.942	.263	.031	0	.622	.75	.820

fixed point, that is, points x close to 0 have orbits that converge to 0; fixed points p where nearby points diverge from p are said to be *repelling*. Other points x_0 give more interesting orbits but require tedious amounts of calculation best relegated to a computer. Table 5.1 shows the first 20 iterates in the orbits for various values of x_0. For example, as indicated in this table,[6] when $x_0 = .1$, $x_1 = L_4(.1) = .36$, $x_2 = L_4(.36) = .922$, $x_3 = L_4(.922) = .289$.

The process of determining the long term behavior of orbits of a given dynamical system is known as *orbit analysis*. For the cases shown in the table, note that the orbit of $x = .25$ converges to the fixed point .75, whereas the orbit of $x = .5$ converges to the fixed

---

point in this usage is associated graphically with a "geometrical" point on a line or in a plane as in Algorithm 5.1.

[6]These values were generated to 15-digit accuracy using MathCad.

TABLE 5.2 Behavior of Orbits of $L_c = cx(1-x)$.

c	Behavior of orbits
.50	all orbits converge to 0
.75	all orbits converge to 0
1.00	all orbits converge to 0, but very slowly
1.50	all orbits converge to 1/3
2.00	all orbits converge to 1/2
3.00	all orbits converge very slowly to 2/3 oscillating from one side of 2/3 to the other as they do so
3.25	all orbits converge to a period 2 cycle
3.50	all orbits converge to a period 4 cycle
3.55	all orbits converge to a period 8 cycle
4.00	there is no pattern whatsoever for a given x_0
5.00	some orbits diverge to $-\infty$, but many others do not

point 0. Orbits of other initial points under L_4 do not seem to exhibit any particular pattern. If orbits of logistic functions $L_c(x)$ for values of c other than 4 are considered, other types of behavior also appear. The summary of some of these behaviors is given in Table 5.2. For values of c greater than the so-called *Feigenbaum point* (approximately 3.56995), orbits of many initial values x_0 under L_c seem to hop around the line wildly and randomly.[7]

The orbit of a initial point under a logistic function can also be constructed graphically using the step-by-step procedure described in Algorithm 5.1 to generate a construction known as a *web diagram* similar to that shown in Figure 5.2. This method, while lacking the precision of numerical calculations, should enhance visual understanding of the process. If you have access to a computer or programmable calculator, you may want to automate the tracing of orbits according to the algorithm. Sources for appropriate BASIC programs are listed at the end of the chapter.

Algorithm 5.1 (Orbit Tracing for Logistic Function L_c)
A. Given an integer n and an initial variable value x_0:

---

[7]For a detailed discussion of this constant and the period-doubling phenomenon, see Chapter 11 in Peitgen et al., *Chaos and Fractals: New Frontiers of Science*.

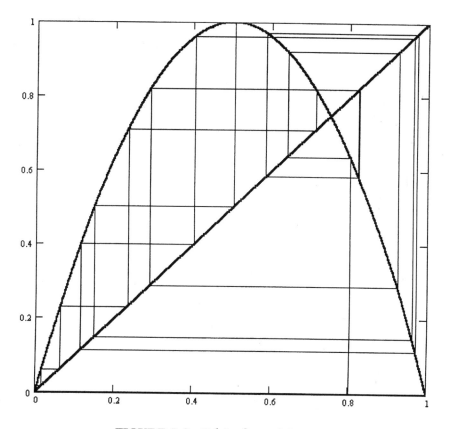

FIGURE 5.2   Orbit of $x_0 = 0.8$, $c = 4$.

    (1) On a graph showing both a logistic function L_c and the line $y = x$, locate the point Z on the x-axis that has its x-coordinate equal to x_0.

    (2) On the line $y = x$, locate the point with x-coordinate also equal to x_0 and label it x_0.

B. Beginning at the location of the current point x_i, draw a vertical segment (upward or downward) along the line $x = x_i$ until the segment intersects the graph of L_c. Let x_{i+1} be the value of the y-coordinate of this intersection point.

C. From this intersection point, draw a horizontal segment (either right or left) until the segment intersects the graph of the diagonal line $y = x$. Label the intersection point x_{i+1}.

D. If $i + 1 = n$, stop. Otherwise return to step B.

Exercises (Logistic Functions)

1. For each c-value ($c = 1, 2, 3, 4, 5$):

   a. Construct a graph showing both $y = L_c(x)$ and $y = x$ for $0 \le x \le 1$.

   b. On this graph, carry out the construction of Algorithm 5.1 (with $n = 5$) to find the next 5 entries in the orbit of $x_0 = .2$ under L_c.

   c. On the same graph, use a second color to carry out the Algorithm 5.1 construction (again with $n = 5$) to find the next 5 entries in the orbit of $x_0 = .8$ under L_c.

   d. Do you expect any of the orbits shown on your various graphs to eventually converge? If so, indicate which ones and give the apparent limit point of each. Would you expect any of the orbits to become chaotic? If so, indicate which ones and why.

2. For $x_0 = .2$ and each c-value ($c = 1, 2, 3, 4, 5$):

   a. Use a computer or calculator to find the entries in the orbit $\{x_0, x_1, \ldots, x_{10}\}$ under $L_c(x)$.

   b. Do these results support or contradict the conjectures you made about apparent limit points and chaotic behavior in the previous exercise? Explain.

3. Explain what happens when you apply the construction of Algorithm 5.1 to the points $x_0 = 0$; $x_0 = 1$. Will your results be the same for all values of c?

4. Explain the mathematics behind the "construction" in Algorithm 5.1; that is, why does this construction lead to successive elements in the orbit of the given initial point?

5. Assume that p is a fixed point of the function f (i.e., $f(p) = p$).

   a. Show that for any positive integer n, p is a fixed point of the function $f^n = f \circ f \circ f \circ \ldots \circ f$ (n times).

   b. What will be true about the orbit of p under iteration by f?

   c. What will be true about orbits of other points x_0 under f that include $x_i = p$ for some $i > 0$.

6. Explain the steps in the proof of the following theorem:[8]

---

[8] Ignace I. Kolodner, *The American Mathematical Monthly* 71 (64) p. 906.

Theorem

If for some k, f^k has exactly one fixed point p, that is $f^k(p) = p$, then p is also a fixed point of the function f, that is, $f(p) = p$.

Proof

$f^k(f(p)) = f^{k+1}(p) = f(f^k(p)) = f(p)$. Thus, $f(p) = p$. ∎

7. For which values of c does a logistic curve L_c appear to have a nontrivial fixed point? Describe the location of this nontrivial fixed point in terms of its graph.

8. Explain why a logistic function will never have more than one nontrivial fixed point.

9. On the graphs of functions L_c with a nontrivial fixed point p, describe how you could graphically find an initial value $x_0 \neq p$ such that the orbit of x_0 converges to the fixed point p in exactly one iteration. In exactly two iterations. Will you always be able to find such initial values. Explain.

10. For each of the following, assume that L_c is a logistic function:

    a. Show that the nontrivial fixed point of a function L_c is equal to $p = (c-1)/c$

    b. Find the nontrivial fixed point of L_c for each of the values $c = 1.5, 2, 3, 4, 5$.

    c. Explain why there is no nontrivial fixed point of L_c when $c \leq 1$.

    d. Show that the slope of L_c at its nontrivial fixed point p is equal to $m_p = 2 - c$.

11. For a logistic function L_c, assume that $x = p$ is a nontrivial fixed point of L_c, and that m_p is the slope of L_c at p.

    a. Using diagrams, explain the following: The attracting or repelling nature of p under L_c will be the same as that of 0 under iteration by $f(x) = m_p x$, that is, if x is a point "close" to p it will be attracted to (or repelled from) p under iteration by L_c in the same way that the point $x - p$ is attracted to (or repelled from) p under iteration by $f(x) = m_p x$.

    b. If $m_p < -1$, use diagrams to show how the previous reasoning indicates that p is a repelling point, whereas if $m_p > -1$, p is an attracting point. What happens if $m_p = -1$?

c. For which values of c will L_c have a nontrivial repelling point, a nontrivial attracting point. Explain your reasoning.

12. Recall that logistic functions are often used to model population growth where x represents the population as a percentage of an upper limit.

    a. For the general logistic function $L_c(x) = cx(1 - x)$ what is this upper limit on the population? Report your answer in terms of c.

    b. For models of population growth based on logistic functions L_c:

       i. Are there any limits on the possible values of c? Explain.

       ii. Of what value is knowing the nontrivial fixed point of L_c if the fixed point is attracting? If repelling?

The following exercise requires the use of computers or appropriate calculators.

13. Use computer- (or calculator-) generated traces of orbits to develop conjectures about the apparent long term behavior of orbits of initial points x_0 (where $0 < x_0 < 1$) under a logistic function L_c in each of the cases described below. In cases where there is a non-trivial fixed point, determine if this point is attracting or repelling. For each case, give a clear statement of your conjecture and justify your reasoning.

    (a) $c \leq 1$ (b) $1 < c < 3$ (c) $c = 3.2$ (d) $c = 3.48$

Summary

To summarize this brief introduction to chaos theory, we note that the dynamic systems in which chaos arises are *deterministic* since they evolve according to precise rules given by equations which are usually not linear and often involve several variables. However, even when the equations of a system are not very complicated, the systems can be unstable due to their *sensitive dependence on initial conditions*.

    As a result, the behavior described by the system can become extremely complicated and, in the long run, *unpredictable*. And in cases like weather models, where we know the initial conditions somewhat imprecisely, very slight differences in the values of these initial conditions may lead to vastly different results. This leads to a dim future for long-range weather forecasting.

It is now realized that no new better simulation of weather on more accurate computers of the future will be able to predict the weather more than about fourteen days ahead, because of the very nonlinear nature of the evolution of the state of the weather. [Robinson, p.1]

Thus, the innocuous sounding *butterfly effect* provides a major counterexample to the classical assumption that arbitrarily small influences do not have arbitrarily large effects.

5.1.3 Famous Sets in Chaos Theory

The previous brief introduction of chaotic behavior provides a basis for understanding a collection of sets that play significant roles in chaos theory, namely *Julia sets*, and the even more well known *Mandelbrot set*. Julia sets are named after the French mathematician Gaston Julia, who together with Pierre Fatou, invented and studied these sets in the early 20th century. The Mandelbrot set is named after the contemporary French mathematician Benoit Mandelbrot whose work from the 1950s through the 1970s at IBM in New York is generally recognized as the foundation of fractal geometry. With this connection, it is most appropriate that the Mandelbrot set has become a "logo" for fractal geometry and chaos theory. Its spectacular color representations generated by high speed modern computers are appreciated by mathematicians and nonmathematicians alike.

Julia Sets

The way the graphical representation of a Julia set is obtained is distinctly different from the usual mathematical process of plotting a curve representing a function. For a function f of one real variable, the latter process, commonly known as "graphing the function," involves substituting a real number x_1 for the variable x in the function expression; computing the result, $x_2 = f(x_1)$; and plotting the point with coordinates (x_1, x_2) on a two-dimensional Cartesian coordinate graph. However, to obtain a representation for the Julia set of a function f, an initial variable value, usually denoted x_0, is substituted into the function expression yielding a new value $x_1 = f(x_0)$. This new value is then used to produce a value $x_2 = f(x_1)$ and this process is iterated repeatedly to produce the orbit of x_0. This iteration continues until the long term orbit behavior can be identified. Then the point x_0 is plotted in a color indicating this orbit behavior. Generally, the points with bounded orbits are shown in black.

Definition 5.1
For a given function f, the set of points whose orbits are bounded under iteration of the function f is called the *filled Julia set of f*. The boundary of a filled Julia set is called the *Julia set*.[9]

Logistic functions have associated Julia sets, but since the initial values used for logistic functions consist only of single-variable real numbers, the graphical representation of such Julia sets is merely a set of points on the x-axis, and hence rather uninteresting. To obtain two-dimensional Julia sets, we move into the realm of complex functions, that is, functions whose domain and range are sets of complex numbers. Here when an initial complex value z_0 produces a bounded orbit, the point z_0 is plotted, that is, colored black, in the two-dimensional complex plane. Some of the simplest functions that yield interesting Julia sets are the quadratic complex functions of the form $Q_c(z) = z^2 + c$, where each complex constant c yields a different function in this family and hence a different shaped Julia set.

In the Julia set illustrations in Figure 5.3, points of the complex plane shown in black have very predictable orbits, for example, the orbits either converge to specific points or cycle. In color illustrations, points depicted with colors have orbits that diverge to infinity. Different colors indicate different "speeds" with which the orbits diverge to infinity. As Definition 5.1 indicates, the boundary between the set of black points and the set of colored (in our case white) points is the *actual* Julia set while the boundary and its interior are called the *filled* Julia set. For example, for the function $Q_0(z) = z^2$, points z where $|z| < 1$ all have orbits that converge to 0. Points z, where

---

[9]The *boundary* of a set is the collection of points for which every neighborhood contains an element of the set as well as an element not in the set.

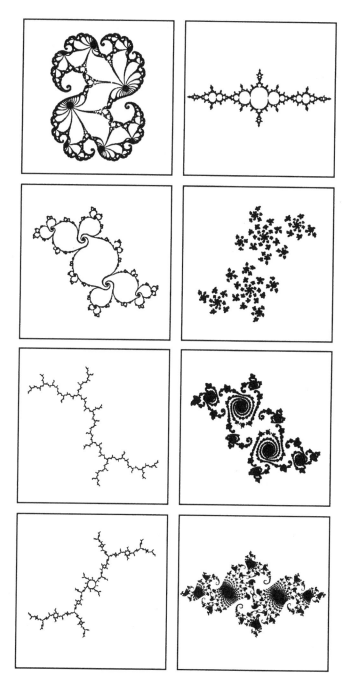

FIGURE 5.3 Some samples of Julia sets. [Peitgen et al., *Chaos and Fractals: New Frontiers of Science*, Springer-Verlag]

$|z| > 1$ all have orbits that diverge to infinity. Thus, the Julia set of Q_0 is exactly the set of points on the circle $|z| = 1$. However, points on this "simple" Julia set exhibit the same unpredictable behavior that points on any Julia set exhibit under iteration by its defining function; namely, any point on the circle $|z| = 1$ has an orbit that does not "escape," that is, diverge, to infinity but the point itself is *arbitrarily* close to other points whose orbits under Q_0 eventually hit any nonzero point in the plane. Thus, just as in the case of Lorenz's weather model, there is *sensitive dependence on initial conditions*.

As might be expected from such complicated properties, Julia sets can be extremely intricate, and come in a vast array of shapes. One indication of the range of diversity in their shapes is the fact that some Julia sets are connected, that is, they are in one piece, while others are totally disconnected and thus described by the picturesque term "fractal dust."

The Mandelbrot Set

As complicated as Julia sets appear, there is another set that is more complicated and has been labeled "the most complex object in mathematics." Mandelbrot discovered this set in the late 1970s when he attempted to make generalizations about Julia sets. Whereas individual members of the family of complex quadratic functions, $Q_c(z) = z^2 + c$, each determine a Julia set in the z-plane, the Mandelbrot set is plotted in the c–plane and represents a catalog of the entire function family $\{Q_c(z)\}$. The characteristic property of Julia sets catalogued by the Mandelbrot set is that of *connectedness*—whether or not the Julia set of Q_c consists of exactly one piece.

Definition 5.2

The *Mandelbrot set* is the set of complex numbers c such that the Julia set for the function $Q_c(z) = z^2 + c$ is connected.

At first glance, this set appears to be nearly impossible to find, since determining whether a single complex point c is in the set would seem to require not only finding the entire Julia set for the function Q_c but also determining whether this Julia set is connected. Fortunately, there is a more efficient method of determination as a result of the following theorem discovered by Julia and Fatou before 1920, making their result one of the earliest in chaos theory:

Theorem 5.1

The Julia set corresponding to the function Q_c, for a specific c, is connected if and only if for all critical points z of Q_c, the orbit of z does not diverge to infinity.

A *critical point* of a function f is, as you recall from elementary calculus, a number z such that $f'(z) = 0$. Since our functions are of the form $Q_c(z) = z^2 + c$, the only critical point of each is $z = 0$. Thus, the previous theorem leads to the following corollary making the determination of a Mandelbrot set far easier.

Corollary

A complex number c is in the Mandelbrot set if and only if the value 0 is in the filled Julia set of Q_c.

Graphical representations of the Mandelbrot set usually show the set itself in black. This means a point c in the complex plane is colored black if the orbit $Q_c(0) = c$, $Q_c(Q_c(0)) = c^2 + c$, $Q_c(Q_c(Q_c(0))) = (c^2 + c)^2 + c$, etc., is bounded. If on the other hand, the values in this orbit diverge to infinity, or, in practice if they become greater than 2 in absolute value (in which case the orbit will diverge to infinity), the iteration is broken off and the point c is colored white. In some cases, white is not used for points in this second set; instead, gradations of color are used to indicate how long the iteration proceeded before being stopped. For example, if the iteration stopped after 10 steps (because the value became 2 or greater), the point is colored red, after 20 steps, orange, etc. These colors then show types of contours in the area outside the actual Mandelbrot set and create the magnificent colored pictures you may have seen. Using elementary properties of complex numbers, it can be shown that the Mandelbrot set lies entirely within the region in the c-plane where $|c| < 2$ as shown in Figure 5.4.

Even though the first images of the Mandelbrot set were published only in 1980, the set has already undergone intensive study and numerous interesting properties have been catalogued. For a

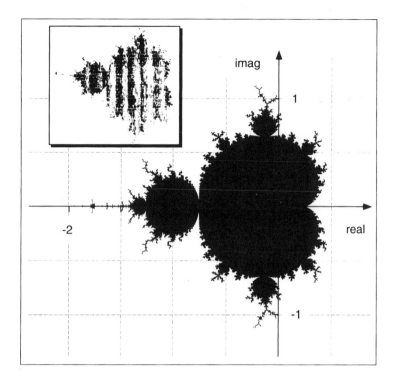

FIGURE 5.4 The Mandelbrot set—old and new rendering. The insert shows an original printout from Mandelbrot's experiment. We have produced the large Mandelbrot set using a modern laser printer and a more accurate mathematical algorithm.

description of many of these, see Chapter 14 in *Chaos and Fractals* by Peitgen, Jürgens, and Saupe.

5.2 Need for a New Geometric Language

When we examine the development of a process over a period of time, we speak in terms used in chaos theory. When we are more interested in the structural forms which a chaotic process leaves in its wake, then we use the terminology of fractal geometry, which is really the geometry whose structures are what give order to chaos. [Peitgen et al., (1992), pp. viii]

Julia sets and the Mandelbrot set, as well as other complicated geometric shapes that arise in chaos theory, cannot be adequately described using the figures of traditional Euclidean geometry. Instead, their descriptions require the language of *fractal geometry*. Even though most of the research developments in fractal geometry have occurred since the advent of high-resolution computer graphics, this geometry had its beginnings nearly a century ago with the development of several strange sets, including the *Cantor set*, the *Koch* and *Peano curves*, and the *Sierpinski triangle* and *carpet*. The Cantor set was discovered by Henry Smith in 1875, but named after Georg Cantor, the founder of set theory, who used the set as an example of an uncountably infinite set of measure zero. This same abstract mathematical object acquired practical significance when Mandelbrot's work at IBM on data transmission errors led to his realization that their occurrence in bursts was similar in appearance to the Cantor set. Algorithms for the Cantor set as well as for the Koch curve and the two Sierpinski shapes (the latter three were developed between 1900 and 1920) will be given later. With these as examples, you will develop an algorithm for the Peano curve that should enable you to explain why its behavior led Steen to describe it as follows: "It meandered so much that it passed through every point in a unit square!" [Steen, p. 123]. And all of this should lead to an appreciation of Mandelbrot's colorful depiction:

> These new structures were regarded ... as 'pathological' ... as a 'gallery of monsters,' akin to the cubist painting and atonal music that were upsetting established standards of taste in the arts at about the same time. The mathematicians who created the monsters regarded them as important in showing that the world of pure mathematics contains a richness of possibilities going far beyond the simple structures that they saw in Nature. Twentieth century mathematics flowered in the belief that it had transcended completely the limitations imposed by its natural origins. [Mandelbrot, *The Fractal Geometry of Nature* p. 3.]

In fact, it is Mandelbrot who coined the term "fractal" to describe these strange sets.

> I coined *fractal* from the Latin adjective *fractus*. The corresponding Latin verb *frangere* means "to break": to create irregular fragments. It is therefore sensible— and how appropriate for our needs!— that, in

addition to "fragmented" (as in *fraction* or *refraction*) *fractus* should also mean "irregular," both meanings preserved in fragment. [Mandelbrot, p. 4]

As we will indicate later, Mandelbrot originally gave a definition for his new fractal sets, but later expressed regret for having done so. Similarly, before giving any formal indication of the nature of fractals, we will explore fractal examples and investigate three major concepts intrinsic to the creation and understanding of fractals, namely self-similarity, dimension, and iterated function systems. In these investigations we will make extensive use of iteration just as we did in orbit analysis.

5.2.1 Fractal Examples

To appreciate the fragmented nature of fractals, it is necessary to look at specific examples. The two explored in this section, namely, the Cantor set and the Koch curve, are among the early examples of fractals. Both can be generated from an *initial set* by iterating, or repeating, a process over and over. This is done by following a step-by-step procedure known as an *algorithm* that involves repeated iteration of the same process. In theory, this repetition would be continued forever; in practice, we can create a figure resembling the final fractal to any given resolution by a finite number of repetitions of the generating process. Strictly speaking, the initial set, also known as the *stage* 0 figure, and the *stage n* figures (the figures resulting after *n* stages in the process) are called *prefractals*, while the term *fractal* is reserved for the figure that results from infinite repetition of the generation process.

The Cantor Set

The Cantor set is generated by beginning with a segment (usually assumed to have length 1) and removing the open middle third of this segment (leaving the endpoints). The process of removing the open middle third of each remaining segment is then repeatedly

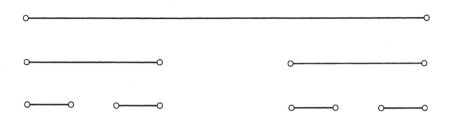

FIGURE 5.5   Stages 0, 1, and 2 in Cantor set generation.

iterated using the procedure described in Algorithm 5.2. Figure 5.5 shows the first three stages in this generation. As noted previously, the actual Cantor set is the set of points remaining after infinite repetition of this process.

Algorithm 5.2 (Generating a Cantor Set)
- *Initial Set (Stage 0):* A segment.
- *Stage 1:*
  - a. Trisect the segment, that is, divide the segment into three congruent subsegments.
  - b. Remove the middle subsegment of the trisected segment, leaving the endpoints.
- *Stage n (n ≥ 2):* Repeat the procedure of Stage 1 on each of the 2^{n-1} remaining congruent segments.

Exercises (Cantor Sets)

1. Beginning with a unit length line segment,[10] use Algorithm 5.2 to carry out the first four stages in the generation of the Cantor set.

2. How many subintervals exist in the stage 4 Cantor set? How long is each?

3. How many subintervals exist in the stage 5 Cantor set? In the stage 10 Cantor set? In the stage n Cantor set? How long are the subintervals in each of these stages?

---

[10] For easy measurement, you may want to use 8.1 cm as your unit length.

4. Verify that the (final) Cantor set is nonempty and actually contains an infinite number of points.

5. What is the length of the Cantor set? Explain.

The Koch Curve

The Koch curve is another well known fractal that is often used to illustrate some of the basic concepts of fractal geometry. Generating a Koch curve involves trisecting each input segment to create three congruent subsegments, constructing an equilateral triangle on the middle subsegment, and then erasing the base of this triangle. The procedure is detailed in Algorithm 5.3.

Algorithm 5.3 (Generating a Koch Curve)
- *Initial Set (Stage 0):* A segment.
- *Stage 1:*
  a. Trisect the segment, i.e., divide each segment into three congruent subsegments.
  b. On the middle subsegment, construct an equilateral triangle with the middle subsegment as its base.
  c. Remove the subsegment base of the newly constructed triangle. (Figure 5.6.)
- *Stage n ($n \geq 2$).* Repeat the procedure of Stage 1 on each of the 4^{n-1} new congruent segments.

Exercises (Koch Curves)

The following exercise asks you to carry out the first three stages in the generation of a Koch curve simultaneously on the three sides of an equilateral triangle. The final figure generated by infinite iteration of this procedure is known as a *Koch snowflake*. As you will see, the Koch snowflake not only demonstrates the fractal properties of Koch curves but also leads to an interesting paradox.

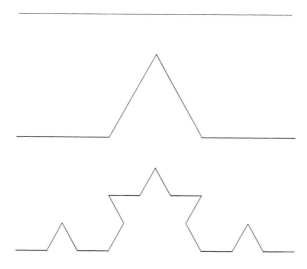

FIGURE 5.6   Stages 0, 1, and 2 in Koch curve generation.

6. Construct an equilateral triangle using either paper and pencil[11] (so you can erase) or dynamic geometry software. For the following, assume that the sides of your triangle have length of one unit.

   Then, for n = 1, 2, 3,

   a. Construct a stage n Koch curve on all three sides of the original triangle, creating a stage n Koch snowflake. For each value of n, carry our the computations below before modifying the construction to obtain the next $(n + 1)$ stage.

   b. Compute the number and length of the segments in your stage n Koch snowflake, as well as the perimeter and area of this snowflake. Report these in the appropriate row in Table 5.3. (Note: You will find it easiest to generalize your results for the next exercise if you express all of your answers using the same pattern; for example, you may want to express them as products and/or sums of powers of the numbers 3 and 4.)

7. By generalizing the patterns you observe, find the perimeter and area for the stage 10 Koch snowflake; for the stage n Koch snowflake.

---

[11]The construction works especially well on triangular isometric dot paper. On such paper, locate the triangle vertices 27 (or an integer multiple of 27) "dot spaces" apart.

TABLE 5.3 Koch Snowflake Data.

	Number of Segments	Segment Length	Perimeter	Area
Stage 0	3	1		
Stage 1				
Stage 2				
Stage 3				
Stage 10				
Stage n				

8. Use your formula for stage n to determine the length of the perimeter of the (final) Koch snowflake. In particular, determine if the length is finite or infinite. Explain your answers.

9. What is the area of the Koch snowflake? How does it compare to the area of the original equilateral triangle?

10. What is the paradox presented by your answers to the previous two exercises? How can it be explained?

5.2.2 The Measurement Dilemma

The Koch curve illustrates some of the problems that arose when mathematicians tried to apply to fractals their usual notions of measurement. Meaningful Euclidean measurements cannot account for the new detail revealed in fractal sets under increasing magnification. This inadequacy is well illustrated by an attempt to measure lengths of fractal-like natural curves such as coastlines and national boundaries. An attempt to measure any one of these curves using different scales of Euclidean measurement (taking into account these changes of scale) leads to different results. Likewise, if the same scale of measurement is used for each measurement, but the curve is increasingly magnified, Euclidean measurement cannot account for the increasing detail shown. In fact, this measurement problem played a significant role in the development of fractal geometry. Mandelbrot discovered that English scientist Lewis F. Richardson[12] had noted that encyclopedias in Spain and Portugal had discrepancies of twenty percent in the estimated length of their common boundary (987 versus 1214 km).[13] Mandelbrot's subsequent article "How Long Is the Coast of Britain?" made the problem of measuring national boundaries and coastlines more widely known.

Measuring Coastlines

An indication of the way coastlines have been measured historically is given in Table 5.4. The information in this table and the footnotes come from the *1998 World Almanac* (p. 541). The footnotes for Table 5.4 indicate that the reported lengths were obtained using a technique known as *divider measurement*. This is a standard way of measuring lengths of irregular curves and makes use of a divider, a tool similar to a noncollapsible compass where the two divider legs have identical points.[14] The directions below describe a regimen for measuring curve lengths using a divider.

Divider Measurement of Curve Length
Directions: Label an initial point P_0 on the curve. With the divider set for a fixed opening ℓ (referred to as the *step-length*), place one point

---

[12]Richardson also worked with early mathematical models for weather forecasting. In his book *Weather Prediction by Numerical Process* (1922) he described his procedures and his vision for a weather center where 64,000 people working in shifts could produce forecasts faster than the weather could advance [Richardson, p. 219].

[13]Reported in "The problem of contiguity: An appendix of statistics of deadly quarrels," *General Systems Yearbook* 6 (1961): 139-187.

[14]In practice, a compass with pencil inserted can be used as a divider.

TABLE 5.4   U.S. Coastline by States (in statute miles).

State	Coastline[a]	Shoreline[b]	State	Coastline[a]	Shoreline[b]
Atlantic Coast	2,069	28,673	Gulf Coast	1,631	17,141
Connecticut	0	618	Alabama	53	607
Delaware	28	381	Florida	770	5,095
Florida	580	3,331	Louisiana	397	7,721
Georgia	100	2,344	Mississippi	44	359
Maine	228	3,478	Texas	367	3,359
Maryland	31	3,190			
Massachusetts	192	1,519	Pacific Coast	7,623	40,298
New Hampshire	13	131	Alaska	5,580	31,383
New Jersey	130	1,792	California	840	3,427
New York	127	1850	Hawaii	750	1,052
North Carolina	301	3,375	Oregon	296	1,410
Pennsylvania	0	89	Washington	157	3,026
Rhode Island	40	384			
South Carolina	187	2,876	Arctic Coast, Alaska	1,060	2,521
Virginia	112	3,315	United States	12,383	88,633

Source: NOAA, U.S. Commerce Department.

[a] Coastlines: Figures are lengths of general outline of seacoast. Measurements were made with a unit measure of 30 minutes of latitude [approximately 35 miles] on charts as near the scale of 1:1,200,000 as possible. Coastline of sounds and bays is included to a point where they narrow to width of unit measure, and includes the distance across at such point.

[b] Shorelines: Figures obtained in 1939-40 with a recording instrument on the largest scale maps then available. Shoreline of outer coast, offshore islands, sounds, bays, rivers, and creeks is included to the head of tidewater or to a point where tidal waters narrow to a width of 100 feet.

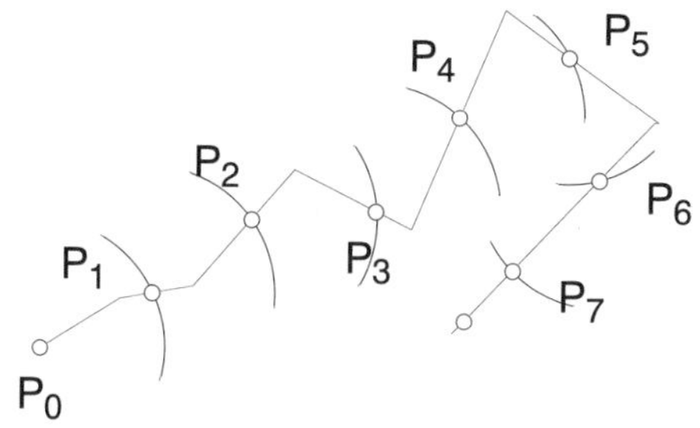

FIGURE 5.7 Divider measuring.

of the divider on P_0 and rotate the divider around this point until the second point of the divider lands on another point on the curve. Mark and label this second point as P_1. Then with the divider point fixed at P_1, rotate the divider until the other point lands on a third point of the curve. Mark and label this point P_2 (Fig. 5.7.). Continue this process of "walking the divider" along the curve until for some integer n the point P_n coincides with, or falls less than, one step-length from,

- the end of the curve, if the curve is not closed; or
- the original point P_0, if the curve is closed.

The *divider-measure* of the curve length is then given by the number $L = n\ell$ where n is the number of *divider steps* using a *step-length* ℓ.

Exercises (Divider Measure)

11. Finding the divider-measure of the perimeter of a Koch snowflake constructed from segments one unit long:

  a. Set the step-length to one unit, i.e., the length of the sides of the original equilateral triangle. Let P_0 be one of the original triangle vertices. How many divider steps lie along the perimeter? What is the corresponding divider-measure of the curve?

  b. Now assume that your step-length is $\frac{1}{3}$ unit long, i.e., $\frac{1}{3}$ as long as the original sides of the equilateral triangle. Using the same point as P_0 and the same technique, how many steps lie along the perimeter this time? What is the divider-measure of the perimeter according to this measurement?

    c. Repeat the previous exercise assuming that the step-length is $\frac{1}{9}$ as long as the original sides.

    d. Why do divider-measures obtained by using decreasing step-lengths yield increasingly larger values for the perimeter of the Koch snowflake? Is there an upper bound on these lengths?

12. Would divider-measures with decreasing step-lengths yield increasingly larger values for the perimeter length of a circle or of a regular polygon such as a square? Would there be an upper bound on the lengths so determined. Explain.

13. What would happen to divider-measures of a coastline obtained by using decreasing step-lengths?

14. Give a possible explanation for the different lengths reported for the common boundary between Spain and Portugal. (Note: You may want to consider the magnification ratios used to make a standard size map of each country.)

15. Use the idea of divider measurement to explain the differences reported in Table 5.4 for the lengths of coastlines and shorelines.

5.2.3 Self-Similarity

The examples examined so far, and the difficulty in measuring them, confirm the irregular and fractured nature suggested by Mandelbrot's term *fractal*. However, we will discover that fractals actually possess a special type of symmetry "across scale" known as self-similarity. This scale invariance makes fractals appear the same under higher and higher magnification.[15] And as the following quotation suggests, the concept of self-similarity is central to fractal geometry.

> The key idea in fractal geometry is *self-similarity*. An object is self-similar if it can be decomposed into smaller copies of itself. Thus self-similarity is the property in which the structure of the whole is contained in its parts. [Hastings, p. 1]

---

[15]This property is beautifully illustrated in videos where the camera continues to zoom in on a small section of the fractal. As the zooming continues, the viewer sees the original fractal shape appear repeatedly.

The "magnification" mappings that map the smaller parts onto the object itself (or inversely, map the object onto each of its smaller parts) are implemented mathematically using transformations described in Chapter 3. Thus, whereas a set of points can be called *self-congruent*, if there is a nonidentity isometry mapping the set onto itself, that is, if the set is *invariant* under the isometry, we will see that a set of points is described as *self-similar* if it is in "some sense" invariant under a (nonidentity) similarity.[16] To define *self-similarity* more precisely, we will use the geometric concept of *tiling*. As defined by Grünbaum and Shephard, a *plane tiling* is a countable family of closed sets that cover the plane without gaps or overlaps (except at vertices and edges) [Grünbaum and Shephard, p. 16]. In order to keep track of the scaling (i.e., magnification) factors, we will use the terminology *s-scale tiling*.

Definition 5.3
A set of points α is said to be *(strictly) self-similar* with *scaling factor s*, if α can be tiled with subsets, each of which can be mapped onto the original set α using a similarity with ratio s. Such a tiling is called an *s-scale tiling*; the subsets are called *tiles*; and s is called the *scaling factor* of the tiling.

The self-similarity properties of the Cantor set and Koch curve become evident when we note that these two examples are constructed by iterating the same transformation at smaller and smaller scales. However, since the construction of other fractals frequently involves more than one transformation and the transformations used may be more general than similarity transformations, the *self-similarity* property defined above will need to be generalized.

Exercises (Self-Similarity)

16. Sketch an illustration showing that a square has a 2-scale tiling.

---

[16]Mandelbrot has an interesting discussion of *self-similarity invariance* in *The Fractal Geometry of Nature*, p. 18.

17. For what other values of s, does a square have s-scale tilings? Explain your answer.

18. What must be true about the size of the scaling factors s in Definition 5.3? For a given self-similar set α, is the scaling factor unique? Explain your answer.

19. Self-similarity of the Cantor set:

   a. Explain why the Cantor set is self-similar with scaling factor 3; determine the number of tiles in such a 3-scale tiling; and describe the location of each tile relative to the entire set.

   b. For *each* tile in the tiling you described in a, name a specific similarity that will map the tile onto the entire Cantor set.

   c. What role does the number 3 play in the similarities you described?

   d. Give two more possible scaling factors $s \neq 3$ for the Cantor set and determine the number of tiles in the corresponding s-scale tilings of the Cantor set.

20. Self-similarity of the Koch curve:

   a. Explain why the Koch curve is self-similar. What is the smallest possible scaling factor for this curve?

   b. Explain why there is more than one possible scaling factor for the Koch curve. Name two possible scaling factors; and for each, give the number of tiles required and describe the tile locations relative to the entire Koch curve.

   c. For *each* tile in the tiling of the Koch curve with the smallest possible scaling factor, name a specific similarity that will map the tile onto the entire Koch curve. (You may want to describe a particular similarity as a product of specific transformation.)

21. Assume that α is a (strictly) self-similar set of points with scaling factor s that can be tiled as in Definition 5.3 with tiles $\alpha_1, \alpha_2, \ldots, \alpha_n$. Prove each of the following:

   a. The original set α can be mapped onto any of the tiles α_i with a similarity. (What would be the ratio of such a similarity?).

   b. Any two of the tiles α_i and α_j are congruent.

   c. If the distance between two given points in the set α is given by K and ℓ is the distance between the corresponding points in one of the s-scale tiles α_i, then $s = K/\ell$.

22. As indicated in this section, a set α can be called *self-congruent* if there is a nonidentity isometry mapping α onto itself. Will a self-similar set β necessarily have a nonidentity similarity mapping β onto itself? Explain.

5.3 Fractal Dimension

The fractal dimension of a set is a number that tells how densely the set occupies the metric space in which it lies. It is invariant under various stretchings and squeezings of the underlying space. [Barnsley, p. 3]

As indicated by the dilemma of trying to find the length of a coastline and the Koch curve, attempts to measure the length (or, in other cases, area or volume) of a fractal are futile. Applying traditional methods of size measurement to highly irregular fractals leads to meaningless results. Instead, Mandelbrot and others discovered that to make any meaningful statement about the size of a fractal, they needed to resort to assigning it a dimension value; but in order to do so, the concept of dimension had to be expanded.

5.3.1 Expanding Topological Dimension

Mathematicians have formulated a number of dimension concepts, but that in most common use (known as topological dimension) involves the number of directions or degrees of freedom inherent in an object. Using this notion, the objects of traditional Euclidean geometry are all assigned non-negative integer dimensions. For example, a point is assigned dimension 0, a line segment is assigned dimension 1, a square is assigned dimension 2, and a cube is assigned dimension 3. One way of explaining this assignment is to simply begin by assigning dimension 0 to a point and then inductively assigning dimensions to other objects by determining the dimension of the "smallest" set whose removal will disconnect it, that is, separate it into two or more distinct parts. The dimension then assigned to the original set is one more than that of the "smallest disconnecting" set. So since a line can be disconnected when a single point, (a set of dimension 0) is removed, lines are assigned dimension 1. Removing a point from a square will not disconnect it; however, removing an appropriate segment (a set of dimension 1), can disconnect it. So squares are assigned dimension 2. Likewise disconnecting a cube requires the removal of an appropriate 2-dimensional set, so cubes are assigned dimension 3. Using this assignment, we sometimes refer to points, segments, squares and cubes as d-cubes where d takes on the values 0, 1, 2, and 3, respectively. Extending this idea further produces the so-called 4-cube, also known as the hypercube, an object that has intrigued many through the ages and is explored in the exercises below.

Exercises (Properties of the Hypercube)

One way to "discover" properties of the hypercube, or 4-cube, is by observing properties of d-cubes for smaller values of d, finding patterns that appear, and then generalizing these to predict properties for $d = 4$.

1. Fill in numerical values in Table 5.5 in rows corresponding to $d = 2$ and $d = 3$.

2. Use predictions based on the values already in cells in the same column to fill in row $d = 4$ in Table 5.5.

3. For the general d-cube, fill in the final row in Table 5.5 with a formula containing the variable d.

Another way to investigate properties of the hypercube is to observe how a $(d - 1)$-cube can be used to generate a d-cube for $d = 1, 2, 3$. Exercises 4 through 7 indicate how this can be done. It may help to think of your points, segments, squares, etc., as being made out of chalk and leaving "chalk trails" as they are dragged.

4. Show how a point can be "dragged" to trace out a segment of unit-length with one endpoint of the segment at the initial position of the point, and the second endpoint at the final position of the point.

5. Show how the number of points (vertices) and segments (sides) of a square can be determined by dragging a unit-length segment in a direction perpendicular to the segment and counting both initial and

TABLE 5.5 Elements of a d-Cube.

d	Points	Segments	Squares	Cubes	Hypercubes
0 (point)	1	0	0	0	0
1 (segment)	2	1	0	0	0
2 (square)					
3 (cube)					
4 (hypercube)					
d (d-cube)					

final positions of points and segments. Also count the segments traced out by dragging the points, and the square traced out by dragging the segment.

6. Explain how this procedure could be used to obtain a cube from a square. Again, verify that your counts of vertices, segments, squares, and cubes come out correctly.

7. Finally, imagine dragging a cube in a direction "perpendicular to itself" to trace out a hypercube and make a count of its various elements. Compare your results with those you obtained in Table 5.5.

To understand how fractals can be assigned dimensions, it is necessary to extend the concept of topological dimension. Two such extensions are *self-similarity* dimension and *box* dimension. Both of these are explored in this section. A third variant called *divider* dimension is introduced in the exercises, while the even more generalized *Hausdorff–Besicovitch* dimension will be mentioned later in the context of Mandelbrot's early definition of fractals. All of these variants are referred to using the generic term *fractal dimension*. And at this early stage in the development of fractal geometry, the commonly accepted practice is to determine the fractal dimension of a set of points by using the dimension variant deemed to be the most appropriate for the set. Fortunately, when the fractal dimension of a set can be computed in more than one way, the computations usually yield the same value. And as the examples will demonstrate, most (but not all) fractal sets will have noninteger fractal dimension.

5.3.2 Self-Similarity Dimension

To assign fractals a *self-similarity dimension,* it is helpful to consider how segments, squares, and cubes can be tiled with a number of smaller tiles such that magnification of each tile by an integer scaling factor (using the same scaling factor for each tile) results in an object congruent to the original. To illustrate this, note that a segment can be tiled using two segment-shaped tiles (meeting at the midpoint of the original segment) so that magnification of each tile by the scaling factor 2 creates a segment congruent to the original. Similarly, a square can be tiled by four square-shaped tiles so that magnification of each tile by the scaling factor 2 (doubling each side) creates a square congruent to the original. The exercises below explore the continuation of this procedure leading to an equation relating an object's dimension d, the scaling factor s, and the number of tiles N in an s-tiling of the object.

Exercises (Self-Similarity)

8. For $s = 2$, sketch a figure illustrating a segment tiled with segment-shaped tiles such that magnification of any one of the tiles by the scaling factor s creates a segment congruent to the original. Sketch a similar figure for $s = 3$.

9. Sketch similar illustrations for a square for scaling factors 2 and 3.

10. Sketch similar illustrations for a cube for scaling factors 2 and 3.

11. Fill in the data requested in Table 5.6 using the suggestions below:

    a. For the segment, square, and cube use your previous illustrations.

    b. For the 4-cube and the generic d-cube, generalize from the patterns appearing in the previous rows of the table.

12. Find an equation giving the apparent relation between the dimension d of an object, the scaling factor s applied to magnify the tiles and the

TABLE 5.6 Dimension Data for Euclidean d-Cubes.

Original Object	Dimension (d) of Object	No. (N) of Tiles Congruent to Original After Magnification by:	
		Scaling Factor $s = 2$	Scaling Factor $s = 3$
Segment	1		
Square			
Cube			
4-Cube			
d-Cube			

number N of tiles that become congruent to the original object after magnification by s.

13. Assume that $\overline{AB}$ is a segment with endpoints $A(0, 0)$ and $B(1, 0)$, and that C is the midpoint of $\overline{AB}$. Find the 3×3 matrices of the similarities required to map segments $\overline{AC}$ and $\overline{CB}$ onto the segment $\overline{AB}$. (You'll need to make use of homogeneous coordinates for points.) What role does the scaling factor have in these matrices?

As you may have discovered, the equation relating the dimension d of the d-cube to N, the number of subobjects congruent to the original d-cube after magnifying by scaling factor s, is $N = s^d$. This equation is used to define the self-similarity dimension of objects. To make the language of the new definition less awkward and more precise, we will use the term *s-scale tiling* introduced in Definition 5.3.

Definition 5.4

Let α be a self-similar set and let N be the number of tiles in an s-scale tiling of α. Then the *self-similarity dimension d* of α is given by $N = s^d$.

Since we now have both *self-similarity* and *topological* dimensions, we will adopt the following convention to distinguish between the two. Dimension as defined by Definition 5.4 will always be labeled *self-similarity dimension*, whereas the more common topological dimension will be referred to simply as *dimension*. Since self-similarity dimension is a generalization of (topological) dimension, this distinction is less significant than it first appears.

In exploring self-similarity dimension it is useful to have fractal examples other than the Cantor set and the fractal curves introduced up to this point. Another well known fractal for which the self-similarity dimension can be readily computed is the Sierpinski triangle. Algorithm 5.4 gives a deterministic method for generating this set. The actual construction of the Sierpinski triangle involves "removing" portions of the original figure at each stage, but in our representations of this triangular figure we will use color to indicate the remaining portions. This coloring procedure requires that at each stage we keep track of the portion to be "removed," that is, left uncolored.

Algorithm 5.4 (Generating a Sierpinski Triangle)
- *Initial Set (Stage 0):* A triangle.
- *Stage 1:*
    a. Construct the midpoint of each side of the triangle.
    b. Construct segments between the midpoints of the three sides.
    c. Mark for "removal" the new *middle* subtriangle by placing a small dot in its interior.
- *Stages 2 through n:* Repeat the procedure of Stage 1 on each of the 3^{n-1} new congruent *unmarked* triangles. (Fig. 5.8.)
- "Remove" the marked sub-triangles.[17]

Exercises (Self-Similarity Dimension)

14. Solve the equation given in Definition 5.4 to give an expression for d.

15. Using the scaling factor $s = 3$, find the self-similarity dimension of the Cantor set.

---

[17]The procedure for doing this will vary depending on the construction method used. For paper and pencil constructions, merely shade the unmarked subtriangles and remove the dots marking the others.

FIGURE 5.8 Stages 0, 1, and 2 in generation of Sierpinski triangle.

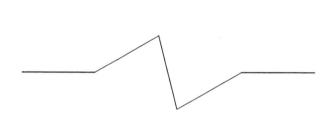

FIGURE 5.9 Stages 0 and 1 in generation of a Koch-like curve.

16. Using another appropriate scaling factor $s \neq 3$, again find the self-similarity dimension of the Cantor set. Does your answer agree with that found in Exercise 15? Should it?

17. Compute the self-similarity dimension of the Koch curve using two different scaling factors. How do your answers compare? Will this always happen? Explain.

18. Figure 5.9 shows stages 0 and 1 in the generation of a Koch-like curve.[18] At each stage, every segment is replaced by 5 new congruent segments, each one-fourth as long as the replaced segment.

    a. Sketch stage 2 in the generation of this curve.

    b. Determine the self-similarity dimension of the fractal curve.

---

[18]The curve is described by Donald Davis [Davis, p. 307].

19. Exploring the Sierpinski triangle:

   a. Use Algorithm 5.4 and an initial *equilateral* triangle to carry out stages 1 through 4 in the generation of the Sierpinski triangle either on paper[19] or by using dynamic geometry software.

   b. By analyzing the procedure used in Algorithm 5.4, determine a possible scaling factor for the Sierpinski triangle and compute its self-similarity dimension.

   c. What is the area of the Sierpinski triangle?

20. Draw stages 0 and 1 in the generation of a fractal curve with self-similarity dimension $d = \ln 6/\ln 4$ and write out an algorithm for the generation of your fractal. Explain why the resultant fractal will have the required dimension. (There is more than one way to do this.) [Davis, p. 307]

21. Stages 0 and 1 in the generation of the Peano curve are shown in Figure 5.10. Note that the congruent replacement segments are all one-third the size of the segment they replace.

   a. Write an algorithm for generating stages 1 through n of this curve.

   b. Draw stage 2 in the generation of this curve.

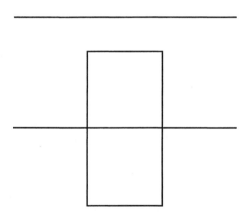

FIGURE 5.10   Stages 0 and 1 in generation of Peano curve.

---

[19]This works especially well on triangular isometric dot paper. On such paper, place the triangle vertices 16 (or an integer multiple of 16) "dot spaces" apart.

  c. Compute the self-similarity dimension of the Peano curve.

  d. Use the value of the self-similarity dimension of the Peano curve to explain Steen's description of its meandering nature. (See quote at beginning of Section 5.2.)

5.3.3 Box Dimension

Whereas self-similarity dimension applies only to sets that are strictly self-similar, there are more generalized dimensions that can be applied to sets that are only "approximately" self-similar, including *natural fractals* like coastlines. One of these generalizations that moves in the direction of the more esoteric Hausdorff–Besicovitch dimension is called *box dimension*.[20] Here the term *box* refers to a segment, a square, or a cube, that is, a d-cube of the appropriate dimension d. To understand how box dimension generalizes self-similarity dimension, recall that the self-similarity dimension d of a set α is given by the equation $N = s^d$ where s is the scaling-factor and N is the number of tiles in an s-scale tiling of α. Solving for d yields

$$\textit{Self-similarity dimension:}\quad d_S = \frac{\ln N}{\ln s} \qquad (A)$$

When a set α is strictly self-similar and we have determined an appropriate scaling factor s, it is possible to tile the set with congruent s-tiles. Using the number of these tiles as N in Equation (A) above, we can immediately compute the fractal dimension of α. However, when α is not strictly self-similar, we cannot tile it with congruent "shrunken" copies of itself. So in good mathematical fashion, we approximate such a covering. To do so, we do not attempt to use smaller versions of the original set, but instead choose a box-shaped set with a side length ℓ and place a grid of these boxes over the set α. The dimension d of the box chosen depends on the nature of the set α. For example, even though it may seem that the appropriate box shape for any curve should be that of a segment, curves that are extremely

---

[20] Box dimension is sometimes referred to as *capacity* dimension [Robinson, p. 358].

"wiggly" are usually covered with square grids as shown in Figure 5.11.

With the grid in place, we count the number of boxes that contain at least some portion of the set α. Then we reduce the side-length ℓ and repeat this procedure with the same box shape. Clearly, the number of boxes required varies as ℓ changes since, as we reduce the side length of our boxes to achieve better fits, the number of "covering" boxes will generally increase. We use the notation $N(\ell)$ to represent the number of covering boxes of side-length ℓ. In theory this process is iterated over and over as ℓ continues to shrink, thus explaining the need for the limit in the definition below. The reason for the choice of the denominator should become apparent after you do the exercises.

Definition 5.5
For a bounded set α, let $N(\ell)$ denote the minimum number of boxes of length $\ell > 0$ required to cover α. Then the box dimension of α is given by

$$\text{Box dimension:} \quad d_B = \lim_{\ell \to 0} \frac{\ln N(\ell)}{\ln (1/\ell)} \qquad (B)$$

Notice that the box dimension of an object is defined only when the limit in Definition 5.5 exists. And even in cases where the limit does exist, its value may not be obvious. However, the definition does give us a way to estimate the box dimension by evaluating the quotient in Equation (B) for several lengths ℓ. In practice, data points $(\ln(1/\ell), \ln N(\ell))$ are plotted and linear regression is used to find the line of best fit for the data. The slope of this line is then used as the box dimension.

Exercises (Box and Divider Dimensions)

22. Use Definition 5.5 and square boxes to show that the box dimension of a solid square is 2. [*Hint:* You may want to assume your square has side lengths of one unit and use boxes with side length $1/2^n$ for increasing values of n. Be sure to explain why the result you get using boxes with these side lengths will be the actual box dimension.]

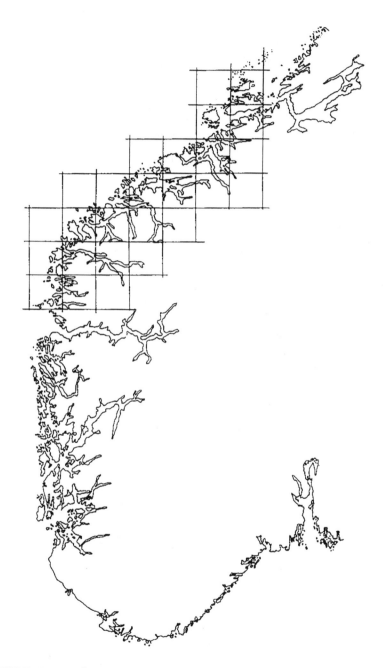

FIGURE 5.11 The coast of the southern part of Norway. The outline was traced from an atlas and digitized at about 1800 × 1200 pixels. The square grid indicated has a spacing of $\delta \sim 50$ km. [Reprinted from Feder, *Fractals*, Plenum Press, p. 7.]

23. Let C be the Cantor set generated from a segment of unit length.

    a. What is the appropriate d-cube to use in measuring the box dimension of C?

    b. Which value(s) of the box side-length ℓ yield the "best-fitting" boxes?

    c. How do these "best" values of ℓ relate to the scale-factors s used to determine the self-similarity dimension of C?

    d. Compute the box dimension of C. How does your value compare with the self-similarity dimension of C?

24. Let K be the Koch-like curve generated from a segment of unit length. (Stage 1 of this curve is shown in Figure 5.9.) Use a procedure similar to that in the previous exercise to determine the box dimension of K. Again compare your answer with the self-similarity dimension of K.

25. Find the box dimension of the Sierpinski triangle. Be sure to explain and illustrate the procedure you use.

26. The fractal known as the *Sierpinski carpet* has a solid square as its initial set. In stage 1 of the generation, the square is subdivided into 9 congruent subsquares, and the middle subsquare is removed. In stages 2 through n, the procedure of stage 1 is repeated on each of the remaining congruent subsquares.

    a. Construct stage 1 and stage 2 Sierpinski carpets.

    b. How many subsquares will remain at the end of stage 3? At the end of stage n?

    c. Find the fractal dimension of the (final) Sierpinski carpet using self-similarity dimension and using box dimension. How do your results compare?

    d. How much is the area reduced at each stage? What is the area of the Sierpinski carpet?

27. A 3-D version of the Sierpinski carpet is known as a *Sierpinski sponge*. The initial set for the sponge is a cube. In stage 1 of the generation, the cube is subdivided into 27 congruent subcubes, and the middle subcube and its 6 nearest neighbor cubes are removed. In stages 2 through n, the procedure of stage 1 is repeated on each of the remaining congruent subcubes.

    a. Find the fractal dimension of the (final) Sierpinski sponge.

b. How much is the volume reduced at each stage? What is the volume of the Sierpinski sponge?

c. Find the surface area of the Sierpinski sponge.

28. In the self-similarity exercises at the end of Section 5.2, the following property for a self-similar set α was derived:

Assume that α is a self-similar set with an s-scale tiling consisting of congruent sets α_i. If K is the distance between two given points in α, and ℓ is the distance between the corresponding points in α_i, then $s = K/\ell$. (C)

a. Use natural logarithms to find the relation this yields between $\ln s$ and $\ln(1/\ell)$.

b. Use your previous result to explain the relation between the denominators in Equations (A) and (B); in particular, explain why the value of K does not appear in Equation (B).

29. Explain in general terms why the box dimension of a strictly self-similar set will be the same as its self-similarity dimension.

Definition 5.6 (Divider Dimension of Curves)
If L is the divider length of curve $\mathcal{A}$ obtained using step length ℓ, then d_ℓ, the *divider dimension* of $\mathcal{A}$, is given by the equation below. (*Note:* In this equation C is a constant independent of steplength.)

$$\text{Divider Dimension:} \quad L = C\,\ell^{1-d_\ell} \qquad (D)$$

30. Suppose that the length of curve $\mathcal{A}$ is computed once using step lengths ℓ_1, yielding divider measure L_1 for its length; and again using step lengths ℓ_2, yielding L_2 for its length. If we assume that the two divider dimensions computed from these two measurements are equal, i.e., $d_{\ell_1} = d_{\ell_2} = d$, show that d can be found without knowing the value of C. (Note: Because of the assumption of equality, we can only assert that our value for d is an approximation of the actual divider dimension of $\mathcal{A}$.)

31. Mandelbrot presents Richardson's data for measuring the west coast of Britain as follows:

- If dividers with step length $\ell = 100$ km are used, then the total length is 1700 km.

- If dividers with step length $\ell = 10$ km are used, then the total length is 3020 km.

Use this data and the result from Exercise 30 to determine an approximate value for the fractal dimension of the west coast of Britain. [Problem modified from Davis, p. 310.]

32. Use the result from Exercise 30 to determine the approximate fractal dimension of coastlines of two different states using the data from Table 5.4. Note that both coastline and shoreline lengths reported for the same state can be considered as coastline measurements using different divider lengths.

33. To show that the relation in Definition 5.6 is true for self-similar curves:

    a. Let A be a self-similar curve with scaling factor s. Explain why, for certain values of ℓ, a divider measurement of A with step length ℓ can be said to be an "approximate" tiling of A with segments of length ℓ. For tilings that fit best, how is ℓ related to the scaling factor s? (Be sure to indicate if there is more than one possible value of ℓ.) How can the fit of such a tiling be made even better?

    b. Find an equation relating L, the curve's length determined by the divider measurement, to the tile length ℓ and the number of tiles N. Solve your equation for N.

    c. In the formula giving the self-similarity dimension (Definition 5.4), replace N by your above result and use Equation (C) to replace s. Then solve for the divider length L to verify Equation (D). What does the constant C represent in this equation?

5.4   Iterated Function Systems*

A fractal set generally contains infinitely many points whose organization is so complicated that it is not possible to describe the set by specifying directly where each point in it lies. Instead, the set may be defined by 'the relations between the pieces.' [Barnsley, p. 4]

So far the examples of fractals we have explored, namely, the Koch curve and various Sierpinski sets, are all *strictly self-similar*, that is, each can be tiled with congruent tiles where the tiles can be mapped onto the original using similarities with the same scaling factor; or inversely, the original object can be mapped onto the individual tiles using similarities with a common scaling factor.

However, as the above quotation indicates, there are so called *fractals* with such complexity that they are not self-similar in this strict sense. To construct objects with such complicated organizations would seem to require very involved procedures. However, the key to their construction is that the "relations between the pieces" of such fractals can be described using relatively small sets of the affine transformations covered in Chapter 3.

5.4.1 A Sierpinski Introduction

To begin our consideration of *fractal generating transformations*, we will find a set of three so called *Sierpinski* transformations that can be used in combination to generate the Sierpinski triangle.

Exercises (The Sierpinski Transformations)

In the exercises below, assume that the initial set used to generate the Sierpinski triangle is equilateral $\triangle ABC$ as shown in Figure 5.12.

1. Describe the location of three tiles that form a 2-scale tiling of the Sierpinski triangle in Figure 5.12. For each tile, specify a dilation (giving both its center and ratio) that maps the entire Sierpinski triangle onto the tile.

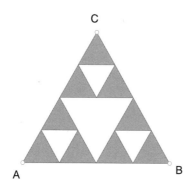

FIGURE 5.12 Stage 2 in the generation of a Sierpinski triangle.

Note: We will call the transformations found in Exercise 1, the *Sierpinski transformations*.

2. As you probably discovered, the three Sierpinski transformations each leave one of the vertices of $\triangle ABC$ invariant. Using the notation T_1, T_2, and T_3 to represent the transformations that leave A, B, and C invariant, respectively, describe the image of $\triangle ABC$ under each of the composite transformations below. In your description, indicate the stage in the Algorithm 5.4 generation in which the image would first appear.

      (a) $T_1 \circ T_2$ (d) $(T_3)^2 \circ T_1$

      (b) $T_2 \circ T_1$ (e) $T_1 \circ T_3 \circ T_1$

      (c) $T_1 \circ T_2 \circ T_3$ (f) $(T_2)^3 \circ (T_3)^2$

3. How could a sequence of these three transformations be used to generate a stage 2 Sierpinski triangle? A stage 3 Sierpinski triangle? A stage n Sierpinski triangle?

4. Let P and Q be two distinct points in the plane. How will the distance between their images under a Sierpinski transformation T compare to the distance between the original points, i.e., compare $d(T(P), T(Q))$ and $d(P, Q)$? Explain why the result will be the same for each of the three transformations.

5. Assume that Z is the invariant point of a Sierpinski transformation T and $P \neq Z$ is any other point.

    a. What happens to the distance $d(Z, T^n(P))$ as n increases?

    b. What does this tell you about the limit of the orbit of P under iteration by T?[21]

    c. Will the limit of the orbit in part (b) depend on the point P? On the transformation T? Explain.

6. Assume that homogeneous coordinates of the three vertices are $A(0, 0, 1)$, $B(2, 0, 1)$, and $C(1, \sqrt{3}, 1)$. Write out a 3×3 matrix representation for each Sierpinski transformation.

7. Use your transformation matrices to find the images of the three vertices A, B, and C under each of the three Sierpinski transformations.

---

[21] As before the orbit is the infinite sequence $\{P, T(P), \ldots, T^n(P), \ldots\}$.

As the previous exercises demonstrate, a stage n Sierpinski triangle (for any natural number n) can be generated by finite iteration of the three Sierpinski transformations where at any stage the three transformations are, in effect, simultaneously applied to the output from the previous stage. Thus, it seems reasonable to expect that the actual Sierpinski triangle would result from an infinite iteration of this process of simultaneous application of the three transformations. Such an application process is said to be *deterministic* in contrast to a *stochastic*, or *random* application process in which each transformation T_i is assigned a probability p_i and the transformation to be applied at each step in the iteration is chosen randomly with probability p_i.[22] When this *random* application process is used to iteratively apply the three Sierpinski transformations to individual points, the resultant procedure is commonly known as the *chaos game*. In practice, computers are used to play this game; however, a short hands-on version of this game serves to illustrate random sequencing of function iteration.

Rules for Chaos Game
Required Equipment: Each player will need a 6-sided die, a transparency pen, and a transparency on which the vertices of an equilateral triangle are marked and labeled with the letters A, B, and C. (To be effective, all transparencies should contain congruent sets of vertices so similarly labeled vertices coincide when the transparencies are stacked.)

A. Assign A to the faces 1 and 2 of the die, B to the faces 3 and 4, and C to the faces 5 and 6. Finally, plot (but do not label) a point X_0 somewhere in the triangle.

B. Roll the die. Then plot (but do not label) the point X_1, which lies halfway between X_0 and the vertex determined by the die. (Note: The labels X_i are used only to clarify the directions. To avoid clutter, you should avoid labeling the points you plot.)

C. Roll the die again and plot the point X_2, which lies halfway between X_1 and the vertex determined by the die.

---

[22]The sum of these assigned probabilities p_i must be 1.

D. The game continues by iterating the previous procedure, i.e., at each step a new point is plotted that lies halfway between the previous point and the vertex indicated by the rolled die.

Exercises (The Chaos Game)

8. Using the rules above, play the chaos game for about 10 minutes, plotting each point on the same clear plastic transparency. To make this go quickly, merely estimate distances. After you finish, stack your transparency together with those made by others to see an image that should bear some resemblance to the Sierpinski triangle.[23]

9. Explain why the chaos game is actually using the Sierpinski transformations found in the previous exercise set.

10. If a fair die is used in the chaos game, each of the three Sierpinski transformations is chosen with probability $\frac{1}{3}$. If these probability assignments were changed, would the appearance of the image change? Explain.

The activities below all refer to the specific transformations described in the rules for the chaos game described above. As in the exercise set for the Sierpinski transformations, assume that homogeneous coordinates of the three vertices are $A(0, 0, 1)$, $B(2, 0, 1)$, and $C(1, \sqrt{3}, 1)$ and use the transformation matrices found in those exercises.

11. Carefully plot the points A, B, and C. On this same graph, plot *and* label the first 5 points that result from playing the chaos game as detailed below.

   a. Beginning with the point $X_0 = A$, randomly choose one of the three Sierpinski transformations to apply to X_0. Use the matrix representation of this transformation to compute the coordinates of X_1, the image of X_0 under this transformation. Then plot X_1.

   b. Continue iterating the procedure described in part (a) to plot and label points X_2, X_3, X_4, and X_5.

---

[23]The desired effect requires a sufficient number of points plotted on transparencies containing congruent copies of the triangle vertices. There should be enough points obtained when 10 or more play the game, each for 10 minutes or so. Fewer players will need to play for a longer period.

12. Explain why all of your points X_i ($i = 0, \ldots, 5$) are located in the actual Sierpinski triangle. Would this happen if you chose a point other than A for X_0? Explain.

13. (Optional) Use a computer or calculator to carry out a much longer simulation of the chaos game. Possible methods include:

   - Using computer programs available as freeware on the web or commercially. For sources of such programs see the website http://www.stolaf.edu/people/cederj/geotext/info.htm

   - Entering code for such a program. Sources of code for BASIC programs and for programs written for CASIO and Texas Instrument graphing calculators are listed at the end of this chapter.

   - Writing and using your own program.

5.4.2 IFS Basics

The set of Sierpinski transformations is an example of an iterated function system (IFS). Notice that the three Sierpinski transformations are all similarity transformations with the same ratio r. Since $r < 1$, the transformations are *contractive*, that is, the transformations decrease the distance between points making image points closer together than their corresponding pre-images. Thus, if any one of the Sierpinski transformations is individually iterated, the image of any initial set under this iteration will shrink to a point. However, when the three transformations are iterated as a system in either deterministic or random order they appear to generate the Sierpinski triangle.

In general, an iterated function system need not consist only of similarities all with the same ratio, or even of similarities with different ratios. IFS transformations may also include affine transformations (shears, and strains or combinations of these with similarities), thus allowing direction specific scaling factors as well as changes in angles. We formalize these ideas in the following definitions.

Definition 5.7

An affine transformation T is *contractive* if there is a constant c, $0 \leq c < 1$ such that for all points X and Y, $d(T(X), T(Y)) \leq c\,d(X, Y)$. The constant c is called the *contraction factor of T*.

Definition 5.8

An *iterated function system (IFS)* is a finite set of contractive[24] affine transformations.

As in our previous work with logistic functions, we are interested in the long term behavior of iterated function systems. In particular, we wish to know whether repeated iterations of the transformations involved will lead to a limit image. Since an IFS consists of multiple transformations, a precise determination of the limiting behavior of their infinite iteration requires mathematical results from advanced analysis and topology. However, we can achieve a general understanding of the behavior of iterated function systems and their utilization of affine transformations by carefully exploring the behavior of a few specific systems. We begin our explorations by examining systems in which the iteration is carried out in deterministic fashion.

Deterministic Iteration

In the case of deterministic iteration, it is customary to use a set of multiple points as the initial input. We will represent such an initial set using the boldface notation $\mathbf{A_0}$. The transformations of the IFS are then iteratively applied in a stage-by-stage procedure in which the output of any stage is considered to be a *collage*, or union, of the images produced by simultaneously applying each of the transformations to the output from the previous stage. When $\mathbf{A_0}$ is a multiple-point set, it follows that the images (sometimes called

---

[24]The requirement that each transformation be contractive is relaxed in more advanced treatments of fractal geometry. It is actually sufficient to require only that the entire transformation set be *contractive*, i.e., the overall effect of iteration of the transformations must continually decrease the distance between points.

d-images to indicate their deterministic generation) will also be multiple-point sets which we will denote A_n. All of this is formalized in Definition 5.9.

Definition 5.9

Let $T_1, \ldots, T_k$ be the transformations of an IFS and let A_0 be an initial set in the common domain of these transformations. Then A_1, the *first d-image of A_0 under the IFS*, consists of the following union of sets obtained by applying each of the transformations T_i once: $A_1 = T_1(A_0) \cup T_2(A_0) \cup \cdots \cup T_k(A_0)$. And similarly A_n, the *nth d-image of A_0 under the IFS*, is given by: $A_n = T_1(A_{n-1}) \cup T_2(A_{n-1}) \cup \cdots \cup T_k(A_{n-1})$. The process of finding these *d*-images is called *deterministic iteration of the IFS* and the sequence of *d*-images $\{A_0, A_1, \ldots, A_n, \ldots\}$ is the *d-orbit of A_0 under the IFS*.

Using the terminology and notation of this definition, we can make a precise statement of our mathematical question: Does the *d*-orbit of A_0 under a given IFS have a limit, and if so, is this limit a fractal?

Exercises (Deterministic Iterated Function Systems)

14. *The Cantor IFS*

   a. Which two affine transformations can be used to generate a Cantor set from an initial segment $A_0 = \overline{PQ}$ (See Algorithm 5.2)? For each, name the invariant points if any, and any other defining properties.

   b. Explain why the set of these two *Cantor transformations* is an IFS.

   c. Draw a diagram showing the initial set A_0 and its first, second, and third *d*-images under this IFS.

    d. Assuming that the initial set A_0 corresponds to the unit interval $[0, 1]$ on the x-axis, find an algebraic representation for each of the two Cantor transformations.[25]

    e. Assuming that A_0 is the same unit interval, use your algebraic representations to find the endpoints of segments contained in the d-images A_n of A_0 under this IFS for $n = 1, 2, 3$.

    f. If the Cantor IFS transformations are applied to the actual Cantor set, what will be true about the d-images produced?

15. *The Sierpinski IFS.* Let $\mathcal{I}$ be the system consisting of the three Sierpinski transformations with invariant points located at the vertices of equilateral $\triangle ABC$ (see the exercises for the Sierpinski transformations).

    a. Assume that the initial set $A_0 = \triangle AB'C'$, where $\triangle AB'C'$ is the small equilateral triangle (and its interior) shown in Figure 5.13. Draw two figures F_1 and F_2 each containing $\triangle ABC$. Use shading to show d-image A_1 in figure F_1, and d-image A_2 in figure F_2. In each figure, indicate which shaded portions resulted from applying T_1, from applying T_2, and from applying T_3.

    b. Assume that the initial set A_0 is a circle (and its interior) located somewhere inside $\triangle ABC$. Draw and label three figures F_0, F_1, F_2 each containing $\triangle ABC$. Draw and use shading to show A_0 in figure F_0, A_1 in figure F_2, and A_2 in figure F_2. Then describe your expectations for the long-term behavior of the d-orbit of this initial set A_0 under $\mathcal{I}$.

    c. Using observations from parts a and b., describe your general expectations for the long-term behavior of the d-orbits of an initial set A_0 under $\mathcal{I}$. In particular, comment on the following: Is there a limit set? If so, are there any points that must be in this limit set and what is the set's shape? Is the behavior dependent on the shape of A_0? On the location of the points A, B, and C?

    d. If the Sierpinski IFS transformations are applied to the actual Sierpinski triangle with vertices A, B, and C, what will be true about the d-images produced?

---

[25] Since the points involved are all on the x-axis, you may want to make use of simple linear equations.

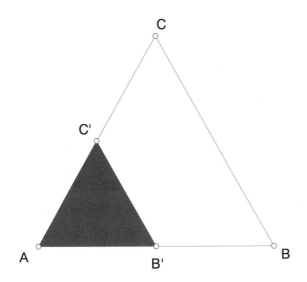

FIGURE 5.13 Equilateral triangles ABC and $AB'C'$.

The limiting behavior of deterministic IFS orbits in a complete metric space (in our case, Euclidean space with the usual distance metric), was formally demonstrated in a 1981 publication by J. Hutchinson.[26] A generalized statement of Hutchinson's results is given in Theorem 5.2.

Theorem 5.2

Let $\mathcal{I}$ be an IFS with domain $\mathbf{S}$, a complete metric space, and assume $\mathbf{A}_0 \subset \mathbf{S}$. Then the d-orbit of $\mathbf{A}_0$ under $\mathcal{I}$ will have a unique limit set $\mathbf{A}_\infty$. Furthermore, the set $\mathbf{A}_\infty$ is independent of the initial set $\mathbf{A}_0$ and invariant under $\mathcal{I}$. $\mathbf{A}_\infty$ is called the attractor of $\mathcal{I}$.

Thus, just as each IFS transformation T has an invariant point that can be found by finding the limit point of the orbit of any point A_0 under T, the IFS itself has an invariant set that can be found by finding the limit set of the d-orbit of any initial set $\mathbf{A}_0$ under the IFS. And, as the name *attractor* suggests, this invariant set $\mathbf{A}_\infty$ is

---

[26] See Hutchinson, pp. 713–747, or Barnsley, Chapter 3. Hutchinson's results, based on Banach's *contraction mapping principle*, are explained and illustrated in Chapter 5 of Peitgen et al., *Chaos and Fractals: New Frontiers of Science*.

attracting, that is, if we deterministically apply the IFS to an initial set, we obtain a sequence of d-images that always "shrink" to this same unique $\mathbf{A_\infty}$. So, the IFS consisting of the two Cantor transformations does generate a unique Cantor set and the IFS consisting of the three Sierpinski transformations generates a unique Sierpinski triangle; where both can be approximated by d-image sets $\mathbf{A_n}$ with the approximation becoming more accurate as n increases.

Random Iteration

As noted above, the Sierpinski triangle can be generated from any initial multiple-point set by deterministic iteration of the three Sierpinski transformations. However, the chaos game also appears to generate the Sierpinski triangle using a step-by-step procedure where each step involves randomly choosing one of these same transformations and applying it to a single point. At first glance, using deterministic iteration on an initial multiple-point set appears to generate an image with a greater resemblance to the Sierpinski triangle with less effort than the chaos game. But a closer examination indicates the immensity of the memory requirements for the deterministic approach. Deterministic generation of the image $\mathbf{A_n}$ requires that every transformation in the system be applied to all the points in the set $\mathbf{A_{n-1}}$, thus requiring storage for the location of each point in $\mathbf{A_{n-1}}$. By comparison, the chaos game requires storage for only one point, since at each step one of the Sierpinski transformations is applied to a single point to produce one image point; the image point (sometimes called an *r-image* to indicate its random generation) is then added to the previous graphical display. In other words, the graphical display at any step shows the accumulation of all previously generated image points.

Definition 5.10

Let $T_1, \ldots, T_k$ be the transformations of an IFS, and X_0 a given point in the common domain of these transformations. Then the *nth r-image of X_0 is $X_n = T_{n_i}(X_{n-1})$* with n_i chosen randomly (with pre-assigned probability) from the set $\{1, 2, \ldots, k\}$. The process of finding these r-images is called *random iteration of the IFS* and the infinite sequence of r-images $\{X_0, X_1, \ldots, X_n, \ldots\}$ is an *r-orbit of X_0 under the IFS*.

As you may have noticed in playing the chaos game, when the initial point X_0 is chosen arbitrarily, the first few r-images of X_0 may not lie in the attractor of the IFS, in this case, the Sierpinski triangle. However, when X_0 is an invariant point of one of the transformations in the IFS, we can show that all r-images of X_0 are elements of $\mathbf{A}_\infty$, the attractor of the IFS. And as n increases, the finite r-orbits $\{X_0, X_1, \ldots, X_n\}$ appear to "fill out" the attractor. Since the attractor of an IFS is dependent only on the transformations involved and not on the initial set, this result may seem less than surprising. But the difference in the sequence of transformation applications between random and deterministic iteration means the result is not automatic. In fact, it is necessary to confirm that the elements in an r-orbit of X_0 under the IFS form a dense covering of $\mathbf{A}_\infty$.[27] This result is summarized below in Theorem 5.3.[28]

Theorem 5.3

If $\mathcal{I}$ is an iterated function system with attractor $\mathbf{A}_\infty$, and X_0 is an invariant point of one of the transformations in $\mathcal{I}$, then the elements in an r-orbit of X_0 under $\mathcal{I}$ form a dense covering of $\mathbf{A}_\infty$.

Since the attractor of an IFS is a limiting set of an infinite process, its complete generation is only theoretically possible. However, with modern high speed computers, it is possible to generate approximations that are within the limits of resolution of the available graphic display equipment. In practice, the computer depiction of an attractor $\mathbf{A}_\infty$ is usually generated by using the far more efficient method of computing a finite r-orbit $\mathbf{X_n}$ with n chosen sufficiently large so that the density of the covering of $\mathbf{A}_\infty$ by $\mathbf{X_n}$ is within the resolution of the computer.

---

[27] I.e., for any point P in the set $\mathbf{A}_\infty$, it is possible to find among the elements of the r-orbit a sequence that converges to P.

[28] For additional details, see Chapter 6 of Peitgen et al., *Chaos and Fractals: New Frontiers of Science.*

The images thus produced often exhibit intricate detail even if they represent an attractor of an IFS consisting of only a small number of transformations.[29] Thus, we have a powerful technique for generating graphical images when an image happens to be the attractor of an IFS, but the real value of the technique will not be apparent until we obtain some understanding of the number and diversity of these "attracting" images.

Exercises (Random Iterated Function Systems)

16. Given an IFS consisting of k transformations, a finite number n and a point X_0 in the domain of the IFS, how many finite r-orbits $\{X_0, X_1, \ldots, X_n\}$ are possible under the IFS? Explain your answer.

17. Given the Sierpinski IFS consisting of the Sierpinski transformations T_1, T_2 and T_3 with invariant points at equilateral triangle vertices A, B, and C, respectively:

    a. If the initial point $X_0 = A$, indicate on a sketch of the stage 3 Sierpinski triangle all possible locations of an r-image X_3 under this IFS. (Be sure to label the vertices A, B, and C.)

    b. Again, assuming that $X_0 = A$, is it possible to arrive at the same point for X_3 using two or more sequences of exactly three transformations T_i? If so, explain where one such point X_3 is located, and give all such sequences.

18. Assume that S is a point in the Sierpinski triangle. Let P_0 be an arbitrary second point (not necessarily in the Sierpinski triangle) and assume that P_k is the kth r-image of P under the Sierpinski IFS: Find a value of k for which the following must be true: $d(P_k, S) < .0001\, d(P_0, S)$. Explain how a generalization of this procedure could be used to show that under iteration by the Sierpinski IFS points are "attracted to the Sierpinski triangle."

19. In the chaos game, the use of a fair die effectively assigns equal probability to each of the three transformations. What would be the effect of changing these probabilities? In particular, what would be the result if one of the probabilities was reduced to zero? Explain.

---

[29] Particularly attractive images are known as *strange attractors*.

20. Show that an invariant point of a transformation T in an IFS will be in the attractor $\mathbf{A}_\infty$ of the IFS.

5.4.3   Designing an IFS for a Target Image

Michael Barnsley used an IFS consisting of four affine transformations to generate the black spleenwort fern that has become another "icon" of fractal geometry (Fig. 5.14). He described a method for finding an IFS to generate a target image in his *Collage Theorem* of 1985.[30] According to Barnsley, the theorem

> ... tells us that to find an IFS whose attractor is "close to" or "looks like" a given set, one must endeavor to find a set of transformations— contraction mappings on a suitable space within which the given set lies—such that the union, or collage, of the images of the given set under the transformations is near to the given set. Nearness is measured using the Hausdorff metric. [Barnsley, p. 95]

In other words, the process of finding appropriate IFS transformations involves finding affine transformations that generate smaller, perhaps distorted, copies of the target image and map these small "copies" to various positions so as to cover the target (Fig. 5.15). The transformed target images need not be congruent and may differ both in size and shape from each other (due to the use of shears, strains, etc.). Also the covering does not have to be a "perfect" tiling; the transformed target images can overlap slightly. Methods of finding and modifying these transformations vary from keyboard manipulation of numerical entries in the transformation matrices to onscreen dragging of transformation images that induces computer calculation of the corresponding matrix entries.

The IFS consisting of the transformations used to generate this "covering" collage can then be applied to an initial point set to generate the target image. Refinements of this process that create remarkably realistic looking pictures of natural objects have been developed. Some have even been patented by Barnsley and his

---

[30]An explicit statement of the theorem is given in Barnsley's *Fractals Everywhere*, 2nd ed., pp. 94–95.

FIGURE 5.14   The Fern. 100,000 game points of the chaos game. Left: generated using equal probability for all contractions. Right: Here the probabilities for choosing the different transformations are not the same. (Source: Peitgen et al., *Chaos and Fractals: New Frontiers of Science*, Springer-Verlag.)

colleagues.[31] Early applications of these techniques appeared as the landscape of the Genesis planet in the movie *Star Trek II: The Wrath of Khan* and the surface of the moons of Endor and outlines of the Death

---

[31] For example, the " basic mathematics [of the so-called fractal transform discovered in 1988] forms the core of US Patent #5065447 jointly held with Alan Sloan, cofounder of Iterated Systems, Inc. . . . " [Barnsley and Hurd, p.xi]

FIGURE 5.15 Leaf collage. Design stages for a leaf: scanned image of a real leaf and a polygon capturing its outline (top), collage by 7 transformed images of the polygon and the attractor of the corresponding IFS (bottom). (Source: Peitgen et al., *Chaos and Fractals: New Frontiers of Science*, Springer-Verlag.)

Star in *The Return of the Jedi*.[32] More recent examples of pictures generated this way, along with a detailed description of the math-

---

[32] Dewdney, "Computer Recreations" in the December 1986 *Scientific American* contains color photos of a computer-generated mountain scene and a computer-generated scene from the Genesis sequence in the movie *Star Trek II*.

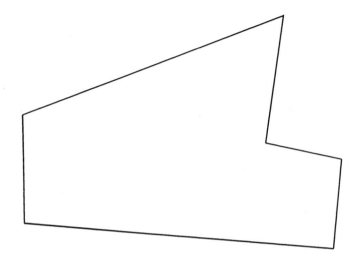

FIGURE 5.16 Target image.

ematical ideas behind their generation, are contained in Barnsley and Hurd's book, *Fractal Image Compression*. The remarkable photo-like quality of these pictures is especially amazing considering that the information required to produce them consists primarily of numerical entries for the matrix representations of a relatively small number of affine transformations.

Exercises (Finding Image-Generating IFS Transformations)

21. On a copy of the target image shown in Figure 5.16, sketch four smaller transformed target images that form a covering of the original target image. Describe the general type of affine transformation that could be used to produce each of your transformed target images.

5.4.4   Are IFS Attractors Fractal?

So far the term *fractal* has been left undefined even though it has been used in naming several examples. To determine the exact nature of sets that we wish to deem "fractals," we first note that the attractor resulting from deterministic application of an IFS consisting only of similarities, all with the same ratio $r < 1$, will be strictly self-similar in the sense of Definition 5.3. Thus, the magnification of any of the individual tiles described in this definition will produce the exact same detail found in the original. But the previous discussion suggests that a "fractal" may exhibit only a resemblance of self-similarity since magnification of any small part of an image generated by random iteration of an IFS can, at best, produce detail that "closely" resembles that of the attractor of the IFS. Furthermore, the transformations used in either type of IFS need not be similarities but can also be contractive affinities. All of this suggests that in order for *fractals* to include images generated from these more generalized iterated function systems using either deterministic or random iteration, we need to broaden the concept of self-similarity by not only generalizing the types of transformations that can be used, but also, by expanding our interpretation of self-similarity from an exact to a stochastic sense.

5.5 Finally—What Is a Fractal?

Typically, fractals are extremely irregular curves or surfaces that wiggle enough to partially fill the gap between one dimension and the next higher one? [Steen, p. 122]

As noted previously, the term "fractal" was invented by Mandelbrot to describe geometric shapes that in simplistic terms can be described as very *fractured*. In 1977, Mandelbrot gave the following formal definition, a definition over which he later expressed reservations:

Mandelbrot's Early Definition
A *fractal* is a set for which the Hausdorff–Besicovitch dimension strictly exceeds the topological dimension. [Mandelbrot, p. 361]

A complete understanding of this definition requires a formal presentation of *H–B (Hausdorff-Besicovitch) dimension*, a concept whose explanation requires a significant amount of analysis and topology. However, for a general understanding, it is sufficient to point out that the H–B dimension is a generalization of the *box dimension* described earlier and like box dimension, the H–B dimension of a fractal set is usually a noninteger.

In 1983, Mandelbrot explained his reservations about defining fractals in terms of dimensions and the desire to define them instead in keeping with the formal definition of geometry introduced at the beginning of Chapter 3.

> I feel. . . that the notion of fractal is more basic than any particular notion of dimension. A more basic reason for not defining fractals resides in the broadly held feeling that the key factor to a set's being fractal is invariance under some class of transform[ation]s but no one has yet pinned this invariance satisfactorily [Mandelbrot, *Proceedings*. p. 1675]

Later in 1987, Mandelbrot, in a widely quoted communication, described fractals as shapes "made of parts similar to the whole in some way." [Feder, p. 11] Intentionally vague, this characterization, together with our preceding investigations, suggests that the defining characteristic of fractals is a generalized version of *self-similarity*, where the generalization includes the use of affine transformations.

Definition 5.11

A set of points α is said to be *(strictly) self-affine* if α can be tiled with subsets, each of which can be mapped onto the original set α using an affine transformation.

Notice that this definition does not require that the affine transformations used to map individual tiles onto the original set be alike. So, for example, the magnification factors used may differ for each transformation and a single transformation may even involve magnifications by different factors in different directions.

Even with this generalization, it is still difficult to make the definition of a fractal precise. The various so called "fractal" examples introduced in this chapter demonstrate not only the need to generalize the *self-similar* requirement to a *self-affine* requirement, but also the need to include stochastic as well as deterministic interpretations of the *self-affine* requirement. In particular, the Koch curve and Sierpinski triangle (the latter as generated by Algorithm 5.4) clearly satisfy the original strict version of self-similarity. However, to include the Sierpinski triangle as generated by the chaos game IFS, we need to allow the interpretation of self-similarity in a stochastic sense. When including Julia sets, we note that some Julia sets require not only random application of the generating transformations but also the use of transformations even more general than affine transformations. All of this should further explain the challenge of formulating a precise definition of *fractal* and the extreme difficultly in computing the dimension of many fractals. In fact, as Devaney notes, the exact dimension for many Julia sets is unknown. [Devaney (1990), p. 147] These and other "open" questions continue to occupy mathematical researchers. The research that will eventually firm up the foundations of this new mathematics involves not only mathematicians but numerous others interested in applications of fractal geometry in both the sciences and the social sciences, in particular, economics. Thus, it is appropriate that we consider the ways in which the term "fractal" is used both in mathematical and scientific research. In his 1997 publication, *Fractal River Basins: Chance and Self-Organization*, Rodríguez–Iturbe emphasizes that "fractals are objects in which properly scaled portions are identical (in a deterministic or statistical sense) to the original object." [Rodríguez–Iturbe, pp. 145-146] Based on this description and the Mandelbrot description given above, we will adopt the definition below.

Definition 5.12

A *fractal* is a set of points that is self-affine either in a *deterministic* or *stochastic* sense.

It may seem that this definition allows any "strange" set to be labeled a fractal. However, the Mandelbrot set is commonly agreed to be nonfractal even though ever increasing magnifications of the set appear to show similar shapes over and over. But as Mandelbrot indicates in the quotation below, closer observation reveals surprising new shapes which continue to appear under these same magnifications.

> In the Mandelbrot set, nature (or is it mathematics?) provides us with a powerful visual counterpart of the musical idea of 'theme and

variation': the same shapes are repeated everywhere, yet each repetition is somewhat different.... It leaves us no way to become bored, because new things appear all the time, and no way to become lost, because familiar things come back time and time again. Because [of] this constant novelty, this set is not truly fractal by most definitions; we may call it a borderline fractal, a limit fractal that contains many fractals. Compared to actual fractals, its structures are more numerous, its harmonies are richer, and its unexpectedness is more unexpected.[33] [Peitgen et al., *Chaos and Fractals*, p. 841]

Also, so called *natural fractals*, that is, physical objects appearing to be fractal, will not be exactly, or perhaps even statistically, self-similar. However, as Donald Davis indicates in the quote below, there is general agreement on the required level of self-similarity these objects must exhibit to be considered as fractals.

For physical objects, one does not require statistical self-similarity at all magnifications. It is generally agreed that a physical object may be considered to be a fractal if it has statistical self-similarity over a range of magnifications in which the largest is at least ten times the smallest. [Davis, p. 298]

5.6　Applications of Fractal Geometry

[F]ractal geometry is first and foremost a new "language" used to describe the complex forms found in nature. But while the elements of the "traditional language"—the familiar Euclidean geometry—are basic visible forms such as lines, circles and spheres, those of the new language do not lend themselves to direct observation. They are, namely, algorithms, which can be transformed into shapes and structures only with the help of computers. In addition, the supply of these algorithmic elements is inexhaustibly large; and they are capable of providing us with a powerful descriptive tool. Once this new language has been mastered, we can describe the form of a cloud as easily and

---

[33] As edited from an interview in the video *Fractals: An Animated Discussion*.

precisely as an architect can describe a house using the language of traditional geometry. [Peitgen et al., (1992) pp. v–viii]

The meandering nature of fractals is, as Steen indicates, "...a good idealization of the geometry of river networks and of the vascular network in a body: To do their job, rivers and veins must pass within a small distance of every point of the territory they serve." [Steen, p.123] It is precisely this meandering nature of fractals that makes them important. Mandelbrot notes: "The importance of fractals lies in their ability to capture the essential features of very complicated and irregular objects and processes in a way that is susceptible to mathematical analysis." [Peterson, p.42] The fractal forms generated by computers are used by mathematicians and scientists to model a variety of natural phenomenon such as trees, coastlines, rivers, mountains, mineral veins, vascular systems, etc. The widespread applications of fractal geometry as well as the speed with which these were being recognized in the late 1980s is indicated by a sampling of articles that appeared in the space of three months at the end of 1987. These articles describe applications ranging from physical chemistry ["Steady-state chemical kinetics on fractals: Geminate and nongeminate generation of reactants," *Journal of Physical Chemistry*, Oct. 22 '87 (91: 5555–5557)] to acoustics ["Fractal finite element mesh generation for vibration problems," *Journal of the Acoustical Society of America*, Nov. '87] to economics ["Tomorrow's shapes: The practical fractal," *The Economist*, Dec. 26, '87 (305: 99–103)]. The enthusiasm with which fractal geometry was often endorsed is indicated by the introductory statement in the latter article:

> It is no accident that the inventor of fractal geometry, Dr. Benoit Mandelbrot, works for IBM. His new science is a child of the computer age. Without the calculating power to explore its weird avenues, and electronic pictures to fire the imagination, fractal geometry would have remained a mathematical oddity. Instead, it may overtake Euclid. [p. 99]

Since then, a number of books containing numerous applications have been published. These include Hastings and Sugihara, *Fractals: A User's Guide for the Natural Sciences* (1993) and Bunde and Havlin (1994) *Fractals in Science*. Once more, an apparently esoteric mathematical subject has become the source of a magnitude of practical applications leading to an irony that Mandelbrot delightfully points out.

> Nature has played a joke on the mathematicians. The 19th century mathematicians may have been lacking in imagination, but Nature was not. The same pathological structures that the mathematicians invented to break loose from the 19th century naturalists turn out to be inherent in familiar objects all around us. [Mandelbrot, pp. 3–4].

Furthermore, this wealth of applications threatens to overwhelm interest in the intriguing mathematics and the many open mathematical questions still remaining in fractal geometry. Concerned about this possibility, Barnsley issues a concluding warning:

> It seems now that deterministic fractal geometry is racing ahead into the serious engineering phase. Commercial applications have emerged in the areas of image compression, video compression, computer graphics and education. This is good because it authenticates once again the importance of the work of mathematicians. However, sometimes mathematicians lose interest in wonderful areas once scientists and engineers seem to have the subject under control. But there is so much more mathematics to be done. What is a useful metric for studying the contractivity of the vector recurrent IFS of affine maps in $\Re^2$? What is the information content of a picture? Measures, pictures, dreams, chaos, flowers and information theory—the hours of the days keep rushing by: do not let the beauty of all these things pass us by too. [Barnsley, (1993) concluding remarks in Forward]

5.7   Suggestions for Further Reading

The following sources contain a wealth of information about fractals and related topics.

Abbott, E. A. (1991). *Flatland*, Princeton NJ: Princeton University Press. (A reprint of the classic introduction to the fourth dimension together with a must-read introduction by Banchoff that explains the social satire Abbott uses.)

Banchoff, T. F. (1990). "Dimension," In *On the Shoulders of Giants*, Edited by Lynn Arthur Steen. National Academy Press, Washington DC.

Barcellos, A. (1984). The fractal geometry of Mandelbrot. *College Mathematics Journal* 15: 98–114.

Barnsley, M. (1993). *Fractals Everywhere*, 2nd ed. San Diego, CA: Academic Press.

Barnsley, M., and Hurd, L. (1993). *Fractal Image Compression*. Wellesley, MA: AK Peters, Ltd. (Presents the mathematics behind the CD *Microsoft Encarta*, a multimedia encyclopedia for which all the pictures are fractals.)

Bunde, A. and Havlin, S. (Eds.) (1994). *Fractals in Science* New York: Springer-Verlag. (Includes PC or Mac diskette of interactive programs for fractal models.)

Cibes, M. (1990). The Sierpinski triangle: Deterministic versus random models. *Mathematics Teacher* 83: 617–21.

Crownover, R. M. (1995). *Introduction to Fractals and Chaos*, Boston: Jones & Bartlett.

Darst, R., Palagallo, J. and Price, T. (1998). Fractal tilings in the plane. *Mathematics Magazine*, Vol. 71, No. 1: 12–23.

Davis, D. (1993). *The Nature and Power of Mathematics*. Princeton NJ: Princeton University Press. (Writing for the liberal arts student, Davis provides substantial introductions to non-Euclidean geometry, number theory, and fractals. The fractal chapter (Chapter 5) focuses on their appealing beauty and includes several relevant BASIC programs.)

Devaney, R. L. (1989). *An Introduction to Chaotic Dynamical Systems*, 2nd ed. Redwood City, CA: Addison-Wesley.

Devaney, R. L. (1990). *Chaos, Fractals, and Dynamics: Computer Experiments in Mathematics*. Menlo Park, CA: Addison-Wesley.

Devaney, R. and Keen, L., (Eds.) (1989). *Chaos and Fractals: The Mathematics Behind the Computer Graphics*, proceedings of Symposia in Applied Mathematics, Vol. 39, AMS.

Dewdney, A. K. Computer recreations. *Scientific American*, August 1985, December 1986, July 1987, November 1987, February 1989, May 1990.

Edgar, G. A. (1990). *Measure, Topology, and Fractal Geometry*, New York: Springer-Verlag.

Eglash, R. (1999). *African Fractals: Modern Computing and Indigenous Design*. New Brunswick NJ: Rutgers University Press.

Feder, J. (1988). *Fractals*, New York: Plenum Press.

Frøyland, J. (1994). *Introduction to Chaos and Coherence*, Philadelphia: Institute of Physics Publishing.

Gleick, J. (1988). *Chaos: Making a New Science*, New York Penguin.

Goldenberg, E. P. (1991). Seeing beauty in mathematics: Using fractal geometry to build a spirit of mathematical inquiry." *MAA Note:*

Visualization in Teaching and Learning Mathematics, Washington, DC: MAA.

Hastings, H., and Sugihara, G. (1993). *Fractals: A User's Guide for the Natural Sciences*, Oxford: Oxford University Press. (The introduction contains a brief chronology of fractals, and Chapter 3, "Dimension of Patterns," provides a a well-written extension of ideas presented in this text.)

Holmgren, R. A. (1996). *A First Course in Dynamical Systems*, 2nd ed., New York, Springer-Verlag.

Hutchinson, J. E. (1981). Fractals and self similarity. *Indiana University Mathematics Journal*, Vol. 30, No. 5:713–747. (Provides the mathematical foundations for IFSs.)

Jürgens, H., Peitgen, H–O., and Saupe, D. (1990). The language of fractals. *Scientific American*, August 1990: 60–67.

Lauwerier, H. (1991). *Fractals: Endlessly Repeated Geometrical Figures*, Princeton NJ: Princeton University Press.

Lorenz E. (1993). *The Essence of Chaos*, Seattle, WA: University of Washington Press.

Mandelbrot, B. B. (1983). *The Fractal Geometry of Nature*. Rev. ed. New York: W. H. Freeman & Co.

Mandelbrot, B. B. (1984). On fractal geometry and a few of the mathematical questions it has raised. *Proceedings of the International Congress of Mathematicians*, August 16–24 (1983):1661–1675. Warsaw: Polish Scientific Publishers.

Peitgen, H., and Saupe, D. (Eds.) (1988). *The Science of Fractal Images*. New York: Springer-Verlag.

Peitgen, H., Jürgens, H., and Saupe, D. (1992). *Chaos and Fractals: New Frontiers of Science* New York: Springer-Verlag. (Contains most of the two-volume text *Fractals for the Classroom*.)

Peitgen, H., and Richter, P.H. (Eds.) (1986). *The Beauty of Fractals: Images of Complex Dynamical Systems*. New York: Springer-Verlag.

Peterson, I. (1984). Ants in labyrinths and other fractal excursions. *Science News* 21: 42–43.

Richardson, L. F. (1922). *Weather Prediction by Numerical Process*. Republished by Dover Publications (1965).

Robinson, C. (1995). *Dynamical Systems: Stability, Symbolic Dynamics, and Chaos*, Ann Arbor, MI: CRC Press.

Rodríguez–Iturbe, I. (1997). *Fractal River Basins: Chance and Self-Organization*. Cambridge: Cambridge University Press.

Ruelle, D. (1991). *Chance and Chaos*. Princeton, NJ: Princeton University Press.

Steen, L. A. (1977). Fractals: A world of nonintegral dimensions. *Science News* 112: 122–123.

Stewart, I. (1987). The two-and-a-halfth dimension. *The Problems of Mathematics*. Oxford: Oxford University Press.

Stewart, I. (1989). *Does God Play Dice? The Mathematics of Chaos*. Oxford: Blackwell.

Wegner, T., and Peterson, M. (1991). *Fractal Creations*. Mill Valley, CA: The Waite Group Press.

Other Fractal Resources

Software, Programs, and Websites

Macintosh Software

Fractal Attraction. (1992). Kevin D. Lee, Yosef Cohen. Uses IFS (iterated function systems) to generate fractals with either random or deterministic algorithms. The IFS codes can be specified either by making numerical entries in a spreadsheet-like display or by using click and drag techniques. Allows interactive application of the collage theorem to create fractal generation of predetermined images. Includes an informative 80-page manual. Currently out of print, but well worth the effort to find.

FractaSketch 2.0 (1998). Peter Van Roy. Creates fractals at specified levels by iterating a template, i.e., by replacing each segment in the prior level with a copy of the template, and displays the fractal dimension of the resulting fractal. Templates can be created by click and drag techniques. Available from Dynamic Software, PO Box 13991, Berkeley, CA 94701.

PC Software

James Gleick's CHAOS: The Software. (1990). Originally written by Josh Gordon, Rudy Rucker, and John Walker for Autodesk, Inc. to accompany Gleick's book, it includes the following programs: The Mandelbrot Sets, Magnets and Pendulum, Toy Universes, The Chaos Game, Strange Attractors and Fractal Forgeries. For the current web address from which the software can be obtained, see the website below.

FRACTINT. A freeware fractal generator created and constantly upgraded and improved by the Stone Soup team. For the current web address from which the software can be obtained see the website below.

Websites

For a list of several websites containing fractal information, information about more fractal software, and other resources see
http://www.stolaf.edu/people/cederj/geotext/info.htm

BASIC Computer Programs

Bannon, Thomas J. (1991). Fractals and Transformations. *Mathematics Teacher* 84: 178–85. Programs incorporating IFS algorithms for graphical display of the Dragon curve, the Koch curve, and the Sierpinski triangle. True BASIC programs generating the Sierpinski triangle using both deterministic and random algorithms.

Davis, Donald (1993). *The Nature and Power of Mathematics.* Princeton University Press. Programs for iterating logistic functions and for graphical display of orbits, the Lorenz attractor, Julia sets, and the Mandelbrot set.

Devaney, Robert L. (1990). *Chaos, Fractals, and Dynamics: Computer Experiments in Mathematics.* Menlo Park CA Addison-Wesley. Programs for computing orbits by iterating functions and for graphical display of Julia sets, the Mandelbrot set, and the Sierpinski triangle.

Peitgen, Heinz-Otto, Jürgens, Hartmut, and Saupe, Dietmar (1992). *Chaos and Fractals: New Frontiers of Science*, New York: Springer-Verlag. Programs for graphical iteration, the Koch curve, the Sierpinski triangle, the chaos game for the fern, and for graphical display of Cantor, Mandelbrot, and Julia sets.

Programs for Graphing Calculators

Peitgen, Heinz-Otto, Jürgens, Hartmut, and Saupe, Dietmar (1991–2) *Fractals for the Classroom—Strategic Activities, Volume 1.* New York: Springer-Verlag and NCTM. Programs for simulating the chaos game for both the CASIO and Texas Instrument graphing calculators.

Videos

The Beauty and Complexity of the Mandelbrot Set: School Edition (1989; 47 min.). A richly illustrated video-lecture by John H. Hubbard of Cornell University. The talk describes iteration and its use in creating pictures of the Julia set and the Mandelbrot set. Available from The Science Television Co., P O Box 2498, Times Square Station, New York, NY 10108.

Chaos, Fractals and Dynamical Systems (1989; 63 min.). ISBN 1-878310-00-3. Robert Devaney. Tells the mathematical story behind chaos, fractals, and dynamical systems. Computer-generated diagrams and graphs give a visual introduction to the concepts. Available from The Science Television Co., P O Box 2498, Times Square Station, New York, NY 10108.

Focus on Fractals (1990; 23 min.). An "entry level introduction" with some narration featuring footage from the Dr. John Hamal Hubbard Dynamical Systems Laboratory. Contains four zooms of the Mandelbrot set, two Julia set promenades, and a 3D rendition of the Lorenz attractor. Available from Art Matrix, PO 880NA, Ithaca, NY 14851-0880

Fractals: An Animated Discussion (1990; 63 min.). Heinz-Otto Peitgen et al. A combination of animated sequences and interviews with Benoit Mandelbrot and Edward Lorenz, accompanied by music composed according to fractal principles. Available from W.H. Freeman, New York.

Fractals: the colors of infinity (1994; 30 min.) An explanation of the Mandelbrot set and the revolutions in thought resulting from its discovery. Includes interviews with Benoit Mandelbrot, Michael Barnsley and Ian Stewart. Available from Films for the Humanities and Sciences, P.O. Box 2053, Princeton NJ 08543-2053.

The Hypercube: Projections and Slicing (1978; 15 min.). A Banchoff/Strauss Production that uses computer graphics to describe the three and four dimensional cubes and the forms they create when rotated around various axes; discusses perspective and shows shapes that evolve when a three and four dimensional cube is sliced at various points. Available from International Film Bureau.

Mandelbrot Sets and Julia Sets (1990; 2 hrs.). Animated zooming (no narration) into the Mandelbrot set, from the Cornell National Supercomputer Facility and the Dr. John Hamal Hubbard Dynamical Systems Laboratory. Available from Art Matrix, PO 880, Ithaca, NY 14851-0880.

Euclid's Definitions, Postulates, and the First 30 Propositions of *Elements, Book I*

A

Definitions

1. A *point* is that which has no part.
2. A *line* is breadthless length.
3. The *extremities of a line* are points.
4. A *straight line* is a line which lies evenly with the points on itself.
5. A *surface* is that which has length and breadth only.
6. The *extremities of a surface* are lines.
7. A *plane surface* is a surface which lies evenly with the straight lines on itself.
8. A *plane angle* is the inclination to one another of two lines in a plane which meet one another and do not lie in a straight line.
9. And when the lines containing the angle are straight, the angle is called *rectilineal*.
10. When a straight line set up on a straight line makes the adjacent angles equal to one another, each of the equal angles is *right*, and

Reprinted with permission of Cambridge University Press from *The Thirteen Books of Euclid's Elements*, 2nd ed., pp. 154–155 (1956). Translated by Sir Thomas L. Heath. New York: Dover.

the straight line standing on the other is called *perpendicular* to that on which it stands.

11. An *obtuse angle* is an angle greater than a right angle.
12. An *acute angle* is an angle less than a right angle.
13. A *boundary* is that which is an extremity of anything.
14. A *figure* is that which is contained by any boundary or boundaries.
15. A *circle* is a plane figure contained by one line such that all the straight lines falling upon it from one point among those lying within the figure are equal to one another.
16. And the point is called the *centre* of the circle.
17. A *diameter* of the circle is any straight line drawn through the centre and terminated in both directions by the circumference of the circle, and such a straight line also bisects the circle.
18. A *semicircle* is the figure contained by the diameter and the circumference cut off by it. And the centre of the semicircle is the same as that of the circle.
19. *Rectilineal* figures are those which are contained by straight lines, *trilateral* figures being those contained by three, *quadrilateral* those contained by four, and *multilateral* those contained by more than four straight lines.
20. Of trilateral figures, an *equilateral triangle* is that which has three sides equal, an *isosceles triangle* that which has two of its sides alone equal, and a *scalene triangle* that which has its three sides unequal.
21. Further, of trilateral figures, a *right-angled triangle* is that which has a right angle, an *obtuse-angled triangle* that which has an obtuse angle, and an *acute-angled triangle* that which has its three angles acute.
22. Of quadrilateral figures, a *square* is that which is both equilateral and right-angled; an *oblong* that which is right-angled but not equilateral; a *rhombus* that which is equilateral but not right-angled; and a *rhomboid* that which has its opposite sides and angles equal to one another but is neither equilateral nor right-angled. And let quadrilaterals other than these be called *trapezia*.
23. *Parallel* straight lines are straight lines which, being in the same plane and being produced indefinitely in both directions, do not meet one another in either direction.

The Postulates

1. To draw a straight line from any point to any point.
2. To produce a finite straight line continuously in a straight line.
3. To describe a circle with any centre and distance.
4. That all right angles are equal to one another.
5. That, if a straight line falling on two straight lines makes the interior angles on the same side less than two right angles, the two straight lines, if produced indefinitely, meet on that side on which are the angles less than the two right angles.

The Common Notions

1. Things which are equal to the same thing are also equal to one another.
2. If equals be added to equals, the wholes are equal.
3. If equals be subtracted from equals, the remainders are equal.
4. Things which coincide with one another are equal to one another.
5. The whole is greater than the part.

The First 30 Propositions of *Book I*

1. On a given finite straight line, to construct an equilateral triangle.
2. To place at a given point (as an extremity) a straight line equal to a given straight line.
3. Given two unequal straight lines, to cut off from the greater a straight line line equal to the less.
4. If two triangles have the two sides equal to two sides, respectively, and have the angles contained by the equal straight lines equal, they will also have the base equal to the base, the triangle will be equal to the triangle, and the remaining angles will be equal to the remaining angles, respectively, namely, those which the equal sides subtend.

5. In isosceles triangles, the angles at the base are equal to one another, and, if the equal straight lines be produced further, the angles under the base will be equal to one another.

6. If in a triangle two angles be equal to one another, the sides which subtend the equal angles will also be equal to one another.

7. Given two straight lines constructed on a straight line (from its extremities), and meeting in a point, there cannot be constructed on the same line (from its extremities), and on the same side of it, two other straight lines meeting in another point and equal to the former two, respectively, namely, each to that which has the same extremity with it.

8. If two triangles have the two sides equal to two sides, respectively, and have also the base equal to the base, they will also have the angles equal which are contained by the equal straight lines.

9. To bisect a given rectilinear angle.

10. To bisect a given finite straight line.

11. To draw a straight line at right angles to a given straight line from a given point on it.

12. To a given infinite straight line, from a given point which is not on it, to draw a perpendicular straight line.

13. If a straight line set up on a straight line make angles, it will make either two right angles or angles equal to two right angles.

14. If with any straight line, and at a point on it, two straight lines not lying on the same side make the adjacent angles equal to two right angles, the two straight lines will be in a straight line with one another.

15. If two straight lines cut one another, they make the vertical angles equal to one another.

16. In any triangle if one of the sides be produced, the exterior angle is greater than either of the interior and opposite angles.

17. In any triangle two angles taken together in any manner are less than two right angles.

18. In any triangle the greater side subtends the greater angle.

19. In any triangle the greater angle is subtended by the greater side.

20. In any triangle two sides taken together in any manner are greater than the remaining one.

21. If on one of the sides of a triangle, from its extremities, there be constructed two straight lines meeting within the triangle, the straight lines so constructed will be less than the remaining two sides of the triangle, but will contain a greater angle.

22. Out of three straight lines, which are equal to three given straight lines, to construct a triangle: thus it is necessary that two of the straight lines taken together in any manner should be greater than the remaining one.

23. On a given straight line and at a point on it, to construct a rectilineal angle equal to a given rectilineal angle.

24. If two triangles have the two sides equal to two sides, respectively, but have the one of the angles contained by the equal straight lines greater than the other, they will also have the base greater than the base.

25. If two triangles have the two sides equal to two sides, respectively, but have the base greater than the base, they will also have the one of the angles contained by the equal straight lines greater than the other.

26. If two triangles have the two angles equal to two angles, respectively, and one side equal to one side, namely, either the side adjoining the equal angles, or that subtending one of the equal angles, they will also have the remaining sides equal to the remaining sides and the remaining angle to the remaining angle.

27. If a straight line falling on two straight lines makes the alternate angles equal to one another, the straight lines will be parallel to one another.

28. If a straight line falling on two straight lines makes the exterior angle equal to the interior and opposite angle on the same side, or the interior angles on the same side equal to two right angles, the straight lines will be parallel to one another.

29. A straight line falling on parallel straight lines makes the alternate angles equal to one another, the exterior angle equal to the interior and opposite angle, and the interior angles on the same side equal to two right angles.

30. Straight lines parallel to the same straight line are also parallel to one another.

B

APPENDIX

Hilbert's Axioms for Plane Geometry

Undefined Terms. Point, line, plane, on, between, congruence.

Group I: Axioms of Connection

I.1. Through any two distinct points A, B, there is always a line m.

I.2. Through any two distinct points A, B, there is not more than one line m.

I.3. On every line there exist at least two distinct points. There exist at least three points which are not on the same line.

I.4. Through any three points, not on the same line, there is one and only one plane.

Reprinted with permission of Open Court Publishing Co. from D. Hilbert, *The Foundations of Geometry*, 2nd ed. (1921). Translated by E. J. Townsend, Chicago: Open Court Publishing Co.

Group II: Axioms of Order

II.1. If point B is between points A and C, then A, B, C are distinct points on the same line, and B is between C and A.

II.2. For any two distinct points A and C, there is at least one point B on the line AC such that C is between A and B.

II.3. If A, B, C are three distinct points on the same line, then only one of the points is between the other two.

Definition

By the *segment AB* is meant the set of all points which are between A and B. Points A and B are called the *endpoints* of the segment. The segment AB is the same as segment BA.

II.4. **Pasch's Axiom.** Let A, B, C be three points not on the same line and let m be a line in the plane A, B, C which does not pass through any of the points A, B, C. Then if m passes through a point of the segment AB, it will also pass through a point of segment AC or a point of segment BC.

Note: II.4′. This postulate may be replaced by the *separation axiom*. A line m separates the points of the plane which are not on m into sets such that if two points X and Y are in the same set, the segment XY does not intersect m, and if X and Y are in different sets, the segment XY does intersect m. In the first case X and Y are said to be on the *same side* of m; in the second case, X and Y are said to be on *opposite sides* of m.

Definition

By the *ray AB* is meant the set of points consisting of those which are between A and B, the point B itself, and all points C such that B is between A and C. The ray AB is said to *emanate from* point A.

A point A, on a given line m, divides m into two rays such that two points are on the same ray if and only if A is not between them.

Definition

If A, B, and C are three points not on the same line, then the system of three segments AB, BC, CA, and their endpoints is called the *triangle ABC*. The three segments are called the *sides* of the triangle, and the three points are called the *vertices*.

Group III: Axioms of Congruence

III.1. If A and B are distinct points on line m, and if A' is a point on line m' (not necessarily distinct from m), then there is one and only point B' on each ray of m' emanating from A' such that the segment $A'B'$ is congruent to the segment AB.

III.2. If two segments are each congruent to a third, then they are congruent to each other. (From this it can be shown that congruence of segments is an equivalence relation; i.e., $AB \simeq AB$; if $AB \simeq A'B'$, then $A'B' \simeq AB$; and if $AB \simeq CD$ and $CD \simeq EF$, then $AB \simeq EF$.)

III.3. If point C is between A and B, and C' is between A' and B', and if the segment $AC \simeq A'C'$ and the segment $CB \simeq C'B'$, then segment $AB \simeq$ segment $A'B'$.

Definition

By an *angle* is meant a point (called the *vertex* of the angle) and two rays (called the *sides* of the angle) emanating from the point.

If the vertex of the angle is point A and if B and C are any two points other than A on the two sides of the angle, we speak of the angle *BAC* or *CAB* or simply of angle A.

III.4. If *BAC* is an angle whose sides do not lie on the same line and if in a given plane, $A'B'$ is a ray emanating from A', then there is one and only one ray $A'C'$ on a given side of line $A'B'$, such that $\angle B'A'C' \simeq \angle BAC$. In short, a given angle in a given plane can be laid off on a given side of a given ray in one and only one way. Every angle is congruent to itself.

Definition

If *ABC* is a triangle then the three angles *BAC*, *CBA*, and *ACB* are called the angles of the triangle. Angle *BAC* is said to be *included* by the sides *AB* and *AC* of the triangle.

III.5. If two sides and the included angle of the one triangle are congruent, respectively, to two sides and the included angle of another triangle, then each of the remaining angles of the first triangle is congruent to the corresponding angle of the second triangle.

Group IV: Axioms of Parallels (for a plane)

IV.1. **Playfair's Postulate.** Through a given point A not on a given line m there passes at most one line which does not intersect m.

Group V: Axioms of Continuity

V.1. **Axiom of Measure (Archimedean Axiom).** If AB and CD are arbitrary segments, then there exists a number n such that if segment CD is laid off n times on the ray AB starting from A, then a point E is reached, where $n \cdot CD = AE$, and where B is between A and E.

V.2. **Axiom of Linear Completeness.** The system of points on a line with its order and congruence relations cannot be extended in such a way that the relations existing among its elements as well as the basic properties of linear order and congruence resulting from Axioms I-III and V.1 remain valid.

Note: V. These axioms may be replaced by *Dedekind's axiom of continuity*. For every partition of the points on a line into two nonempty sets such that no point of either lies between two points of the other, there is a point of one set which lies between every other point of that set and every point of the other set.

Birkhoff's Postulates for Euclidean Plane Geometry

APPENDIX **C**

Undefined Elements and Relations. (a) *Points A, B, . . .*; (b) sets of points called *lines, m, n, . . .*; (c) *distance* between any two points: $d(A, B)$ a real nonnegative number with $d(A, B) = d(B, A)$; (d) *angle* formed by three ordered points A, O, B, $(A \neq O, B \neq O)$: $\angle AOB$ a real number (mod 2π). The point O is called the *vertex* of the angle.

Postulate I (Postulate of Line Measure)
The points A, B, . . . of any line m can be out into 1:1 correspondence with the real numbers x so that $|x_B - x_A| = d(A, B)$ for all points A, B.

Definitions
A point B is *between* A and C $(A \neq C)$ if $d(A, B) + d(B, C) = d(A, C)$. The points A and C, together with all points B between A and C, form *segment AC*. The *half-line m'* with *endpoint O* is defined by two points O, A in line m $(A \neq O)$ as the set of all points A' of m such that O is not between A and A'. If A, B, C are three distinct points the three segments AB, BC, CA are said to form a *triangle* $\triangle ABC$ with

Reprinted with permission from G. D. Birkhoff, A set of postulates for plane geometry (based on scale and protractor), *Annals of Mathematics* 33: 329–345 (1932).

sides AB, BC, CA and *vertices A, B, C*. If *A, B, C* are in the same line, $\triangle ABC$ is said to be *degenerate*.

Postulate II (Point–Line Postulate)
One and only one line m contains two given points P, Q(P ≠ Q).

Definitions
If two distinct lines have no points in common they are *parallel*. A line is always regarded as parallel to itself.

Postulate III (Postulate of Angle Measure)
The half-lines m, n, ... through any point O can be put into 1:1 correspondence with the real numbers a (mod 2π) so that if A ≠ O and B ≠ O are points of m and n, respectively, the difference $a_n - a_m$ (mod 2π) is ∠AOB. Furthermore if the point B on n varies continuously in a line r not containing the vertex O, the number a_n varies continuously also.

Definitions
Two half-lines *m, n* through *O* are said to form a *straight angle* if $\angle mOn \equiv \pi$. Two half-lines *m, n* through *O* are said to form a *right angle* if $\angle mOn \equiv \pm\pi/2$, in which case we also say that *n* is *perpendicular* to *m*.

Postulate IV (Similarity Postulate)
If in two triangles $\triangle ABC$, $\triangle A'B'C'$ and for some constant k > 0, $d(A', B') = kd(A, B)$, $d(A', C') = kd(A, C)$, and $\angle B'A'C' = \pm\angle BAC$, then also $d(B', C') = kd(B, C)$, $\angle C'B'A' = \pm\angle CBA$, $\angle A'B'C' = \pm\angle ACB$.

Definitions
Any two geometric figures are *similar* if there exists a 1:1 correspondence between the points of the two figures such that all corresponding distances are in proportion and corresponding angles are all equal or all negatives of each other. Any two geometric figures are *congruent* if they are similar with $k = 1$.

D

APPENDIX

The SMSG Postulates for Euclidean Geometry

Undefined Terms. Point, line, plane.

Postulate 1
Given any two different points, there is exactly one line which contains both of them.

Postulate 2 (The Distance Postulate)
To every pair of different points there corresponds a unique positive number.

Postulate 3 (The Ruler Postulate)
The points of a line can be placed in correspondence with the real numbers in such a way that:
  i. *To every point of the line there corresponds exactly one real number.*
  ii. *To every real number there corresponds exactly one point of the line.*
  iii. *The distance between two points is the absolute value of the difference of the corresponding numbers.*

Reprinted from SMSG, *Geometry: Student's Text*, A.C Vroman, Pasadena, CA (1965).

Postulate 4 (The Ruler Placement Postulate)

Given two points P and Q of a line, the coordinate system can be chosen in such a way that the coordinate of P is zero and the coordinate of Q is positive.

Postulate 5

(a) Every plane contains at least three noncollinear points. (b) Space contains at least four noncoplanar points.

Postulate 6

If two points lie in a plane, then the line containing these points lies in the same plane.

Postulate 7

Any three points lie in at least one plane, and any three noncollinear points lie in exactly one plane. More briefly, any three points are coplanar, and any three noncollinear points determine a plane.

Postulate 8

Any two different planes intersect, then their intersection is a line.

Postulate 9 (The Plane Separation Postulate)

Given a line and a plane containing it, the points of the plane that do not lie on the line form two sets such that:

   i. each of the sets is convex.

   ii. if P is in one set and Q is in the other then the segment $\overline{PQ}$ intersects the line.

Postulate 10 (The Space Separation Postulate)

The points of space that do not lie in a given plane form two sets such that:

   i. each of the sets is convex.

   ii. if P is in one set and Q is in the other, then the segment $\overline{PQ}$ intersects the plane.

Postulate 11 (The Angle Measurement Postulate)

To every angle $\angle BAC$ there corresponds a real number between 0 and 180.

Postulate 12 (The Angle Construction Postulate)

Let $\overrightarrow{AB}$ be a ray on the edge of the half-plane H. For every number r between 0 and 180 there is exactly one ray $\overrightarrow{AP}$, with P in H, such that in $\angle PAB = r$.

Postulate 13 (The Angle Addition Postulate)

If D is a point in the interior of $\angle BAC$, then $m\angle BAC = m\angle BAD + m\angle DAC$.

Postulate 14 (The Supplement Postulate)

If two angles form a linear pair, then they are supplementary.

Postulate 15 (The SAS Postulate)

Given a correspondence between two triangles (or between a triangle and itself), if two sides and the included angle of the first triangle are congruent to the corresponding parts of the second triangle, then the correspondence is a congruence.

Postulate 16 (The Parallel Postulate)

Through a given external point there is at most one line parallel to a given line.

Postulate 17

To every polygonal region there corresponds a unique positive number.

Postulate 18

If two triangles are congruent, then the triangular regions have the same area.

Postulate 19

Suppose that the region R is the union of two regions R_1 and R_2. Suppose that R_1 and R_2 intersect at most in a finite number of segments and points. Then the area of R is the sum of the areas of R_1 and R_2.

Postulate 20

The area of a rectangle is the product of the length of its base and the length of its altitude.

Postulate 21

The volume of a rectangular parallelepiped is the product of the altitude and the area of the base.

Postulate 22 (Cavalieri's Principle)

Given two solids and a plane, if for every plane which intersects the solids and is parallel to the given plane the two intersections have equal areas, then the two solids have the same volume.

E

APPENDIX

Some SMSG Definitions for Euclidean Geometry

1. The *distance* between two points is the positive number given by the distance postulate (Postulate 2). If the points are P and Q, then the distance is denoted by PQ.

2. A correspondence of the sort described in Postulate 3 is called a *coordinate system* for the line. The number corresponding to a given point is called the *coordinate* of the point.

3. B is *between* A and C if (1) A, B, and C are distinct points on the same line, and (2) $AB + BC = AC$.

4. For any points A and B the *segment* $\overline{AB}$ is the set whose points are A and B, together with all points that are between A and B. The points A and B are called the *endpoints* of $\overline{AB}$.

5. The distance AB is called the *length* of the segment $\overline{AB}$.

6. Let A and B be points of a line L. The ray $\overrightarrow{AB}$ is the set which is the union of (1) the segment $\overline{AB}$ and (2) the set of all points C for which it is true that B is between A and C. The point A is called the *endpoint* of $\overrightarrow{AB}$.

7. If A is between B and C, then $\overrightarrow{AB}$ and $\overrightarrow{AC}$ are called *opposite rays*.

Reprinted from SMSG, *Geometry: Student's Text*, A.C. Vroman, Pasadena, CA (1965).

8. A point B is called a *midpoint* of a segment $\overline{AC}$ if B is between A and C, and $AB = BC$.

9. The midpoint of a segment is said to *bisect* the segment. More generally, any figure whose intersection with a segment is the midpoint of the segment is said to *bisect* the segment.

10. The set of all points is called *space*.

11. A set of points is *collinear* if there is a line which contains all the points of the set.

12. A set of points is *coplanar* if there is a plane which contains all the points of the set.

13. A set A is called *convex* if for every two points P and Q of A, the entire segment $\overline{PQ}$ lies in A.

14. Given a line L and a plane E containing it, the two sets determined by Postulate 9 are called *half-planes*, and L is called an *edge* of each of them. We say that L *separates* E into the two half-planes. If two points P and Q of E lie in the same half-plane, we say that they lie *on the same side* of L; if P lies in one of the half-planes and Q in the other, they lie on *opposite sides* of L.

15. The two sets determined by Postulate 10 are called *half-spaces*, and the given plane is called the *face* of each of them.

16. An *angle* is the union of two rays which have the same endpoint but do not lie in the same line. The two rays are called the *sides* of the angle, and their common endpoint is called the *vertex*.

17. If A, B, and C are any three noncollinear points, then the union of the segments $\overline{AB}$, $\overline{BC}$, $\overline{AC}$ is called a *triangle*, and is denoted by $\triangle ABC$; the points A, B, and C are called its *vertices*, and the segments $\overline{AB}$, $\overline{BC}$, and $\overline{AC}$ are called its *sides*. Every triangle determines three angles, $\triangle ABC$ determines the angles $\angle BAC$, $\angle ABC$, and $\angle ACB$, which are called the *angles* of $\triangle ABC$.

18. Let $\angle BAC$ be an angle lying in plane E. A point P of E lies in the *interior* of $\angle BAC$ if (1) P and B are on the same side of the line $\overleftrightarrow{AC}$ and (2) P and C are on the same side of the line $\overleftrightarrow{AB}$. The *exterior* of $\angle BAC$ is the set of all points of E that do not lie in the interior and do not lie on the angle itself.

19. A point lies in the *interior* of a triangle if it lies in the interior of each of the angles of the triangle. A point lies in the *exterior* of a

triangle if it lies in the plane of the triangle but is not a point of the triangle or of its interior.

20. The number specified by Postulate 11 is called the *measure of the angle*, and is written as $m\angle BAC$.

21. If $\overrightarrow{AB}$ and $\overrightarrow{AC}$ are opposite rays, and $\overrightarrow{AD}$ is another ray, the $\angle BAD$ and $\angle DAC$ form a *linear pair*.

22. Angles are *congruent* if they have the same measure. Segments are *congruent* if they have the same length.

23. Given a correspondence $ABC \leftrightarrow DEF$ between the vertices of the two triangles. If every pair of corresponding sides are congruent, and every pair of corresponding angles are congruent, then the correspondence $ABC \leftrightarrow DEF$ is a *congruence between the two triangles*.

24. If the sum of the measure of two angles is 180, then the angles are called *supplementary*, and each is called a *supplement* of the other.

25. If the two angles of a linear pair have the same measure, then each of the angles is a *right angle*.

26. Two intersecting sets, each of which is either a line, a ray, or a segment, are *perpendicular* if the two line which contain them determine a right angle.

27. The *perpendicular bisector* of a segment in a plane is the line in the plane which is perpendicular to the segment and contains the midpoint.

F

APPENDIX

The ASA Theorem

Theorem F.1

If, in nondegenerate triangles $\triangle ABC$ and $\triangle A'B'C'$, $\angle CAB \simeq \angle C'A'B'$, $\angle ABC \simeq \angle A'B'C'$, and $\overline{AB} \simeq \overline{A'B'}$, then $\angle BCA \simeq \angle B'C'A'$, $\overline{BC} \simeq \overline{B'C'}$, and $\overline{AC} \simeq \overline{A'C'}$.

The proof of this theorem is given in each of three axiom systems. Hilbert's Birkhoff's, and SMSG's.

Proof I. (Based on Hilbert's axioms)
We begin by proving the following lemma. ∎

Lemma

If, in nondegenerate triangles $\triangle ABC$ and $\triangle A'B'C'$, $\overline{AB} \simeq \overline{A'B'}$, $\overline{AC} \simeq \overline{A'C'}$, and $\angle CAB \simeq \angle C'A'B'$, then $\overline{BC} \simeq \overline{B'C'}$, $\angle ABC \simeq \angle A'B'C'$, and $\angle BCA \simeq \angle B'C'A'$.

Proof

Let triangles $\triangle ABC$ and $\triangle A'B'C'$ be given as in the hypothesis of the lemma. Then $\angle ABC \simeq \angle A'B'C'$ and $\angle BCA \simeq \angle B'C'A'$ by Axiom III-5. Hence, all that remains is to prove $\overline{BC} \simeq \overline{B'C'}$.

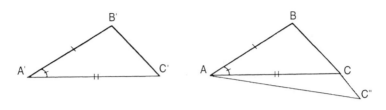

FIGURE F.1

On ray $\overrightarrow{BC}$ find C'' such that $\overline{BC''} \simeq \overline{B'C'}$ (III-1), and construct $\overline{AC''}$ (I-1) (Fig. F.1). If $C = C''$, then $\overline{BC''} \simeq \overline{BC}$, and hence $\overline{BC} \simeq \overline{B'C'}$.

If $C \neq C'$ the three points B, C, C'' are distinct since $\triangle ABC$ and $\triangle A'B'C'$ are nondegenerate triangles. Furthermore, since C'' is on ray $\overrightarrow{BC}$, either C is between B and C'', or C'' is between B and C.

Case 1: C is between B and C''. Since $\overline{AB} \simeq \overline{A'B'}$, $\overline{BC''} \simeq \overline{B'C'}$, and $\angle ABC \simeq \angle A'B'C'$, $\angle C''AB \simeq \angle C'A'B'$ (III-5). But $\angle C'A'B' \simeq \angle CAB$. Thus, $\angle C''AB \simeq CAB$.[1] So ray $\overrightarrow{AC} = \text{ray}\overrightarrow{AC''}$ (III-4), and hence $\overline{AC''} = \overline{AC}$ (I-1). Therefore, C and C'' each lie on both AC and BC so $C = C''$. But this is a contradiction.

Case 2: C'' is between B and C. In this case a contradiction is obtained in a similar manner. Hence, $C = C''$, and as a result $\overline{BC} = \overline{B'C'}$.

Let triangles $\triangle ABC$ and $\triangle A'B'C'$ be as given in the hypothesis. Then by the preceding lemma it suffices to show $\overline{AC} \simeq \overline{A'C'}$. On ray $\overrightarrow{AC}$ find C'' such that $\overline{AC''} \simeq \overline{A'C'}$ (III-1) and construct BC'' (I-1). If $C = C''$, then $\overline{AC} = \overline{AC''}$, and hence $\overline{AC} \simeq \overline{A'C'}$. If $C \neq C''$, the remainder of the proof is analogous to the proof of the lemma. ∎

Proof II (Based on Birkhoff's axioms)
Let triangles $\triangle ABC$ and $\triangle A'B'C'$ be as given in the hypothesis. Then by the definition of congruence $d(A, B) = d(A'B')$, $\angle CAB = \pm\angle C'A'B'$, $\angle ABC = \pm\angle A'B'C'$. We will assume that $\angle CAB = \angle C'A'B'$, $\angle ABC = \angle A'B'C'$ since the proof is similar in the other case. Using Postulate IV and the definition of congruence it suffices to show $d(A, C) = d(A', C')$. If $d(A, C) \neq d(A', C')$, then without loss

---

[1]Note that we need to establish the transitivity of angle congruence.

of generality $d(A, C) < d(A'C')$. Let C'' be a point of ray $\overrightarrow{AC}^2$ such that $d(A, C'') = d(A', C')$ (I), and consider BC'' (II). Now $\angle C'A'B' = \angle CAB$. Furthermore since ray $\overrightarrow{AC} = $ ray $\overrightarrow{AC''}$ (II), $\angle CAB = \angle C''AB$ (III). Therefore $\angle C'A'B' = \angle C''AB$. In addition $d(A', C') = d(A, C'')$ and $d(A', B') = d(A, B)$. Hence, $\angle A'B'C' = \angle ABC''$ (IV). This implies that $\angle ABC'' = \angle ABC$ so ray $\overrightarrow{BC} = $ ray $\overrightarrow{BC''}$ (III). Therefore, C and C'' are each contained in BC and AC and so $C = C''$. It follows that $d(A, C) = d(A, C'')$. Since $d(A, C'') = d(A', C')$ this implies $d(A, C) = d(A', C')$. ∎

Proof III (Based on the SMSG axioms)

Let triangles $\triangle ABC$ and $\triangle A'B'C'$ be as given in the hypothesis. By Postulate 15 it suffices to show $\overline{AC} \simeq \overline{A'C'}$. If $\overline{AC} \not\simeq \overline{A'C'}$, then by definition of congruent segments, $\overline{AC} \neq \overline{A'C'}$. Without loss of generality, we can assume $AC < A'C'$. Let C'' be a point of line AC such that $\overline{AC''} \simeq \overline{A'C'}$ (Fig. F.2). Consider line BC'' (Post. 1). Now $m\angle CAB = m\angle C''AB$ (Post. 11) and $m\angle CAB = m\angle C'A'B'$ by the definition of congruent angles. Hence, $m\angle C''AB = m\angle C'A'B'$; so $\angle C''AB \simeq \angle C'A'B'$. Furthermore, $\overline{A'C'} \simeq \overline{AC''}$ by the definition of congruent segments, and $\overline{A'B'} \simeq \overline{AB}$ by hypothesis. Therefore, $\angle ABC'' \simeq \angle A'B'C'$ (Post. 15), i.e., $m\angle ABC'' = m\angle A'B'C' = m\angle ABC$. This implies ray $\overrightarrow{BC''} = $ ray $\overrightarrow{BC}$ (Post. 12). And since line $AC = $ line AC'' (Post. 1), it follows that C and C'' are each points of both lines AC and BC. Hence, $C = C''$. Therefore, $\overline{AC} \simeq \overline{AC''}$, so $\overline{AC} = \overline{AC''} \simeq \overline{A'C'}$. ∎

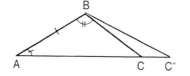 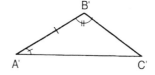

FIGURE F.2

[2]Here it is necessary to show that this notation is well defined.

References

Aaboe, A. (1964). *Episodes from the Early History of Mathematics*. New York: L. W. Singer.

Abbott, E. A. (1991). *Flatland*, Princeton NJ: Princeton University Press.

Adler, C. F. (1967). *Modern Geometry: An Integrated First Course*. New York: McGraw-Hill.

Adler, I. (1966). *A New Look at Geometry*. New York: John Day Co.

Adler, I. (1968). What shall we teach in high school geometry? *Mathematics Teacher* 61: 226–238.

Albert, A. A., and Sandler, R. (1968). *An Introduction to Finite Projective Planes*. New York: Holt, Rinehart and Winston.

Aleksandrov, A. D. (1969). Non-Euclidean geometry. In *Mathematics: Its Content, Methods, and Meaning*, Edited by A. D. Aledsandrov, A. N. Kolmogorov, and M. A. Lavrent'ev. Vol. 3, pp. 97–189. Cambridge, MA: M. I. T. Press.

Anderson, I. (1974). *A First Course in Combinatorial Mathematics*. Oxford: Clarendon Press.

Artzy, R. (1965). *Linear Geometry*. Reading, MA: Addison-Wesley.

Audsley, W. J. (1968). *Designs and Patterns from Historic Ornament*. New York: Dover.

Banchoff, T. F. (1990). Dimension. In *On the Shoulders of Giants*. Edited by Lynn Arthur Steen. National Academy Press, Washington DC.

Barcellos, A. (1984). The fractal geometry of Mandelbrot. *College Mathematics Journal* 15: 98–114.

Barker, S. F. (1964). *Philosophy of Mathematics*. Englewood Cliffs, NJ: Prentice-Hall.

Barker, S. F. (1984). Non-Euclidean geometry. In *Mathematics: People, Problems, Results*. Edited by D. M. Campbell and J. C. Higgins. Vol. 2, pp. 112–127. Belmont, CA: Wadsworth.

Barnsley, M. (1993). *Fractals Everywhere*, 2nd ed. San Diego, CA: Academic Press.

Barnsley, M., and Hurd, L. (1993). *Fractal Image Compression*. Wellesley, MA: AK Peters, Ltd.

Beck, A., Bleicher, M. N., and Crowe, D. W. (1972). *Excursions into Mathematics*. New York: Worth Publishers.

Benedicty, M., and Sledge, F. R. (1987). *Discrete Mathematical Structures*. Orlando, FL: Harcourt Brace Jovanovich.

Birkhoff, G. D. (1932). A set of postulates for plane geometry, based on scale and protractor. *Annals of Mathematics*, 33: 329–345.

Blake, I. F., and Mullin, R. C.. (1975). *The Mathematical Theory of Coding*. New York: Academic Press.

Blumenthal, L. (1961). *A Modern View of Geometry*. San Francisco: W. H. Freeman.

Bold, B. (1982). *Famous Problems of Geometry and How to Solve Them*. New York: Dover.

Borsuk, K. (1960). *Foundations of Geometry: Euclidean and Bolyai–Lobachevskian Geometry*, Amsterdam: North–Holland.

Bourbaki, N. (1950). The architecture of mathematics, *American Mathematical Monthly* 57: 221–232.

Boyer, C. B. (1956). *History of Analytic Geometry*. New York: Scripta Mathematica.

Bronowski, J. (1974). The music of the spheres. In *The Ascent of Man*, pp. 155–187. Boston: Little, Brown.

Bruck, R. H., and Ryser, H. J. (1949). The non-existence of certain finite projective planes. *Canadian Journal of Mathematics*. 1: 88–93.

Bunde, A., and Havlin, S. (Eds.) (1994). *Fractals in Science* New York: Springer-Verlag.

Burn, R. P. (1975). *Deductive Transformation Geometry*. Cambridge: Cambridge University Press.

Caldwell, J. H. (1966). Chapter 11: The plane symmetry groups. In *Topics in Recreational Mathematics*. Cambridge, U.K.: Cambridge University Press.

Cibes, M. (1990). The Sierpinski triangle: Deterministic versus random models. *Mathematics Teacher* 83: 617–21.

Cipra, B. A. (1988). Computer search solves an old math problem. *Science* 242: 1507–1508.

Copeland, R. (1979). *How Children Learn Mathematics: Teaching Implications of Piaget's Research*, 3rd ed. New York: Macmillan.

Courant, R., and Robbins, H. (1941). *What Is Mathematics?* London: Oxford University Press.

Coxeter, H. S. M. (1957). *Non-Euclidean Geometry*, 3rd ed. Toronto: University of Toronto Press.

Coxeter, H. S. M. (1961). *The Real Projective Plane*, 2nd ed. Cambridge: Cambridge University Press.

Coxeter, H. S. M. (1969). *Introduction to Geometry*, 2nd ed. New York: Wiley and Sons.

Coxeter, H. S. M. (1987). *Projective Geometry*, rev. 2nd ed. New York: Springer-Verlag.

Coxford, A. F., and Usiskin, Z. P. (1971). *Geometry: A Transformation Approach*. River Forest, IL: Laidlow Bros.

Cromwell, P. R. (1997). *Polyhedra*. Cambridge, U.K.: Cambridge University Press.

Crowe, D. (1986). *HiMAP Module 4: Symmetry, Rigid Motions, and Patterns*. Arlington, MA: COMAP.

Crownover, R. M. (1995). *Introduction to Fractals and Chaos*, Boston: Jones & Bartlett.

Darst, R., Palagallo, J., and Price, T. (1998). Fractal tilings in the plane. *Mathematics Magazine*, Vol. 71, No. 1: 12–23.

Davis, D. M. (1993). *The Nature and Power of Mathematics*. Princeton, NJ: Princeton University Press.

Devaney, R. L. (1990). *Chaos, Fractals, and Dynamics: Computer Experiments in Mathematics*. Menlo Park, CA: Addison-Wesley.

Devaney, R. and Keen, L., (Eds.) (1989). *Chaos and Fractals: The Mathematics Behind the Computer Graphics*, Proceedings of Symposia in Applied Mathematics, Vol. 39, AMS.

Devlin, K. (1994). *Mathematics: The Science of Patterns*. New York: Scientific American Library.

Dewdney, A. K. Computer recreations. *Scientific American*, August 1985, December 1986, July 1987, November 1987, February 1989, May 1990.

Dieudonné, J. (1981). The universal domination of geometry. *Two-year College Mathematics Journal* 12:227–231.

Dodge, C. W. (1972). *Euclidean Geometry and Transformations*. Reading, MA: Addison-Wesley.

Dorwart, H. (1966). *The Geometry of Incidence*. Englewood Cliffs, NJ: Prentice-Hall.

Dubnov, I. A. (1963). *Mistakes in Geometric Proofs*. Boston: Heath.

Eccles, F. M. (1971). *An Introduction to Transformational Geometry*. Menlo Park, CA: Addison-Wesley.

Edgar, G. A. (1990). *Measure, Topology, and Fractal Geometry*, New York: Springer-Verlag.

Edgerton, S. Y. (1975). *The Renaissance Rediscovery of Linear Perspective*, New York: Basic Books.

Eglash, R. (1999). *African Fractals: Modern Computing and Indigenous Design*. New Brunswick NJ: Rutgers University Press.

Eves, H. (1972). *A Survey of Geometry*, rev. ed. Boston: Allyn and Bacon.

Eves, H. (1976). *An Introduction to the History of Mathematics*, 4th ed. New York: Holt, Rinehart and Winston.

Ewald, G. (1971). *Geometry, An Introduction*. Belmont, CA: Wadsworth.

Farmer, D. W. (1996). *Groups and Symmetry*, Vol. 5, Mathematical World. AMS.

Faulkner, J. E. (1975). Paper folding as a technique in visualizing a certain class of transformations. *Mathematics Teacher* 68: 376–377.

Feder, J. (1988). *Fractals*, New York: Plenum Press.

Fehr, H. F., Eccles, F. M., and Meserve, B. E. (1972). The forum: What should become of the high school geometry course. *Mathematics Teacher* 65: 102ff.

Fey, J. (Ed.) (1984). *Computing and Mathematics: The Impact on Secondary School Mathematics*. Washington, DC: NCTM.

Fishback, W. T. (1964). *Projective and Euclidean Geometry*. New York: Wiley and Sons.

Fisher, J. C. (1979). Geometry according to Euclid. *American Mathematical Monthly* 86: 260–270.

Frøyland, J. (1994). *Introduction to Chaos and Coherence*, Philadelphia: Institute of Physics Publishing.

Gallian, J. (1996). Error detection methods. *ACM Computing Surveys* 28(3): 504–517.

Gans, D. (1955). An introduction to elliptic geometry. *American Mathematical Monthly* 62 (7, part II): 66–73.

Gans, D. (1958). Models of projective and Euclidean space. *American Mathematical Monthly* 65: 749–756.

Gans, D. (1969). *Transformations and Geometries*. New York: Appleton-Century-Crofts.

Gans, D. (1973). *An Introduction to Non-Euclidean Geometry*. New York; Academic Press.

Gardner, M. (1959). Euler's spoilers: The discovery of an order-10 Graeco-Latin square. *Scientific American* 201 (5): 181–188.

Gardner, M. (1966). The persistent (and futility) of efforts to trisect the angle. *Scientific American* 214 (6): 116–122.

Gardner, M. (1975). On tessellating the plane with convex polygon tiles. *Scientific American* 233 (1): 112–117.

Gardner, M. (1978). The art of M. C. Escher. In *Mathematical Carnival*, Edited by M. Gardner, pp. 89–102. New York: Alfred A. Knopf.

Gardner, M. (1981). Euclid's parallel postulate and its modern offspring. *Scientific American* 254(4): 23–24.

Gardner, M. (1989). *Penrose Tiles to Trapdoor Ciphers*. New York: W. H. Freeman & Co.

Garner, L. E. (1981). *An Outline of Projective Geometry*. New York: Elsevier/North-Holland.

Gensler, H. J. (1984). *Gödel's Theorem Simplified*. Lanham, MD: University Press of America.

Gleick, J. (1988). *Chaos: Making a New Science*, New York: Penguin.

Golos, E. (1968). *Foundations of Euclidean and Non-Euclidean Geometry*. New York: Holt, Rinehart and Winston.

Goldenberg, E. P. (1991). Seeing beauty in mathematics: Using fractal geometry to build a spirit of mathematical inquiry. *MAA Note: Visualization in Teaching and Learning Mathematics*, Washington, DC: MAA.

Grabiner, Judith V. (1988). The centrality of mathematics in the history of western thought. *Mathematics Magazine* 61(4): 220–230.

Gray, J. (1979). *Ideas of Space: Euclidean, Non-Euclidean, and Relativistic*. Oxford: Clarendon Press.

Greenberg, M. (1980). *Euclidean and Non-Euclidean Geometries*, 2nd ed. San Francisco: W. H. Freeman.

Gruenberg, K. W., and Weir, A. J. (1967). *Linear Geometry*. New York: Van Nostrand Reinhold.

Grünbaum, B. (1981). Shouldn't we teach geometry? *Two-Year College Mathematics Journal* 12: 232–238.

Grünbaum, B., and Shephard, G. C. (1987). *Tilings and Patterns*. New York: W. H. Freeman.

Guggenheimer, H. W. (1967). *Plane Geometry and Its Groups*. San Francisco: Holden-Day.

Haak, S. (1976). Transformation geometry and the artwork of M. C. Escher. *Mathematics Teacher* 69: 647–652.

Hartshorne, R. (1967). *Foundations of Projective Geometry*. New York: W. A. Benjamin.

Hastings, H., and Sugihara, G. (1993). *Fractals: A User's Guide for the Natural Sciences*, Oxford: Oxford University Press.

Heath, T. L. (1921). *A History of Greek Mathematics*. Oxford: Clarendon Press.

Heath, T. L. (1956). *The Thirteen Books of Euclid's Elements*, 2nd ed. New York: Dover.

Henderson, L. D. (1983) *The Fourth Dimension and Non-Euclidean Geometry in Modern Art*. Princeton, NJ: Princeton University Press.

Hilbert, D. (1921). *The Foundations of Geometry*, 2nd ed. Translated by E. J. Townsend. Chicago: Open Court Publishing Co.

Hilbert, D., and Cohn–Vossen, S. (1952). *Geometry and the Imagination*, translated by P. Nemenyi. New York: Chelsea.

Hoffer, W. (1975). A magic ratio recurs throughout history. *Smithsonian* 6(9): 110–124.

Hofstadter, D. R. (1984). Analogies and metaphors to explain Gödel's theorem. In *Mathematics: People, Problems, Results.* Edited by D. M. Campbell and J. C. Higgins. Vol. 2, pp. 262–275. Belmont, CA: Wadsworth.

Holmgren, R. A. (1996). *A First Course in Dynamical Systems*, 2nd ed., New York: Springer-Verlag.

Hutchinson, J. E. (1981). Fractals and self similarity. *Indiana University Mathematics Journal*, Vol. 30, No. 5:713–747.

Iaglom, I. M. (1962). *Geometric Transformations*, Vols. 1, 2, 3. Translated by Shields. New York: Random House.

Ivins, W. M. (1964). *Art and Geometry: A Study in Space Intuitions*. New York: Dover.

Jacobs, H. (1974). *Geometry*. San Francisco: W. H. Freeman,

Jeger, M. (1969). *Transformation Geometry*. English version by A. W. Deicke and A. G. Howson. London: Allen & Unwin.

Johnson, D. A. (1973). *Paper Folding for the Mathematics Class*. Washington, DC: NCTM.

Johnston, B. L., and Richman, F. (1997). *Numbers and Symmetry: An Introduction to Algebra*. New York: CRC Press.

Jones, O. (1986). *The Grammar of Ornament*. Ware England: Omega Books.

Jürgens, H., Peitgen, H–O, and Saupe, D. (1990). The language of fractals. *Scientific American*, August 1990: 60–67.

Kaplansky, I. (1969). *Linear Algebra and Geometry: A Second Course.* Boston: Allyn & Bacon.

Kelly, P., and Matthews, G. (1981). *The Non-Euclidean Plane: Its Structure and Consistency*. New York: Springer-Verlag.

Kennedy, H. C. (1972). The origins of modern axiomatics: Pasch to Peano. *American Mathematical Monthly* 79: 133–136.

King, J., and Schattschneider, D. (1997). *Geometry Turned On! Dynamic Software in Learning, Teaching and Research*, MAA Notes 41. Washington, D.C.: MAA.

Klein, F. (1897). *Famous Problems of Elementary Geometry*: Boston: Ginn & Company.

Kline, M. (1963). *Mathematics: A Cultural Approach*. Reading, MA: Addison-Wesley.

Kline, M. (1964). Geometry. In *Mathematics in the Modern World: Readings from Scientific American*, pp. 112–120. San Francisco: W. H. Freeman.

Kline, M. (1968). Projective geometry. In *Mathematics in the Modern World: Readings from Scientific American*, pp. 120–127. San Francisco: W. H. Freeman.

Kline, M. (1972). *Mathematical Thought from Ancient to Modern Times*. New York: Oxford University Press.

Knorr, W. R. (1986). *The Ancient Tradition of Geometric Problems*. Boston: Birkhauser.

Kolata, G. (1982). Does Gödel's theorem matter to mathematics? *Science* 218: 779–780.

Lam, C. W. H. (1991). The search for a projective plane of order 10. *The American Mathematical Monthly* 98(4): 305–318.

Lang, S., and Murrow, G. (1983). *Geometry: A High School Course*. New York: Springer-Verlag.

Lauwerier, H. (1991). *Fractals: Endlessly Repeated Geometrical Figures*, Princeton NJ: Princeton University Press.

Lieber, L. R. (1940). *Non-Euclidean Geometry: Or Three Moons in Mathesis*, 2nd ed. Brooklyn, NY: Galois Institute of Mathematics and Art.

Lindquist, M. M., and Schulte, A. P. (1987). *Learning and Teaching Geometry, K–12:1987 Yearbook*, Washington, DC: NCTM.

Lockwood, E. H., and Macmillan, R. H. (1978). *Geometric Symmetry*. Cambridge: Cambridge University Press.

Lockwood, J. R., and Runion, G. E. (1978). *Deductive Systems: Finite and Non-Euclidean Geometries*. Reston, VA: NCTM.

Lorenz E. (1993). *The Essence of Chaos*, Seattle, WA: University of Washington Press.

MacGillavry, C. H. (1976). *Symmetry Aspects of M.C. Escher's Periodic Drawings*, 2nd ed. Utrecht: Bohn, Scheltema & Holkema.

MacLane, S. (1959). Metric postulates for plane geometry. *American Mathematical Monthly* 66: 543–555.

Mandelbrot, B. B. (1983). *The Fractal Geometry of Nature*. Rev. ed. New York: W. H. Freeman & Co.

Mandelbrot, B. B. (1984). On fractal geometry and a few of the mathematical questions it has raised. *Proceedings of the International Congress of Mathematicians*, August 16–24 (1983):1661–1675. Warsaw: Polish Scientific Publishers.

Martin, G. E. (1982a). *The Foundations of Geometry and the Non-Euclidean Plane*, corrected ed. New York: Springer-Verlag.

Martin, G. E. (1982b). *Transformation Geometry: An Introduction to Symmetry*. New York: Springer-Verlag.

Maxwell, E. A. (1961). *Fallacies in Mathematics*. Cambridge: Cambridge University Press.

Maxwell, E. A. (1975). *Geometry by Transformations*. Cambridge: Cambridge University Press.

Maziarz, E., and Greenwood, T. (1984). Greek mathematical philosophy. In *Mathematics: People, Problems, Results*. Edited by D. M. Campbell and J. C. Higgins. Vol. 1, pp. 18–27. Belmont, CA: Wadsworth.

Meschkowski, H. (1964). *Non-Euclidean Geometry*, 2nd ed. Translated by A. Shenitzer. New York: Academic Press.

Meserve, B. E. (1983). *Fundamental Concepts of Geometry*. New York: Dover.

Mihalek, R. J. (1972). *Projective Geometry and Algebraic Structures*. New York: Academic Press.

Mikami, Y. (1974). *The Development of Mathematics in China and Japan*, 2nd ed. New York: Chelsea.

Moise, Edwin E. (1974). *Elementary Geometry from an Advanced Standpoint*, 2nd ed. Reading. MA: Addison-Wesley.

Nagel, E., and Newman, J. R. (1956). Goedel's proof. In *The World of Mathematics* Edited by R. Newman. Vol. 3, pp. 1668–1695. New York: Simon and Schuster.

O'Daffer, P. G., and Clemens, S. R. (1976). *Geometry: An Investigative Approach*. Menlo Park, CA: Addison-Wesley.

Ogle, K. N. (1962). The visual space sense. *Science* 135: 763–771.

Olson, A. T. (1975). *Mathematics Through Paper Folding*. Washington, DC: NCTM.

Osserman, R. (1981). Structure vs. substance: The fall and rise of geometry. *Two-Year College Mathematics Journal* 12: 239–246.

Pedoe, D. (1963). *An Introduction to Projective Geometry*. Oxford: Pergamon Press.

Pedoe, D. (1970). *A Course of Geometry for Colleges and Universities*. Cambridge: Cambridge University Press.

Pedoe, D. (1979). *Circles, A Mathematical View*. New York: Dover.

Pedoe, D. (1983). *Geometry and the Visual Arts*. New York: Dover.

Peitgen, H., and Saupe, D. (Eds.) (1988). *The Science of Fractal Images*. New York: Springer-Verlag.

Peitgen, H., Jürgens, H., and Saupe, D. (1992). *Chaos and Fractals: New Frontiers of Science* New York: Springer-Verlag.

Peitgen, H., and Richter, P.H. (Eds.) (1986). *The Beauty of Fractals: Images of Complex Dynamical Systems*. New York: Springer-Verlag.

Penna, M. A., and Patterson, R. R. (1986). *Projective Geometry and Its Applications to Computer Graphics*. Englewood Cliffs, NJ: Prentice-Hall.

Penrose, R. (1978). The geometry of the universe. In *Mathematics Today: Twelve Informal Essays* Edited by L. A. Steen. pp. 83–125. New York: Springer-Verlag.

Peterson, I. (1984). Ants in labyrinths and other fractal excursions. *Science News* 21: 42–43.

Piaget, J., and Inhelder, B. (1967). *The Child's Conception of Space*. Translated by F. J. Langdon and J. L. Lunzer. New York: W. W. Norton.

Pless, V. (1982). *Introduction to the Theory of Error-Correcting Codes*. New York: Wiley and Sons.

Polya, G. (1971). *How to Solve It*, 2nd ed. Princeton, NJ: Princeton University Press.

Radin, C. (1995). Symmetry and tilings. *Notices of the AMS*, 42(1): pp. 26–31.

Ranucci, E. R. (1974). Master of tessellations: M. C. Escher, 1898–1972. *Mathematics Teacher* 67: 299–306.

Ranucci, E. R., and Teeters, J. E. (1977). *Creating Escher-Type Drawings*. Palo Alto, CA: Creative Publications.

Richardson, L. F. (1922). *Weather Prediction by Numerical Process*. Republished by Dover Publications (1965).

Robertson, J. (1986). Geometric constructions using hinged mirrors. *Mathematics Teacher* 79: 380–386.

Robinson, C. (1995). *Dynamical Systems: Stability, Symbolic Dynamics, and Chaos*, Ann Arbor, MI: CRC Press.

Rodríguez–Iturbe, I. (1997). *Fractal River Basins: Chance and Self-Organization*. Cambridge: Cambridge University Press.

Rosen, J. (1975). *Symmetry Discovered: Concepts and Application in Nature and Science*. Cambridge: Cambridge University Press.

Ruelle, D. (1991). *Chance and Chaos*. Princeton, NJ: Princeton University Press.

Ryan, P. J. (1986). *Euclidean and Non-Euclidean Geometry: An Analytic Approach*. Cambridge: Cambridge University Press.

Sanders, W. J. and Dennis, J. R. (1968). Congruence geometry for junior high school. *Mathematics Teacher* 61: 354–369.

Sawyer, W. W. (1971). *Prelude to Mathematics*. New York: Penguin Books.

Schattschneider, D. (1978). The plane symmetry groups: Their recognition and notation. *The American Mathematical Monthly*, 85:439–450.

Schattschneider, D. (1990). *M. C. Escher: Visions of Symmetry*. New York: W. H. Freeman and Company.

School Mathematics Study Group (1965). *Geometry: Student's Text*, rev. ed. Pasadena, CA: A. C. Vroman.

Seidenberg, A. (1962). *Lectures in Projective Geometry*. New York: Van Nostrand Reinhold.

Senechal, M., and Fleck, G. (Eds.) (1988). *Shaping Space: A Polyhedral Approach*. Cambridge MA: Birkhäuser Boston.

Singer, D. (1997). *Geometry: Plane and Fancy*. New York: Springer-Verlag

Smart, J. R. (1998). *Modern Geometries*, 5th ed. Pacific Grove, CA: Brooks/Cole.

Smith, D. E. (1958). *History of Mathematics*, Vol. 1. New York: Dover.

Solow, D. (1982). *How to Read and Do Proofs*. New York: Wiley and Sons.

Sommerville, D. (1970). *Bibliography of Non-Euclidean Geometry*, 2nd ed. New York: Chelsea.

Steen, L. A. (1977). Fractals: A world of nonintegral dimensions. *Science News* 112: 122–123.

Steen, L. A. (1980). Unsolved problems in geometry. *Mathematics Teacher* 73: 366–369.

Steen, L. A. (Ed.) (1990). *On the Shoulders of Giants: New Approaches to Numeracy*. Washington, D.C.: National Academy Press.

Stevenson, F. W. (1972). *Projective Planes*. San Francisco: W. H. Freeman.

Stewart, I. (1987). The two-and-a-halfth dimension. *The Problems of Mathematics*. Oxford: Oxford University Press.

Stewart, I. (1989). *Does God Play Dice? The Mathematics of Chaos*. Oxford: Blackwell.

Stewart, I., and Golubitsky, M. (1993). *Fearful Symmetry: Is God A Geometer?* London: Penguin Books.

Swetz, F. (1984). The evolution of mathematics in ancient China. In *Mathematics: People, Problems, Results*. Edited by D. M. Campbell and J. C. Higgins. Vol. 1, pp. 28–37. Belmont, CA: Wadsworth.

Teeters, J. C. (1974). How to draw tessellations of the Escher type. *Mathematics Teacher* 67: 307–310.

Thompson, T. M. (1983). *From Error-Correcting Codes Through Sphere Packings to Simple Groups*. The Carus Mathematical Monographs, No. 21. Ithaca, NY: MAA.

Torretti, Roberto (1978). *Philosophy of Geometry from Riemann to Poincaré*. Dordrect, Holland: D. Reidel Publishing Company.

Trudeau, R. J. (1987). *The Non-Euclidean Revolution*. Boston: Birkhäuser.

Tuller, A. (1967). *Modern Introduction to Geometries*. New York: Van Nostrand Reinhold.

Veblen, O., and Bussey, W. H. (1906). Finite projective planes. *Translations of the American Mathematical Society* 7: 241–259.

Washburn, D., and Crowe, D. (1988). *Symmetries of Culture: Theory and Practice of Plane Patterns Analysis*. Seattle: University of Washington Press.

Watson, A. (1990). The mathematics of symmetry. *New Scientist* 17, October 1990: 45–50.

Wegner, T., and Peterson, M. (1991). *Fractal Creations*. Mill Valley, CA: The Waite Group Press.

Wenninger, M. (1966). *Polyhedron Models for the Classroom*. Washington, DC. NCTM.

Wenninger, M. (1979). *Spherical Models*. Cambridge: Cambridge University Press.

Weyl, H. (1989). *Symmetry*. Princeton: Princeton University Press. (Original copyright in 1952).

Whitehead, A. N. (1971). *The Axioms of Projective Geometry*. Cambridge Tracts in Mathematics and Mathematical Physics, No. 4. New York: Hafner Publishing Co.

Wolfe, H. E. (1945). *Introduction to Non-Euclidean Geometry*. New York: Holt, Rinehart and Winston.

Wylie, C. R., Jr. (1964). *Foundations of Geometry*. New York: McGraw-Hill.

Wylie, C. R., Jr. (1970). *Introduction to Projective Geometry*. New York: McGraw-Hill.

Yale, P. B. (1968). *Geometry and Symmetry*. San Francisco: Holden-Day.

Young, J. W. (1930). *Projective Geometry*. The Carus Mathematical Monographs, No. 4. Chicago: Open Court Publishing Co. (for the MAA).

Zage, W. M. (1980). The geometry of binocular visual space. *Mathematics Magazine* 53: 289–294.

Zirakzadeh, A. (1969). A model for the finite projective spaces with three points on every line. *American Mathematical Monthly* 76: 774–778.

Index

Undergraduate Texts in Mathematics

(continued from page ii)

Frazier: An Introduction to Wavelets Through Linear Algebra

Gamelin: Complex Analysis.

Gordon: Discrete Probability.

Hairer/Wanner: Analysis by Its History. *Readings in Mathematics.*

Halmos: Finite-Dimensional Vector Spaces. Second edition.

Halmos: Naive Set Theory.

Hämmerlin/Hoffmann: Numerical Mathematics. *Readings in Mathematics.*

Harris/Hirst/Mossinghoff: Combinatorics and Graph Theory.

Hartshorne: Geometry: Euclid and Beyond.

Hijab: Introduction to Calculus and Classical Analysis.

Hilton/Holton/Pedersen: Mathematical Reflections: In a Room with Many Mirrors.

Hilton/Holton/Pedersen: Mathematical Vistas: From a Room with Many Windows.

Iooss/Joseph: Elementary Stability and Bifurcation Theory. Second edition.

Irving: Integers, Polynomials, and Rings: A Course in Algebra

Isaac: The Pleasures of Probability. *Readings in Mathematics.*

James: Topological and Uniform Spaces.

Jänich: Linear Algebra.

Jänich: Topology.

Jänich: Vector Analysis.

Kemeny/Snell: Finite Markov Chains.

Kinsey: Topology of Surfaces.

Klambauer: Aspects of Calculus.

Lang: A First Course in Calculus. Fifth edition.

Lang: Calculus of Several Variables. Third edition.

Lang: Introduction to Linear Algebra. Second edition.

Lang: Linear Algebra. Third edition.

Lang: Short Calculus: The Original Edition of "A First Course in Calculus."

Lang: Undergraduate Algebra. Second edition.

Lang: Undergraduate Analysis.

Laubenbacher/Pengelley: Mathematical Expeditions.

Lax/Burstein/Lax: Calculus with Applications and Computing. Volume 1.

LeCuyer: College Mathematics with APL.

Lidl/Pilz: Applied Abstract Algebra. Second edition.

Logan: Applied Partial Differential Equations, Second edition.

Lovász/Pelikán/Vesztergombi: Discrete Mathematics.

Macki-Strauss: Introduction to Optimal Control Theory.

Malitz: Introduction to Mathematical Logic.

Marsden/Weinstein: Calculus I, II, III. Second edition.

Martin: Counting: The Art of Enumerative Combinatorics.

Martin: The Foundations of Geometry and the Non-Euclidean Plane.

Martin: Geometric Constructions.

Martin: Transformation Geometry: An Introduction to Symmetry.

Millman/Parker: Geometry: A Metric Approach with Models. Second edition.

Moschovakis: Notes on Set Theory.

Owen: A First Course in the Mathematical Foundations of Thermodynamics.

Palka: An Introduction to Complex Function Theory.

Pedrick: A First Course in Analysis.

Peressini/Sullivan/Uhl: The Mathematics of Nonlinear Programming.

Undergraduate Texts in Mathematics

Prenowitz/Jantosciak: Join Geometries.

Priestley: Calculus: A Liberal Art.
Second edition.

Protter/Morrey: A First Course in Real
Analysis. Second edition.

Protter/Morrey: Intermediate Calculus.
Second edition.

Pugh: Real Mathematical Analysis.

Roman: An Introduction to Coding and
Information Theory.

Roman: Introduction to the Mathematics
of Finance: From Risk Management to
Options Pricing.

Ross: Differential Equations: An
Introduction with Mathematica®.
Second edition.

Ross: Elementary Analysis: The Theory
of Calculus.

Samuel: Projective Geometry.
Readings in Mathematics.

Saxe: Beginning Functional Analysis

Scharlau/Opolka: From Fermat to
Minkowski.

Schiff: The Laplace Transform: Theory
and Applications.

Sethuraman: Rings, Fields, and Vector
Spaces: An Approach to Geometric
Constructability.

Sigler: Algebra.

Silverman/Tate: Rational Points on
Elliptic Curves.

Simmonds: A Brief on Tensor Analysis.
Second edition.

Singer: Geometry: Plane and Fancy.

Singer/Thorpe: Lecture Notes on
Elementary Topology and
Geometry.

Smith: Linear Algebra. Third edition.

Smith: Primer of Modern Analysis.
Second edition.

Stanton/White: Constructive
Combinatorics.

Stillwell: Elements of Algebra: Geometry,
Numbers, Equations.

Stillwell: Elements of Number Theory.

Stillwell: Mathematics and Its History.
Second edition.

Stillwell: Numbers and Geometry.
Readings in Mathematics.

Strayer: Linear Programming and Its
Applications.

Toth: Glimpses of Algebra and Geometry.
Second Edition.
Readings in Mathematics.

Troutman: Variational Calculus and
Optimal Control. Second edition.

Valenza: Linear Algebra: An Introduction
to Abstract Mathematics.

Whyburn/Duda: Dynamic Topology.

Wilson: Much Ado About Calculus.